THE LEACOCK MEDAL TREASURY

THE
LEACOCK MEDAL TREASURY

3 DECADES OF THE BEST OF CANADIAN HUMOUR

Selected by Ralph L. Curry

Lester and Orpen Limited

Also by Ralph L. Curry:
Stephen Leacock: Humorist and Humanist

CATALOGUING IN PUBLICATION DATA

Main entry under title:

The Leacock Medal treasury

ISBN 0-919630-62-6

1. Canadian wit and humor (English).*
I. Curry, Ralph L., 1924-

PN6178.C3L33   C817'.5'408   C76-017093-2

Printed in Canada

to GWEN
to the very supportive Board of the STEPHEN LEACOCK HOME
and finally
to STEPHEN LEACOCK, himself

WINNERS OF THE STEPHEN LEACOCK MEMORIAL MEDAL
Awarded by The Stephen Leacock Associates

1947 *Ojibway Melody* by Harry L. Symons
1948 *Sarah Binks* by Paul Hiebert
1949 *Truthfully Yours* by Angeline Hango
1950 *Turvey* by Earle Birney
1951 *The Roving I* by Eric Nicol
1952 *The Salt Box* by Jan Hilliard
1953 *The Battle of Baltinglass* by Lawrence Earl
1954 *Pardon My Parka* by Joan Walker
1955 *Leaven of Malice* by Robertson Davies
1956 *Shall We Join the Ladies?* by Eric Nicol
1957 *The Grass is Never Greener* by Robert Thomas Allen
1958 *Girdle Me a Globe* by Eric Nicol
1959 No Award Given
1960 *Just Add Water and Stir* by Pierre Berton
1961 *Mice in the Beer* by Norman Ward
1962 *Jake and the Kid* by W.O. Mitchell
1963 *Three Cheers for Me* by Donald Jack
1964 *Homebrew and Patches* by Harry J. Boyle
1965 *Gregory Clark War Stories* by Gregory Clark
1966 *Nursery Rhymes to be Read Aloud by Young Parents with Old Children*
      by George Bain
1967 *Needham's Inferno* by Richard Needham
1968 *And Now . . . Here's Max* by Max Ferguson
1969 *You're Only as Old as You Act* by Stuart Trueman
1970 *The Boat Who Wouldn't Float* by Farley Mowat
1971 *Children, Wives, and Other Wildlife* by Robert Thomas Allen
1972 *The Night We Stole the Mountie's Car* by Max Braithwaite
1973 *Saturday Night at the Bagel Factory* by Don Bell
1974 *That's Me in the Middle* by Donald Jack
1975 *A Good Place to Come From* by Morley Torgov
1976 *The Luck of the Irish* by Harry J. Boyle

The editor and publisher gratefully acknowledge permission from the following to reprint:

From THE ROVING I by Eric Nicol. Reprinted by permission of McGraw-Hill Ryerson Limited.
From GREGORY CLARK WAR STORIES by Gregory Clark. Copyright © Optimum Publishing Company Limited. Reprinted by permission of the publishers.
From NURSERY RHYMES TO BE READ ALOUD BY YOUNG PARENTS WITH OLD CHILDREN by George Bain. Reprinted by permission of Clarke, Irwin & Company Limited.
From THREE CHEERS FOR ME. The Journals of Bartholomew Bandy. Revised Edition. Volume I by Donald Jack, copyright © 1962, 1973 by Donald L. Jack. Reprinted by permission of Doubleday & Company, Inc.
From TRUTHFULLY YOURS by Angeline Hango. Reprinted by permission of Oxford University Press Canada.
From SARAH BINKS by Paul Hiebert. Reprinted by permission of Oxford University Press Canada.
From YOU'RE ONLY AS OLD AS YOU ACT by Stuart Trueman. Reprinted by permission of The Canadian Publishers, McClelland and Steward Limited, Toronto.
From TURVEY by Earle Birney. Reprinted by permission of The Canadian Publishers, McClelland and Stewart Limited, Toronto.
From GIRDLE ME A GLOBE by Eric Nicol. Reprinted by permission of McGraw-Hill Ryerson Limited.
From JAKE AND THE KID by W.O. Mitchell. Reprinted by permission of The Macmillan Company of Canada Limited.
From HOMEBREW AND PATCHES by Harry J. Boyle. Copyright © by Harry J. Boyle. Reprinted by permission of the Canadian Speakers' and Writers' Service Limited.
From THE BATTLE OF BALTINGLASS by Lawrence Earl. Reprinted by permission of George G. Harrap & Company Ltd., London.
From SATURDAY NIGHT AT THE BAGEL FACTORY by Don Bell. Reprinted by permission of The Canadian Publishers, McClelland and Stewart Limited, Toronto.
From THAT'S ME IN THE MIDDLE copyright © 1973 by Donald Jack. Reprinted by permission of Doubleday & Company, Inc.
From JUST ADD WATER AND STIR by Pierre Berton. Reprinted by permission of The Canadian Publishers, McClelland and Stewart Limited, Toronto.
From PARDON MY PARKA by Joan Walker. Reprinted by permission of The Canadian Publishers, McClelland and Stewart Limited, Toronto.
From MICE IN THE BEER by Norman Ward. Reprinted by permission of the author.
From THE GRASS IS NEVER GREENER by Robert Thomas Allen. Reprinted by permission of the author.

Contents

Introduction

The humour of Stephen Butler Leacock has long been considered the cream of Canadian humour, indeed, of the world's humour. Beginning with *Literary Lapses* in 1910, Leacock steadily and regularly furnished the world with its laughter. Called "the Canadian Mark Twain" and "the master satirist," Stephen Leacock almost every year added another volume to his canon of fun. Humour must be, by its very nature, contemporary and timely, and for this reason little of it lasts. Stephen Leacock, however, had the taste of a real artist in selecting his subjects, in choosing his details. Far more than most, he produced material which is still funny. Perhaps his secret was his dedication to the human. Whenever a bank or a government or a style got too big or complicated for the individual, Stephen Leacock stoutly aligned himself with the little man. This kind of humour lasts. One may only note that "My Financial Career" has been reprinted very nearly as often as Mark Twain's "Celebrated Jumping Frog of Calavaras County." With his great sympathy for man bedeviled by conventions and fashions and machinery, Stephen Leacock remains one of the world's great humourists.

At his death in 1944, Leacock left thirty-five joyous books and multitudes of friends and readers. It was only fitting, therefore, that this man should be remembered in some appropriate, permanent way. The usual things were done: the commissioning of a bust by Elizabeth Wynn Wood, the housing of a complete collection of Leacock's works in his beloved Orillia Public Library; but it remained for the Stephen Leacock Associates to mark his memory

1

best in awarding the Stephen Leacock Medal for Humour. The Leacock Medal has been awarded each year, except one, since 1947 for the best book of humour written by a Canadian. Some years the crop has been slim, but as the reader can judge, most of the time the winner had been a proper tribute to a master humourist like Leacock. Since 1973 the Medal has been accompanied by a generous monetary award as well, through the spirited assistance of the Manufacturers Life Insurance Company.

This collection is a further tribute, of course, to Stephen Leacock, but through him it is also a token of respect for those who labour in the same vineyards. Twain and Leacock and Dickens all found that the world is quick to laugh at the joke but very slow to take seriously its creator. Writing humour is hard work. It is skilled work. And we need to applaud more often and more loudly.

Although each medal winner is represented in this present collection, the selections are not arranged chronologically. Indeed, they may seem hardly to be arranged at all, though each selection has been chosen first because of its ability to make us smile and second because it seems to stand on its own feet, needing no setting or support. The editor has tried to position pieces in such a way that the reader does not become sated as he goes through the book. He will instead, it is devoutly to be hoped, continually find something different to laugh at. These writers have little in common except that they are all funny.

The editor has noticed a strong use of first person. More than three-fourths of the selections which appear here are told from this point of view (a 1951 winner is even titled *The Roving I*). One has to be struck, however, that with so much use of "I" there is so little use of ego. This, of course, is in the tradition of the very best of humour. Charles Lamb and Mark Twain and Stephen Leacock frequently placed themselves as the butt of the joke, turning such slings and arrows of absurd fortune as they endured into inspired fun.

With best wishes to the reader then, here's to Stephen and his whole tribe!

Ralph L. Curry
Old Brewery Bay, Orillia, Ontario
1976

Like many of the creators of North American humour, Eric Nicol made his contribution from the ranks of the journalists. His The Roving I – *the 1951 winner – is very largely a reportorial eye. The reader will notice his acute sense of the incongruous scattered through this collection, for Eric Nicol has won the Leacock Medal more often than any other author – in 1951, in 1956 and in 1958.*

ERIC NICOL
from The Roving I

Popular opinion to the contrary, it isn't always springtime in Paris. The other seasons are autumn, winter and tourist.

I arrived at that even more mystical period between the arrival of the first frost and the turning on of the first heat. Paris hotels, stores and cinemas are heated according to the calendar rather than the cold, and a new ice age could move right down the *Champs Elysées* without shaking a single *concierge's* resolve to hold the coal till mid-November. This is known as *la logique française*, which has done so much for philosophy and so little for chilblains.

I soon discovered that I was not the stuff of which Madame Curies are made. During her student days in Paris, Madame Curie kept warm with little more than a burning desire for knowledge. During the few hours that I spent in an unheated room I found that my desire for knowledge wouldn't burn worth a damn. This was a considerable disappointment because I had dried it out thoroughly at a Canadian university. I envied the zeal of an American student who had a fireplace in his room but was forbidden by hotel regulation to have a fire in it, and who hurried in and out with his briefcase in what impressed everybody as inspired scholasticism, until it was discovered that the briefcase brought in wood and packed out ashes.

I moved into the *Maison Canadienne*, which had steam radiators. I had never kissed a steam radiator before. Her embrace was perfunctory but its warmth was sheer historical novel. I'll never forget those first two weeks we had together, the happy gurgle of her pipes, her slight but becoming drool. Then, as I suppose it must to all lovers, there came the morning when I woke up to find that she had turned cold. I'm ashamed to say, I kicked her. That same afternoon I walked in and caught her, stripped, with the plumber. After that things were never quite the same. We lived together, of course, as friends, but my heart was open to the first pair of bedsox that came along.

Worthy and lacklustre as a village parson, the *Maison Canadienne* is a unit of the vast University City on the rim of Paris. In the intellectual mecca of the City students of all races, creeds and colours come together and establish a common bond of hatred for the cafeteria. (In the cafeteria of *La Maison Internationale*, for a trifling 60 francs one is served a rare old gymshoe soup, a slice from the tongue of some abnormally huge animal, never identified, and an eggcup brimming with applesauce fortified by core, pips and bits of bark, which one eats with a spoon left over from the excavation of some unknown tunnel.) The *Maison Canadienne* smacks of clean living. Clean living is anathema to any artist. If he gets enough of it it'll ruin him. You can't be both Baudelaire and an Eagle Scout. And everybody that comes to Paris is an artist or is willing to become one to avoid clean living.

So, it's much harder than in Hemingway's time to find a garret to be Bohemian in. Young American artists, arriving fully equipped with beards and plastic cobwebs, have easeled their way into everything in the Latin Quarter, paying large sums for a garret in first-class state of shambles and with a genuine hole in the roof (often difficult to distinguish from the spurious brace-and-bitter). I simply couldn't afford the sort of room Mimi is accustomed to dying of consumption in. At the *Maison* she would have to make shift on the ping-pong table. I wasn't too happy about this, but after all the *Maison* did have showers, and I might always run into a healthy Mimi.

Besides, I was partially a student, offering up my bugle to the grindstone of post-graduate study at the Sorbonne. I soon discovered the secret of the Sorbonne graduate's breadth of learning. Educators whose taste is jaded by a steady diet of boiled sciencemen should try this recipe sometime:

Instead of the students cutting classes, the professors do. With an even 700 years of teaching experience behind them, the Faculty of the Sorbonne have learned not to be caught in the classroom. Many of the professors manage to be out of town during the school year. A student from Guadeloupe turns up for his first biology lecture and finds on the door a small, handwritten note saying that the professor is pursuing tree toads in Guadeloupe and won't be visible until the year after next.

If he can't get out of Paris in time to escape the autumnal flux of students, the professor can always die. Owing to a Sorbonne convention of not conceding the death of a professor until five years after his behavior has become suspect as excessively meditative, the student can never be sure that he is not trying to invoke a ghost. This adds an eerie element to his education, the importance of which can hardly be overestimated.

Naturally, not all the professors succeed in escaping. But those that are left find all sorts of ingenious excuses for not giving their lectures, or at least delaying them as long as possible. Some are busy giving examinations. By giving examinations at the beginning of the term, not only do they eliminate a lot of students who might otherwise try to hear a lecture, cluttering up the halls and creating draughts, but they cut down the period before the Christmas holidays to a handful of lectures hardly worth bothering about.

Well, you ask, how does this make for a panoramic education? Quite simple. Here's the way it works.

Student turns up for, say, a lecture on Comparative Theology. He finds a note on the door. The Comparative Theology professor regrets that he will be unable to meet his Thursday class owing to the fact that he has gone to Hell on business. Now, there is no student lounge, no common room, no snack bar in the Sorbonne. Nowhere to go and relax. Unused classrooms are locked. Even the washroom is guarded by a *concierge* who, though pleasant enough when explaining the paper shortage, will not tolerate social gatherings within his precincts.

The student therefore has the choice of going home to a suspicious family or, even more ghastly, entering the Library. Unless — and this is the gimmick — he goes to some other lecture. For, although the student's own lectures may always be cancelled, he will find another amphitheater open and heated and filling with people. Goaded by conscience and curiosity, hungry for the sound of a human voice, he traipses in with the crowd. First thing he knows he is listening to a brilliant lecture about something he never heard of. New vistas open up. His interest is sparked. He is on his way to a well-rounded education.

I can attest personally to the effectiveness of this oblique approach. Although I never quite trapped a lecture in my own period of French literature, I sat in on some lulus about Early Etruscan Art, the Physiology of Vegetables, and Burial Customs amongst the Ancient Greeks. And while not learning enough about these subjects to discuss them at length, I'm set to heckle anybody else who tries it.

I only wish I could have gotten close enough to the front of the class to have seen one of the professors. A heavy ground fog drifts down the Sorbonne's cold, stone corridors and leaks into the lightless lecture rooms, obscuring the professor from all but those students equipped with radar. Still, it's nice to know he's up there somewhere.

Wait, the fog is clearing.

The lady professor shuffles her notes professionally, deals herself a card off the top, and peers at it through her lorgnette. She's not a bad-looking dish, but that lorgnette could shrivel a man at fifty yards.

The first fact rises glistening from her tongue. All around me heads salaam in unison over notebooks, rise in the order in which their owners will graduate, the dullest still bent as the second fact is resurrected. Standing against the rear wall in the overcrowded classroom, I suddenly feel too old for this form of worship. I study my classmates:

Stocky, bespectacled young women in unconscionably comfortable shoes, ends of orange scarves lolling from coat pockets in some private paroxysm of retching. Those plain girls who walk stomach-first, as a sort of wistful substitute for pregnancy, and who make the highest marks ever.

A couple of boyish English, red-eared, hair combed by hurricane, trousers carbuncled at the knee and jackets leathered at the elbow.

The sleek young Italian priest, black-coated, black-buttoned, face carved into ivory attention.

Black boys, Chinese.

A beautiful French girl, blonde, who moved to her seat with the slow, sinuous grace of a coiling python and took off her coat with a surge of breasts that rocked the entire curriculum.

The room is too warm.

Standing beside me is a girl, another dumpling in the stew. But her face is strangely peaceful. Is she having a religious experience? No, she's fainting. My realization that she is fainting is all her knees have been waiting for. They buckle and I catch her under the armpits. She is very heavy. I look desperately at the lady professor, but she's lorgnetting another note. Nobody has noticed what has happened. I can't think of the French for "fainted" and my wrists are getting tired.

After a while the girl slumps to the floor in spite of me, and while I'm trying to wrestle her erect some people nearby look around. Sensing that the scene we are presenting suggests indecent assault, I shout in English:

"For God's sake open a window!"

This foreign noise attracts the rest of the class, who stare at me with cold suspicion. The lady professor, gradually becoming aware of a disturbance, makes a myopic sweep of the room with her lorgnette. She focuses on me, struggling to lug the guts into the neighbour room. I feel somebody pulling me off the girl. A couple of other females help the recovering fainter out to the corridor, leaving me panting and red and under general opprobrium.

I am the type that, in a crisis, is pushed aside by the person who knows what to do. I only wish he could be there in the first place.

I don't attend any more courses at the Sorbonne.

The *Salle de Travail* of the *Bibliothèque Nationale*, "world's richest library" (*le Guide Bleu*). Average age of students: fifty. Average distance of noses from books: four inches. Only sound, the gentle rustle of beard on manuscript, the whisper of call slips sliding down the pneumatique to stacks below, the chair scrape of somebody quietly retiring to the foyer to drop dead.

Concentration is so heavy the arms are broken off most of the chairs. The readers are straight out of Daguerre's first experiments in photography:

A little man saved from midgetdom only by his bowler. With hands resting on his behind, he fluffs out the wings of his swallowtail coat (*circa* 1885), like a nervous blowfly.

A great grey faceless nun, crucifix sheathed in her bodice, the

Saviour tucked under the blanket with just his head and arms outside, so that he seems to be sleeping warm on that mighty chest.

A gaunt note-taker who is obviously, soundlessly insane. He lays down his pen, his face splits into a mad grin of triumph, he rubs his hands between his knees like a safecracker honing his fingers. Suddenly he is savagely gnawing a knuckle, eager to destroy it. The knuckle is swollen with callous. Then with a slow and graceful smoothing of his hair he returns calm to his note-taking.

Passing through the *Salle* like a coloured streamer — a pretty girl. While at the catalogues academic virgins from Iowa and Ontario kneel and pray into the files, offering themselves to some god of primary sources.

Once, I think I have caught the old gentleman on my left nodding asleep, but he turns out to be blind in the near eye.

Two penitentiary gangways run around the walls, the cells of books. Four million books awaiting the brief parole of a reader. The worst criminals doomed to perpetual confinement. Others brought out for grilling, under magnifying glass, probed by pencil flashlight, backs broken if they prove reticent.

I am intimidated by this library where they won't let you take a book out. They have a guard on the door to make sure you don't, to ask you to open your briefcase when you leave. You must read your book in the *Salle*. You can't take it home and conveniently lose it under a pile of magazines and old bridge tallies. Since you can't do much else in the *Salle*, you are more or less forced to read the book. An insidious process. After a while you come to enjoy reading. Nothing sharpens a pleasure like knowing it is a restricted privilege.

Perhaps that helps explain why France is a nation of voracious readers. Perhaps we in Canada need fewer glib lending libraries in which books are as blatantly available as the latest issue of Real Screen Garbage. Perhaps Canada would be better informed if a book were as hard to take out as a bottle.

Anyhow, the *Bibliothèque Nationale* knows how to play hard to get. After you've submitted the call slip for a book you have time to step out for a glass of wine, or even a quick trip around the world. Deep in the subterranean warrens of the Library, batteries of gnomes are contriving reasons for not finding the book, or at least for finding the wrong book.

For this reason it is a good idea to bring along your own book to read until your slip comes back stamped with time, date, condition of tract, and the notation that the book you've asked for either is already out or was never written. In any event you do read, because the medallion heads of Aristotle, Plato and Horace, circling the cupola, are watching you with a cold, clear eye, and there's a queue of people waiting for a seat in the *Salle*. A remarkable queue indeed.

In France you take a book along, whatever you're going to do, because the doing is bound to take longer than you planned. France's high degree of literacy is founded on solid inefficiency.

Even Paris is irritating, if you're geared too high. Trained on the American way of life, which is so beautifully banked at the turns that there's never any question of one's not dying on time, I chafed at the pace of Paris:

Crowds block the sidewalk, crystallized around a street vendor hustling a gadget to take skin off new potatoes or fat off old wives. The French can't get over the miracle of oral communication.

In a large department store I linger while the record of my purchase is entered by a dignified person in a dress suit, his script crawling across the page of a ledger designed for doomsday, every dip of the pen into its bottle another banderillo into my impatience.

I try to run for the subway train I hear coming in the *Métro*, but those in front won't let me. They have the crazy idea that five minutes one way or the other don't matter and that neither do I.

At first, only by an effort of will have I understood that the French care less about time than about what happens in it. My reeducation begins with the discovery that most North Americans don't know how to eat. We eat on the run, like marathon swimmers and some other species of queer fish. We snatch breakfast, Adam's apples bobbing in the brief, frantic transmission of coffee and toast. For lunch, perched on spine-blunting stools, we contest a square foot of counter, wolfing a brittle wedge of sandwich and its headstone of withered dill. (Or, worse, we exhume it from a paper bag and pull off the winding sheets of greaseproof paper to find the remains of Mother's bridge-party: tuna that's started to turna.) And dinner, all too often, we pythonize on the double so that Sis can make a movie, Father can listen to "It Pays To Be

Daft," and Mother has time to throw out the empty cans before charging off to her night class in glass-blowing.

Except for a few isolated communities, where the pace of life favours feeding and breeding, we're all teed up for pill meals. In the brutal scramble for scratch we abuse the most innocent and faithful of our appetites, so that later we can keep our ulcers awash in elk's milk. Even during the declining days of Rome, when the Romans were burning the Christian at both ends, they never violated the sanctity of the feast. We may or may not be ripe for the barbarian hordes, but Heaven alone can save us now from the Automat.

The poignancy of this betrayal of the inner man can be felt most keenly after a meal in a good French restaurant, especially if you forget to loosen your belt. For the French not only have gastronomic know-how, they have retained the quaint notion that a café luncheon is an occasion, not for clinching a business deal, but for enjoying food. More than that, at noon in Paris all commerce freezes. Shutters clang closed on shop windows, exterior handles vanish from doors, and during two hours, for the whole length and breadth of the city, the only transaction is that between plate and palate.

In a few weeks, by constant practice, I built up my elapsed time, from ordering of *apéritif* to picking up of change, to an hour and forty minutes. Eating solo, that is. Much better time (anything over two hours) can be made if you're with somebody you can make love to between the salad and the Camembert.

And after a while I learn to descend the subway steps one at a time.

Paris travels mostly underground. Blundering beneath the city in every direction is the *Métropolitain*, which makes up in cheapness what it lacks in speed. Each day four million people tumble into its burrows, to be compressed, dehydrated, garlicized and finally excreted by the elderly blindworms. Throughout the process, Parisians remain composed and gracious. They back on to a crowded train, using that part of their anatomy that provides the softest buffer against those already congealed within.

Stationed on the platform is what could be Robespierre's mother, a *Métro* worker who knows exactly how far the coaches can swell with people without wedging into the bore of the tunnel. When she sees this point being reached she lays aside her knitting and blows a whistle, whereupon the train conductor presses the button that slams the doors shut on those who didn't quite make it.

The inevitable intimacy of travel on the *Métro* during rush hours is supplemented by a more voluntary variety at all hours. It is customary to neck on the *Métro*. Nearly every trainload includes at least one couple nuzzling, kissing or hugging. All ages are eligible, and some of the worst offenders are already married to each other.

Since the trains are well lighted, this unabashed love-making is likely to unnerve the visitor accustomed to the high moral tone of the B.C. Electric or Toronto T.C. At least it unnerved me. One Saturday night, mixing with Parisian youth on its way home, I scarcely knew where to look. If I had been with a lady I could have looked down her throat, like the others, but I was just going along for the ride.

Of course in Paris you soon adjust yourself to this sort of thing, unless you come from the stonier parts of Nova Scotia. The French take for granted certain natural functions whose existence we in North America have never openly admitted. Thus in the *Métro*, the cinema, at the café table, or simply on the sidewalk, *monsieur* is at perfect liberty, thanks to this Freedom of Smooch, to plant a pucker on *madame*. That is why, just as every Canadian knows how to skate and every Englishman is at home on the cricket pitch, every Frenchman has a solid grounding in seduction. At the moment there is no agitation amongst Frenchwomen in favour of skating or cricket.

For his ride, with or without romance, the user of the *Métro* pays 10 francs, or roughly three cents. This makes the *Métro* one of the world's cheapest methods of transportation and encourages its workers to strike fairly frequently. When only the wealthy have cars, and you can't get more than five on a bicycle, hugging or no hugging, well, a strike can certainly be a nuisance. . . .

One of the most colourful and celebrated districts of all the world's cities is the Paris Left Bank. As soon as anybody thinks of Paris he thinks of the Left Bank. Even before I left Vancouver, friends were happily discussing the probability of my being slugged there.

Before I left Vancouver, anxious to blend with the Latin Quarter, I developed a greasy look and bought myself a turtleneck sweater. The turtleneck sweater, my friends agreed, merely heightened my resemblance to a turtle.

But I refused to be daunted. I looked forward eagerly to treading the cobblestones of the very streets where Hemingway, Verlaine, Sartre and other greats had written their way to glory. Genius, I knew, lurked in the heavy brush of Left Bank beards. It was there for the flushing. And like a hundred hacks before me, I fingered my own sparse stubble with the light of hope in my eyes.

For several weeks after I reached Paris, however, I wasn't sure which Bank I was living on (besides the Bank of Montreal, that is). The Seine serpentines through Paris, and it depends on which way you're facing whether you're on the Left Bank or the Right Bank. If you're standing on one of the bridges, of course, you know you're not on either Bank, but that's no way to spend a Saturday night.

So, for a while I tried to tell from their relative degree of dissolution the inhabitants of the Left Bank from those of the Right Bank. This didn't work because there are wonderfully dissolute-looking people on both Banks, and they keep crossing one another's lines. Besides, a lot of dissolute-looking people are just passing through town and don't live on either Bank.

In fact I caught somebody, obviously a tourist who didn't know which was the Left Bank, following me as though I might lead him to it. Maybe I did, I don't know. But I dislike having strangers follow me.

If I hadn't been so ashamed of my ignorance as to which was the Left Bank I would have asked someone. But I couldn't bring myself to ask a total stranger, "Où est la Rive gauche?" only to have him give me a funny look and tell me I was standing on it. Like being in the centre of Edmonton and asking where Alberta is.

Besides, with my fractured French, when I asked a passerby a question such as "Où est la Rive gauche?" he invariably and quite boisterously directed me to the nearest sidewalk urinal. This created a fresh crisis, since French people are hospitable enough to make sure you get where they think you want to go, and first thing I knew I'd be in full flight across the city.

I therefore kept my mouth shut and waited for somebody to tip his hand. Sure enough, one night a fellow in a café mentioned that we were sitting on the Left Bank.

Instantly my sideburns lengthened and a deep scar appeared over my eye. Needless to say, I had a beret slung at the ready, and I clapped it on in a twinkling. Too large, it hooded my eyes, making me inscrutable to the point of blindness.

Unfortunately, as I learned later, the Left Bank is not the real district of vice in Paris. I was confusing it with Montmartre, which is on the Right Bank. This helps explain why the waiter of the café raised my beret enough for me to find my way out, at his suggestion, and why I stopped caring which Bank I was on, just so long as I kept out of the Seine. . . .

One of the world's more dangerous professions is that of being a pedestrian in Paris.

The diversity of origins of the cars that roar around Paris helps account for the peculiarly murderous quality of the traffic. Small, fast English cars that haven't quite got the hang of running on the right side of the street; big, faster American cars that fill the street entirely; swarms of tiny, very excitable Italian cars that prefer the sidewalk, all combine with the native transport of the French, who drive as though to be passed were a national disgrace to which death is preferable, especially the death of a pedestrian.

In Paris there is open season on pedestrians all year 'round. Find an elderly Parisian pedestrian and you'll have the ultimate in cunning and agility. Watch him cross the street, inciting a bus to charge, then nipping nimbly behind a stalled taxi that has flooded its carburetor in the excitement of trying to nail him. Beautiful footwork.

The ordinary city bus, which is old and rather near-sighted, lumbers after pedestrians like an arthritic rhinoceros. And as with the rhino, its most dangerous part is its horn. This horn suggests nothing more maleficent than a goosed duck, until you turn to find several tons of steel careening at you. Much of the time the driver honks for the sheer joy of honking, deriving a good deal of tactile pleasure from squeezing the big rubber bulb.

Generally speaking, drivers in Paris are of two types: those who drive with one hand on the horn, and those who drive with both hands on the horn. Except at night. By city by-law beeping is forbidden at night. Instead, cars should blink their lights before running down a pedestrain. One of the charms of Paris night life is the sight of two taxis winking at each other as they trap a pedestrian in a hotbox. And any driver whose lights have failed can harvest a bumper crop before he's chided by a policeman.

The Paris traffic policeman puts a nice rhythm into the chaos by standing in a concrete pillbox and waving cars in all directions. He is especially useful in the large, busy squares. These squares, which are round, give the motorist a chance to circle and take another crack at a pedestrian. The pedestrian's only defence here is to run with other pedestrians in a pack. Most European cars, being small and light, will not take on more than five people, or two bicycles, at once. The Paris taxi will take on anything except passengers.

Before the creation of the atomic bomb, the Paris taxi was rated by connoisseurs as the most destructive force known to man. Every one is familiar with the characteristic tilted-back posture of the cabbie's body, resulting from unremitting effort to push the accelerator through the floorboard.

Only the advanced age of most of the hacks has saved the population from extinction. Most of those that ferried troops to the Marne in World War I have been retired, but their successors have inherited the same bellicose spirit, and anybody who tries to assess France's military potential must take them into account.

Ask the man who's been knocked prone by one. . . .

Christmas comes to Paris. The spirit of faith and goodwill to men creeps in, like a cautious reindeer, amidst the sudden silence of the International Conferences. The meetings of the Big Threes, Big Fours and Big Fives are momentarily fused into a meeting with the Big One.

In the window of the large department store, to merry music coming from nowhere in particular, gaily frocked dolls bow solemnly to each other, a Don Quixote inspires jerky hysteria in the humpbacked jester, and a grand lady in a splendid coach favours all with her gracious if somewhat incessant smile, despite the apparent dislocation of her neck. Past this bright spectacle, their eyes shining with that childfulness that is their ultimate sophistication, file the Parisians, great big adult Parisians, with here and there a child who has managed to squeeze into the parade.

To give the kids an even break, the big department store has devoted two whole floors to toys. Both floors are crowded but a lot of people aren't buying anything. Desperately jolly clerks demonstrate unsinkable rubber ducks and miniature pinball games, but they can't conceal the pricetags. *Le Rapide*, for example, a tiny electric train frantically chasing its own caboose, never escapes the glowering overhang: "10,000 francs." Ten thousand francs is half the monthly wage of many a French workingman.

So the wistful adults admire *Le Rapide* and buy a football. In France this has been a vintage year for footballs. As well there are bugeyed woolly dogs and elephants, and a little red car that buzzes in circles, stops, makes its own hood and door fly open, rams its neighbours, and in all respects duplicates the performance of a Paris taxi.

The dolls are back, too. French dolls wear more eyeshadow and rouge than Canadian dolls, and somehow they convey the impression that, tilted backwards, they would be more likely to cry for Daddy than Momma.

But of course the focus of fascination is the old white-whiskered gent in the red playsuit. In France S. Claus assumes the alias of *Père Noël* and is considerably thinner than in his North American appearances. In postwar Europe, a fat Santa would be vaguely unbelievable.

Outside in the street the bustling shoppers pause a moment before the splendour of the few Christmas trees France has been able to cull from her balding prairie. By no means everyone can afford a tree, even a scraggy pup of a jackpine, but in all the parlours there is something green and gay and warmed by real candles, which amazingly enough are almost as effective as the safe, brittle, electric kind, the kind they have in the gilded salons of the International Conferences. . . .

My first evening at the Paris Opera convinced me that Canada should order a theatre just like it. No, better make it a half-dozen, to make sure the West gets one.

The Paris Opera would bring out the patrician in a sandhog, with its elaborate promenades, mirrors, marble columns, chandeliers, and the usual gay assortment of nude nymphs painted on the ceiling. Airplane neck is an occupational disease for the tourist in France. When in doubt the French artist paints a nude, right above your head. In the gorgeous chambers of the *Hôtel de Ville*, for example, one finds paintings representing the discovery of electricity (nude holding bolt of lightning), the agrarian sciences (nude holding small bunch of barley stalks), the invention of the dynamo (nude looking dynamic), and so on.

Anyhow, it isn't hard to believe that before the latest war the Opera was formal. As I ascended to my seat I seemed to sense a battery of searchlights playing on the fray of my collar. My seat was in the third balcony loges and cost me 185 francs (about 50 cents). All the cheap seats are called loges at the Opera, giving you the aristocratic feeling of being entitled to spit on patrons in the orchestra, where the newly rich sit.

You reach the loges by means of a marble staircase which you instinctively mount slowly and gracefully, back straight, chin up, hand resting lightly on the hilt of the sword (or, as in my case, on the bag of the caramels). The stairs are liberally busted with greats of the operatic past and with members of the *Garde Républicain*, who stand around looking colourful in their dress uniforms, politely resisting attempts of American visitors to pack them off as souvenirs.

You give your ticket to an ancient lady who makes a career of unlocking the doors giving access to your loge, and you follow her into red-plush luxury. You fight off the impulse to wipe your feet before entering. Instead, after tipping the crone, you saunter to whichever is your chair of the six or seven in the box, and sit down to enjoy the vista of people in other loges. Since the tiers of loges rise in successive horsehoes to the ceiling, you can lean over the front of yours and gaze down the décolletage of the ladies in the box below. All this, mind you, and the curtain hasn't even gone up yet.

I hadn't been sitting in my loge five minutes before I began feeling like the Emperor Franz Josef (in his prime). If a lady had offered me her hand, palm downwards, I would undoubtedly have kissed it. My discharge button blossomed into the Order of the Royal Thundermug, or maybe it was a Star of the Knightsblood Dripping. I plucked off my gloves one finger at a time, instead of by the rip in the cuff as usual.

I found myself bowing to people who didn't bow back, so I became distant and aloof. In the third balcony loges you have no trouble being distant. The only people that are more distant are those in the fourth balcony loges.

But by the time the conductor raised his baton I was relishing a sensation that should be available to everyone: being part of a lovely jewelbox set with human faces and ivory shoulders, a proud and sparkling necklace of civilized living.

The opera? *Aida*, and very good, too. The tenor, an old model, tended to ping a bit on the hills, but the Egyptian dancing girls were just what the oculist ordered. . . .

As a mental cathartic, there's nothing better than a visit to a first-class zoo. An evening amongst the existentialists of the *Café de Flore* is not nearly as rewarding.

Paris has a first-class zoo, including a belligerent animal that charges eight francs to stand guard over your bike. The splendid thing about the zoo is that nearly all the animals are free of cages, roaming around large compounds landscaped to resemble their natural habitat, with only a moat to protect the wilder ones from visitors. Since the moats are unseen in horizontal perspective, you look across what seems to be a plain of lions and tigers and water buffalo at perfect liberty to stroll up and ask you the time. At first this effect is quite startling, as the old lady into whose arms I leapt could doubtless testify. None of the animals appear bored or run-down, and the tiger, in particular, pads endlessly back and forth along his parapet, muttering to himself in a way that shows clearly he hasn't abandoned the idea of chewing somebody's head off. For the mountain goats, and people who like to pretend they're mountain goats, the zoo has a man-built mountain of concrete, with an elevator, tunnels and a special room for that popular creature the W-C.

The elephants in their house, chained by the ankle, doing a little lock-step dance in their own dung, for peanuts, are more pitiful than Ophelia. The periscopic head of an ostrich appears over its rock enclosure, with that monstrous dignity that stupidity wears, and follows me to the giraffes, whose heads are lofty enough to persuade me momentarily that God too looks down with gentle eyes. For divine comedy give me a lioness playing with three knockabout clowns of cubs for whom the world hasn't yet learned to stand still, who stagger about in search of the agent responsible for continually pulling the floor out from under them, and fasten ever upon each other.

And for the microcosm of life's essentials take me to that hillside bedlam of monkeys — male monkeys, female monkeys, pig-gybacking baby monkeys, biting one another, conceiving, retriev-ing, exploring fur with the concentration of a psychiatrist, looking privately sad, or putting on a special shining face, a jittery false front, in hope of getting something from outside their world, something from us, all in a paradise of trees to shove one another off, water to drown one another in, and a few places where a monkey can be himself and meditate.

I enjoyed the Paris zoo. The only regrettable incident occurred when a little girl, after being shown the camels and hippos, burst out crying at the sight of me. Can't have everything, I suppose.

Wonderful education for the kiddies, a zoo like that. To hell with the birds and the bees: park the little quizzers for an after-noon in a zoo like the one in the *Bois de Vincennes*. After that, the only question they'll ask is whether they can have the car for the evening.

Considerably less entertaining and much more expensive than the zoo is the Folies Bergère.

The sign above the entrance to the theatre says, in English, "Line up here for tickets." In the queue around me people mum-ble to each other in English, in American, in German. I reflect that if there were anybody from home in Paris, this would be the place to run into him, blatant with baser nature.

The foyer is gaudy in red carpets, gilt and crystal. Behind the bar two bartenders wait confident of the inevitability of thirst after three hours on the theatrical desert ahead. An impassive blonde surrounded by a counter of rubber dolls squeezes one to make it do a little nautch dance. We all pass her by, intent on the larger infamy. We also pass up the programme sellers. What we have come to see will need no identification.

Seated, we have a few moments of hoping to be shocked and wondering how it can be done. The orchestra suddenly blows out the lights with a blare of overture peppy to the point of hysteria and guaranteed, if not to set the pulse racing, at least to discour-age conversation.

The curtain rises on *les girls*. *Les girls* are a naked neologism. To a Frenchman, a *girl* is somebody whose chest has no visible means of support, who is equally destitute of talent, and who parades across the stage with that desperate display of denture that can persuade the more sensitive spectator never to smile again. *Les girls* alternate between too many clothes, for the ladies in the audience, and not enough, for the men, interpolated by comedy as broad as it is long.

I find myself squirming under the implication that this is what the French think English and American and Canadian tourists want, and, worse, that they may be right. A young lady primly dressed in crinolines and buttoned to the neck steps before the curtain and announces the next act. We wonder why, until she turns around to exit and we see that the dress has no seat. The place reeks of mildewed Rabelais. I am shocked, yes, by the realization that what I am watching is naïve, pathetically innocent. It is about as erotic as a side of beef. It misses completely the delicious naughtiness inherent in North American puritanism. I wince to think how the show's producers must flail about for new ways of making nakedness interesting.

For, in Paris the naked body is accepted as calmly and frankly as sunshine. Every park is full of statuary devoted to literal representation of the human form, so that little boys know almost as soon as they can see that little girls are not entirely sugar and spice, while little girls note that frogs and snails and puppy dogs' tails are an incomplete catalogue of what constitutes little boys.

Result: to the adult Parisian mere nudity is banal. The aura of mystery with which Anglo-Saxons like to surround it he can understand just enough to profit by offering them the Folies Bergère and the *boîtes de nuit* (night clubs), which he punningly calls *boîtes d'ennui*.

The naughtiness traditionally associated with Paris is therefore largely an imported product, smuggled in by foreigners in great rolls of inhibitions. Paris doesn't change anybody, it just lets them be unashamed of what they already are.

For some people, especially those from places like Boston or Hamilton, this experience is as gratifying as shucking a girdle after a hot day. Many of them refuse to go home. They won't squeeze back into that darned thing. They want to lie around in the sidewalk cafés and go quietly to seed. And at home their sisters and uncles and cousins cry, "Oh, that awful Paris!" and try to book passage on the next boat.

But even when you understand that much, it's difficult to throw off the prudery of a lifetime. I found that out one day in the

Louvre. I was standing admiring a fine statue of Apollo when I was suddenly engulfed by little schoolgirls, being toured about by their teacher. These little girls, each with a note pad in her fist, gazed up relentlessly at the naked Apollo, then looked at me (in sports jacket and flannels), looked at Apollo, looked more sharply at me, whispered amongst themselves in fast French, and gathered around their teacher, a female. That was how I found myself running red-faced through the Louvre, until I found some nice, neutral Egyptian sarcophagi to stare at while I caught my breath.

I can remember, when I was quite young and entirely dependent on the meagre statuary visible in Vancouver, feeling guilty because I didn't have a figleaf. All grown males worthy of casting in bronze had one, it seemed. I was seriously pondering the possibility of transplanting when the light finally broke through and I realized that I was more evergreen than deciduous.

I walked away from the Folies Bergère feeling much the same way: disillusioned and vaguely insulted. No doubt the reason the French are so clever with clothes is that to them the body is a bit dull, but I felt that I had paid rather dearly to sit and watch them prove it.

A sentimental favourite won the medal in 1965. Gregory Clark in his seventy-third year had been a reporter since 1911, a war correspondent during World War II, and a popular columnist since 1947. A host of grateful readers was glad to see Gregory Clark War Stories *win this coveted award.*

GREGORY CLARK
from Gregory Clark War Stories

As a souvenir of a place, or of an event, a walking stick has it over almost any other trinket. China, glass, get broken; funny hats get moth-eaten; Tyrolean leather pants wither, grow stiff with age; objets d'art get shoved back farther and farther in forgotten bureau drawers. But sticks? Boy, you can fill the back of a clothes closet with them, and they're always there, rattling around, falling over, asserting themselves, year unto year, memories living and vibrant. All you've got to do is pick one up and take it out for a walk, and the full strange, sweet story of it comes back in Technicolor.

This whole-bark Malacca, for instance. It is beautiful, see? A soft, faded golden color; the buff, maybe, of a Kildeer plover. But faintly mottled. And see this odd ridge that runs the full length of the stick? That proves it to be a whole-bark Malacca. This stick is made of a giant grass, no less, that grows in the jungles of Malaya.

I met this stick on the deck of a refugee ship. It was one of the Duchesses, and she was steaming hellbent for Canada across the North Atlantic with 350 English children and 400 adults, and lifeboats enough for about half of us.

We had set sail in the morning, with five destroyers running with us until nightfall, by which time we were round the end of Ireland; and we changed direction, the destroyers left us, and we drove, all dark and sightless, into the North.

It was the queerest ship ever I was in, loud with the clamour and gaiety of children, hundreds of them, from infants of noble name in the charge of frightened Nanas, all up through toddlers, six-year-olds, ten-year-olds, grave spindle-shanked English schoolgirls, very proper. And as I say, we had only so many lifeboats.

We elders, when the first morning dawned, looked out at the sea with wry grins. Now, even if you got the kids into the lifeboats, who would row them? It was the first time being an elder had me really baffled.

So, with chests out and strong legs, and hearty grins, we 400 promenaded the decks amidst the scampering children, and pretended not to be thinking at all, much less thinking about what hammered at our hearts and brains like demons.

Most of the elders were refugees too. We had a famous lord, for example, whose luggage, it was whispered about, contained half the wealth of Britain, with which he had been entrusted to bring to Ottawa for safekeeping. Three knob-headed Scotsmen among us were reputed to have, under their brindle thatches, practically all the knowledge of nuclear physics that was then known in Britain. You see, it was quite a cargo for a romantic man to inspect.

I saw this cane, this whole-bark Malacca, in the hands of a sturdy man who was promenading the deck with a very beautiful woman and an equally beautiful child.

He had stiff red hair, and a wide, kind face that reminded me, somehow, of Harpo Marx. But he didn't know beans about handling a walking stick. I fell in behind him, to get a better look at the beautiful stick.

It was clumsy in his hands. He tapped it on the deck as he walked, then tried to swing it jauntily. But he tapped it out of time, out of rhythm with his pacing; and he swung it at the wrong instant of his stride.

About the third time round the deck, he smiled at me across his shoulder.

"You are admiring," he said, in a distinct foreign accent, "my stick."

"I am. It is beautiful."

"Friends gave it to me," he said. I believe it cost £10. That is $40?"

He was astonished at his own statement, and held the Malacca up for our reverent regard.

"In my country," he said, "Hungary, there is an old saying: 'Never refuse a staff to a pilgrim.' "

And with the most glowing smile, he held the Malacca toward me.

"No, no!" I cried, stepping back. "Good heavens, no, I was merely admiring it! I am a fancier of sticks. But please forgive me, I wouldn't dream . . . "

"Never," said the redheaded man, "refuse a staff to a pilgrim. I am very superstitious. I feel very strong I must give you this stick. I am not happy with it. I do not know how to walk with it. I am strangers with it. Please!"

He thrust the Malacca at me.

"My name is Clark," I said helplessly, taking the stick.

"My name is Korda," said the redheaded man.

"Korda!" I froze.

"Ah, not the great Korda, not Alexander. I am only Vincent, his brother, and his art director."

He introduced me to his beautiful wife, his glowing child.

"Down in my cabin," I said, "I have a whole bundle of sticks. Mr. Korda, I will go and pick one which I too will give to a pilgrim. And what is more, I will walk the rest of the voyage with that pilgrim and teach him how to swing and love a stick."

I gave him a blackthorn, with a round crook, a gypsy stick, very finely studded, black as a stallion, lovely to heft.

And when we reached Quebec, all safe and sound, we had walked a hundred miles, talked a thousand things, and Vincent Korda could swing a stick.

Hmmm! Now, see this other stick. It is crab-apple. . . .

George Bain, formerly a journalist for the Toronto Globe and Mail *and currently with the London Bureau of the* Toronto Star, *has a unique distinction in the history of the Leacock Medal. His* Nursery Rhymes to be Read Aloud by Young Parents with Old Children, *the selection in 1966, is the only book of verse ever to win the award.*

GEORGE BAIN

from Nursery Rhymes to be Read Aloud by Young Parents with Old Children

IBEX

If inching up the steep inclines
Which mark the Alps and Apennines
You chanced to meet a sort of goat
With reddish, greyish-brownish coat
And heavy horns that backward curled
(By colour, grey-to-white, and knurled),
An agile, sturdy, close-knit beast
Whose joy in life seemed much increased
To leap with death-defying leap
Across some chasm yawning deep,
I'd say you'd met an Ibex there
— But maybe not; they're awfully rare.

The Ibex is a species of wild Goat. One type is called the *Ibex ibex*, a name that sounds like the sound you get on the phone when the line is busy.

There is also a type called the Chetan Ibex, which is a source of bezoar. Bezoar is a calculus or concentration found in the stomach or intestines of some animals, chiefly ruminants, and is formed of layers of animal matter deposited around some foreign substance.

Bezoar balls are valued in Iran as a cure for various ailments, including poisoning. First you've got to catch your Ibex. Even then, getting it to surrender the bezoar balls is no cinch. Everything would be much easier if the Ibex could be persuaded to lay them, like eggs.

The Ibex you see on the top of the Alps and Apennines will be a male Ibex, because that's the way they run things. The male Ibexes stay up in the hills until October, when they come down to join the ladies. Shortly afterward they return to their crags, leaving their mates to look after the incipient little Ibexes.

This is an arrangement which gives the male Ibex a lot of freedom and saves the female Ibex a lot of climbing. They seem to be very happy with it.

Donald Jack has done more writing for the theatre than any other medium but two of his three books about Bartholomew Bandy and his exploits with the Canadian army overseas in World War I have won the Leacock Medal for Humour, in 1963 and 1974. Bandy, a perfect foil for Jack's puckish sense of the absurd, was introduced in Three Cheers for Me, *the 1963 winner.*

DONALD JACK
from Three Cheers for Me

They withdrew the four companies of the second battalion for rebuilding near Amiens. As Amiens was only twenty miles away, naturally we went on foot. I must have presented a proud sight, marching at the head of my platoon of four men.

After a few miles we had a real road to walk on. Its camber was slight, but the feeling of it underfoot was so unfamiliar after the days of soft ground and mud that we kept staggering sideways like crabs.

We were in rest near Amiens for some weeks. Gradually the reinforcements from Canada got the battalion back to full strength. . . .

The men were delighted to be within deserting distance of a city that, after the battered towns of the front line, seemed to be a teeming metropolis. Not even Amiens' prices could damp their enthusiasm for its relative gaiety.

As for myself, I went into town twice and was pleased to see the stained glass in the cathedral almost unharmed. I got lost the first time I went, and was accosted by a dirty woman. The second time, I drove in with Captain Karley . . . and we had an expensive dinner. Karley grew gay on red wine and champagne and finally vanished with the restaurateur's daughter into the gloomy, cockroach-infested depths of the back rooms, leaving me to get back to camp on foot. I got lost again.

Mostly, though, I stayed in my tent to catch up on sleep, write letters, and read the Good Book intensely.

Rupert refused to enter Amiens but talked to me at all hours of the day and night. Once he sat up on his elbow at three in the

31

morning. "Are you awake?" he asked in a penetrating whisper. He went on without waiting for a reply. "You know, I'm beginning to have doubts."

This was so intriguing that I said, "Doubts? You mean, religion?"

"Certainly not," he said in a shocked tone. "Whatever gave you that idea?"

What indeed.

"I mean about coming through this thing alive."

"Oh," I said. Then, "Why?"

"Well, look what happened to all those others. Some of them were quite devout men. A corporal in my platoon was almost as, well, religious as I, but he was — He always began his letters home, 'Dear sister in Christ,' you know. But they got him the second he went over the top."

We were silent for a moment.

"Bartholomew?"

"Yes?"

"Do you know I've never — well, been with a — " The last word was drowned by a cough.

"A what?"

"A woman," he said angrily.

It took a moment to adjust to this new topic.

"How do you mean?"

"You know."

"You mean —?"

"Yes. Someone I knew back home had been, well, with a woman when he was only nineteen." Rupert was silent for a moment. "I'm twenty-three," he said.

We both contemplated this in such profound silence that I was able to get back to sleep.

I was awakened again at five.

"Bartholomew?"

"Mmm?"

"Have you?"

"What?"

"Been with — "

"You mean — "

"Yes."

"No."

Rupert sighed and went back to sleep. He seemed annoyed with me.

The days passed in orderly officer duties, lectures on gas, Boer War tactics, bugle calls, and a lot of other things I'd learned months before. I took a lot of church parades, shouted "at the halt on the left, form platoon," and managed to get rid of most of my lice.

We dined for a time in Battalion Mess, presided over by the lieutenant colonel, who told a good many dirty stories, skillfully twirling his swagger stick between his fingers the while. Having earned his displeasure, I tried to make myself as inconspicuous as possible, but failed the first day when he noticed I wasn't laughing.

"What's the matter, Bandy, are my little pleasantries too much for your pristine ears?"

Everyone chortled.

"I don't approve of foul stories, sir," I said.

Everyone groaned.

"You don't approve, eh? Frankly, Bandy, you terrify me."

I thought it better to keep quiet.

"But you're inspiring at the same time. Inspiring in your purity. The chaplain tolerates my poor, tired efforts, but you don't."

It was with a shock that I saw the padre was indeed in the mess. He had been sitting there all along with a set smile on his face.

The colonel said a good many more cutting things, but in so inimitable a fashion that everyone was vastly amused.

After that he told disgusting stories every day, looking at me pointedly, as if interested solely in my reaction.

Gradually I saw that he would never leave me alone. Silent dignity having failed, I decided to return to my natural behavior.

On Boxing Day he told a particularly revolting story. By now, everyone had joined in the game of turning pointedly to me at the end of each story, my expression apparently adding to their enjoyment.

"What, Bandy, still not appreciating my little drolleries?" the colonel remarked, tap-tapping at the table with his stick.

"No, sir."

"Perhaps he doesn't understand them?" the adjutant suggested.

"By heavens, Fred, I think you've got something there! That must be the explanation. Admit it now, Bandy; you don't really understand them. Well, let's see. I'll tell another little story, and we'll examine Lieutenant Bandy afterward to see if he understands it. Perhaps, why, perhaps we'll even have him laughing. Well, here goes:

"A farmer was taking his prize cow to market to be inseminated — I won't use the simpler, Saxon word in consideration of Bandy's feelings — and of course also the chaplain's. Eh, Padre?"

The padre smiled and shifted uncomfortably.

"Well, as I said, the farmer was taking the cow to be bulled, and as he was going down a country lane, Giles was sitting on a fence — this is an English joke, Bandy.

" 'Where be you taking cow, George?' Giles asked.

" 'Oi be taking it to market to be bulled.'

"Giles nodded, and George went on his way, but when he got to market the bull wasn't there, so he had to go home. The next day he passed Giles again.

" 'Where be you taking cow, George?' Giles asked.

" 'Oi be taking it to market to be bulled.'

"Giles nodded, and George went on; but again the bull had failed to turn up, so George had to go home again.

"The third day he passed Giles again.

"Where be you taking cow, George?'

" 'Oi be taking it to market to be bulled.'

" 'Oi don't like to seem to be interfering, like,' Giles said, 'but seems to me you be making a regular whore out of that cow.' "

The colonel waited expectantly.

"No, Bandy? No smile? Does Bandy not see the joke?"

"I don't think he knows what inseminated *or* bulled means, sir," the adjutant said.

"Well, let's see. What does it mean, Bandy?"

I told him.

"Excellent! Full marks! A round of applause, please, for Subaltern Bandy."

Everyone clapped heartily, looking at me with gleaming red faces, including, I was saddened to note, Rupert.

"Now, next. Do you know what a market is, Bandy?"

"Yes, sir, where they sell vegetables."

"Fine. Finally, do you know what a whore is? Do you know, Bandy?"

"Yes, sir."

"What is it?"

"An immoral woman, sir."

"Very, very good. So will you now kindly explain to the company the joke. Will you, Bandy?"

"Yes, sir." I thought for a moment. "This farmer George was taking his cow to market to be inseminated by a bull, but the bull wasn't there, which was hardly surprising because they don't allow that kind of thing in the middle of a market. It's not good for the children. George was therefore wasting his time. The usual procedure is for the bull to be brought to the cow. George obviously was an incompetent gentleman farmer devoted to raising hordes of gentlemen, with or without pedigrees.

"Also, sir, as you admitted that it was a market devoted to selling vegetables, George was not merely incompetent but absurd if he expected to find a a bull there. Why, he'd be looking in a china shop next — "

"But this is an English market, Bandy. All sorts of nasty, immoral things go on at English markets," the colonel said, rapping the table angrily.

"Yes, sir, but I happen to know that there weren't any bulls at this particular market; they'd long since slaughtered them off to make swagger sticks out of their pizzles. Did you know that's what swagger sticks were made of, sir?"

"I — " the colonel said.

"It's a fact, sir, so that when you're striding along twirling your swagger stick you are in effect making obscene gestures hardly in keeping with the military proprieties. I don't think the brigadier would like that, sir."

The colonel was in the middle of twirling his stick. He looked at it with a slight start, then put it on the table.

"We're not discussing swagger sticks," he said. "We're discussing markets, and I say there was a bull in that market, do you hear?"

"If you insist, sir."

"I do insist."

"In that case why did George have to take his cow there three times?"

"Because the bull wasn't feeling well," the colonel said. He was about to pick up his stick to rap the table but changed his mind.

Captain Karley murmured: "Personally I think the bull recognized the cow as his cousin. That would explain everything, sir."

"That's right," the colonel said gratefully.

"If they were cousins," Spanner said, "wouldn't that be incest?" He sounded disapproving.

"That would be the end of the world as we know it," I remarked.

"Don't listen to them, sir," the adjutant said, glaring. "This incest business is red herrings."

"Whoever heard of red herrings committing incest?" I said. "Incidentally, are herrings red? I always thought they were brown."

"Certainly they're red," Karley said, "with shame, because they're always committing incest."

The colonel wasn't allowing the initiative to be seized from him. He scratched his face angrily. "It's not the herrings that were guilty of incest," he said. "It's the bull."

"Don't you think the cow was more to blame?" a subaltern asked, timidly. "After all, it was she who made the advances. *Cherchez la femme*, you know," he added as an afterthought.

"Certainly," Karley said spiritedly. "She advanced all the way to market, under fire from Giles."

"So it was really Giles to blame for the whole sorry business," Spanner said. "Holding up the cow's advance. I wouldn't be surprised if he was really a German spy in disguise."

There then ensued a heated discussion about Giles. Becoming bored in the middle of it, I wandered out just as the colonel, in a fit of pique, threw his stick at the phonograph, which was playing a popular song called, "You're the Apple of My Eye, Although You're Rotten to the Core."

My days were now fully occupied in instructing my platoon from the infantry training manual and lecturing on a variety of subjects ranging from gas to the Care and Maintenance of One's Weapon. I let Markis, now a corporal, give the lecture on prophylaxis because he seemed to know more about it than I. I became quite fluent during these lecture sessions, although I rarely knew what I was talking about.

Meanwhile, as the time drew near for our next tour in the trenches, Rupert became more and more morose. On New Year's Eve he disappeared and didn't come back until four in the morning. Shortly after the first of January we went back up, and were ten days in support and five days in the line. . . .

Day after day after day we shivered in the line or huddled in the evil-smelling, rat-infested dugouts. I tried to busy myself looking after the men, but they were resourceful enough, especially Corporal Markis, who was once caught trying to bring in a four-poster from a newly wrecked house. Foiled in this endeavor, he made do with a magnificent spring mattress supported on barbed wire. My new sergeant, called Bunser, was a strange character. He was small and had a dark, blue face, and went around with his shoulders hunched under a cape so that he looked like a bundle of old rags wrapped in waterproofing. For some reason every single member of my platoon was under average height. I felt like Snow White among the seven dwarfs, except that there were more than seven of them.

Every time I went into their dugout, they were playing cards. Everyone in the army seemed to play cards, devotedly, fanatically. I learned how to play poker, just by watching them. Once, Markis, who always won, gave me an interesting lecture on the subject. He also told me that I ought to try it myself; I'd be a natural.

"Why?"

"You got the best poker face I ever saw."

Nothing much happened during that tour. The snipers picked off their usual daily quota.

We had five days of rest, billeted at a farmhouse whose owners, an old French couple, had stayed on even though they had lost all their stock and their fields had been trampled and furrowed into quagmires by boots and gun carriages. I spent my time on work parties, sleeping and watching the airplanes wander back and forth over the lines, and began to envy the pilots. We received a large batch of mail while at rest. I had five letters from home and a brochure from a medical-supply firm in the States offering me a year's supply of pessary rings at an unheard-of discount. The letters from Mother . . . hoped I was keeping up my piano lessons.

The entire Somme front having gone to sleep, we were moved to the Flanders section of the line. The division rattled on rails and stumbled on *pavé* for four days, then to everyone's disgust went straight into the front line.

I had thought the conditions were poor enough in the Somme. They were a bed of roses compared with Ypres. I never saw such an abominable desolation, even though two or three inches of

snow obscured the harsher wounds. The furrows of the front and
support trenches were like poisonous scars. No man's land was a
cesspool, without even the merciful covering of snow, for the
snow had been dissipated by the crumps.

The dugout I shared with Randle and Barayan was carved out
of clay, and the walls trickled.

We were perpetually soaked and trembling with cold. The daily
half-pint of rum was the one bright spot, and watching the others
drink it with obvious relish, it became an increasing effort to resist
the temptation. My teeth clattered audibly, but I was stubborn.
My servant made me numerous cups of coffee, but it was almost
always half cold before it was delivered, and didn't make me any
warmer. Finally, Karley became annoyed with me.

"Man, you'll never get warm unless you start drinking the
stuff."

"But you told me it only keeps you warm for half an hour."

"Half an hour's better than no loaf, isn't it? Do you think, you
stubborn idiot, that they'd include it with the rations and the
ammo if it wasn't a necessity? Drink it, man!"

"I promised my fa — "

"Promised! What does *he* know what it's like out here?"

"We're not prejudiced, you know," Spanner murmured from
the depths of the blanket he was huddled in. "We're quite happy
to go on drinking your ration. It's for your own good."

"For my own good," I repeated. "M'yes, the thin edge of the
wedge."

"Randle is drinking his."

I turned, startled, to Barayan. He was looking at me with his
black eyes gleaming. "What?" I looked at Rupert incredulously.

"Sure," Karley said. "Haven't you noticed he hasn't been selling
it to us lately?"

I stared at Rupert for a moment, then back to Karley, holding
my hands over the candle to warm them. "Anyway, that's nothing
to do with me. I promised, and I always keep my promises."

They all snorted disgustedly. "You're a bumpkin," Selby snapped.

"What do promises matter?" Barayan said.

"They matter to me."

"Oh, God. A man of principle."

"Look, Bandy," Spanner said. "Don't look at it as demon rum.

It's medicine, pure and simple. Now, drink it up like a good boy, and release us from the suspense."

"I can stand the cold."

Karley glared. "Well, we can't stand you standing the cold," he snapped. "Look at your great blank face, man: it's purple. Do you want to go around looking like a baboon's behind? Drink it!"

"No, thanks. I already feel myself going downhill rapidly enough without that. If I started on rum I'd graduate to whisky. Before I knew where I was, I'd be reading novels."

"Once and for all, are you going to drink it?" Karley shouted.

"No."

"Oh, yes you are," Karley said. He stood up. "I order you formally, as your company commander, to drink that rum."

"Go to hell."

There was a dead silence, broken only by the crump of shells, the chatter of machine guns, the droning of a plane, and the squeal of rats. Karley was wide-eyed. Even Spanner had emerged from his blanket, his lean blue jaw slack with astonishment. Rupert was popeyed.

"Did you hear what I heard?" Karley asked faintly.

"I did," Spanner said grimly.

"He swore. He actually used bad language." Karley put his hand to his head and staggered, then sat down weakly, still staring at me. "He actually said 'hell.' "

"Gentlemen." Spanner got up in slow dignity and raised his mug. "A toast."

They all arose.

"To Second Lieutenant Bandy, Bartholomew W., who, on this nineteenth day of January in the year of our Lord nineteen hundred and seventeen, spoke for the first time like a true soldier."

They drank solemnly.

"Gentlemen," Spanner said, "I don't think we need press our Mr. Bandy any further. The thin edge is in; the die is cast. You can lead a horse to water, or rather rum — and this is not entirely irrelevant, for Bandy does resemble a horse — and sooner or later it will drink. It's just a matter of time, now. And time, as everyone knows, is on our side."

That night when Barayan was on duty I asked Rupert if it was true.

"Why not?" There was silence for a moment, then: "You know, Bandy, you have to adjust. You can't be a stick in the mud all your life."

"I can't?"

"No," Rupert said. "After all, this is France, not Canada."

"That's true," I said.

"Life is to be lived."

"Thank you for reminding me."

"But you — you're not getting anything out of it."

"How?"

"Well . . . " Rupert leaned over. "We are in a dangerous situation," he announced.

"Oh?"

"It calls for an adjustment to one's standards, one's — behavior. Take for example . . . " He hesitated. "Well, you don't even know anything, well, about women, for example. Do you?"

"No."

"There you are," he said.

"There who are, where?" I asked curiously. I had an idea this was leading somewhere.

"You haven't lived."

"Have you?" I asked.

He wriggled in his sleeping bag. "Certainly," he said.

"Just because you've been drinking rum?"

"Of course not," he said. "I mean the other."

I thought about it. It was true. I hadn't lived, not even in Toronto, at the university.

"You know, Bandy — you won't mind if I say this, I hope — but you're a terrible prig. Personally, I suspect anyone who goes round parading his piety and moral superiority. It's not superiority at all; it's lack of experience."

"What are you talking about, Rupert?"

"That's another thing. Must you call me Rupert? Everyone else addresses each other by their surnames. We're not at school, you know."

"I'll try to remember. Now will you tell me what you're talking about?"

"I'm not talking about anything," he said crossly.

"What do you mean by experience?"

Rupert, or rather Randle, clicked his tongue and gave an impatient sigh. "You *are* a fool, Bandy. I don't know what I ever saw in you." He plucked morosely at his flea bag. "You know, they're still laughing at you over the beer vats."

He was referring to my reaction when on taking the men for their ablutions one day at rest I found they were using huge beer vats in an abandoned brewery as bathtubs. Only the lice that were building cities in my armpits had overcome my reluctance to dip myself in the officers' vat; I had complained of smelling of beer for two days afterward.

There was a long silence. Rupert started to speak two or three times, but didn't. Finally he said, "And I suppose when you were in Amiens you just went to look at the cathedral."

"Yes, why?"

"One can't spend all one's life looking round churches."

"I only spent a couple of hours. Now, if you'll excuse me, I'm going back to sleep."

I was almost asleep when he said, "I went with a woman."

I sat up. "What woman?"

"How should I know?" he said. He clicked his tongue impatiently "I wasn't interested in her *name*."

"So that's what you meant by experience. When was this?"

"On New Year's Day."

"Oh." I remembered.

Randle lay back with a sigh. "She called me Chéri," he said. "She was very affectionate."

"Well, I hope you looked after yourself," I said, and lay down again.

"How do you mean? She didn't steal my money, if that's what you mean."

"You know what I mean."

"Oh, that. Certainly," he said, loftily.

There was another pause. Then he said with a half-snigger, "though I must admit I was alarmed later when I got a . . . " He coughed. "But it went away."

I sat up again. "You mean a sore?"

"Yes," he almost shouted. "Do you have to be so — so — " He struggled for the word, couldn't find it, and snuggled down into his bag.

"And it went away? How long did it last?"

He sighed noisily. "I didn't mark it on a calendar," he said acidly. "I didn't have my stop watch with me. Now are you satisfied? You know, I'm becoming rather shocked at you, Bandy. This curiosity seems to me definitely unhealthy. A couple of weeks," he added scornfully.

I was forced to sound knowledgeable. "I guess you know the incubation period for the *Spirochaeta pallida* is about two to three weeks."

"You're talking nonsense as usual."

"Are you sure?" I could see he wasn't. "If I were you I'd go to the M.O. tomorrow."

"But I tell you it's gone."

"All the more reason. It's entrenching itself in your bloodstream. You'd better counterattack."   ·

"Oh, Lord, another amateur strategist."

"Good night," I said.

"Are you sure?"

"Yes."

"How?"

"I picked it up," I said.

"*You*'ve got it, too?"

"Certainly not. I mean, I picked up the information. At medical school." I heard him lie down slowly. It was a long time before he answered.

"I think you're bluffing."

I didn't say anything.

"I definitely won't. Never."

I remained silent.

"I'll never go. What would he think? What would everyone think?"

"What does that matter?" I said.

"I'll never," he said, in tones of finality.

But he did and it was and he went, and I never saw him again at the Front. . . .

The first Québecoise to win the Leacock award was Angeline Hango. Truthfully Yours, the story of her bilingual, convent-bound childhood, took the prize in 1949.

ANGELINE HANGO

from Truthfully Yours

During our last trip to the country my love life began. . . . I loved the baker. . . . That baker came every morning and I would dash out of bed and run downstairs to meet him. I hate to admit this but I know that I did not put on a dressing gown because I shall never forget my first dressing gown and I got that when I was about twenty; and no one else ever had one like it. I will tell you about it later. However, I am sure I was quite decently covered with my pyjamas, even though it was not proper. He smiled at me and I was happy the rest of the day. I was so homely, or at least I thought I was, and skinny and shy in a way, that it did not enter maman's head that a man would ever pay any attention to me. I think that she felt that our ignorance of life and our convent upbringing was insurance against our being interested in men. She was wrong. There was not a man around that I was not in love with. Of course, it was a deep secret; at least I hope it was. Maman could not see anything because she was too close to me but I may have looked pretty silly to others. . . .

I remember the wild dreams I concocted while I was lying in bed waiting for the baker to come. I was wishing that when he came to the house he would notice some smoke and then open the door and find the house on fire. Then he would think of me, throw his armful of loaves on the floor and dash upstairs and find me still sleeping. It became a little awkward at that point. I should have looked very beautiful with my hair a charming mass of curls like Ruth Roland's (heroine of the serial movie days) but the fact is that I had straight hair and furthermore it was put up in rags. I hurried to remove the rags and stuff them under my pillow. Then

44

I went on with my dream. He would take me in his arms and carry me away. That thought was so delightful that it was as far as my dream ever went. There was nothing I could add. . . .

Then I loved the dentist. . . . He could have pulled every tooth and I don't think that silly smile would have come off my face. I never took my eyes off him; I looked just like Andy Hardy when he is admiring a sophisticated blonde. I was to go every other day for two weeks, and I lived for every other day. Maman came with me the first time only, and after that she hoped I knew the way to his office. I think the drilling hurt quite a bit, but it was heavenly. Once he blew that little syringe-looking affair down my bosom instead of on my tooth and I was embarrassed, but I giggled and blushed and he laughed, and I thought that he was lovely and playful; but I also knew that I would not tell maman that. I never saw him again. My teeth were terribly good and by the time I needed a new filling I had had many another silent love. That is, I like to think they were silent, but I am afraid that one look at me and all these males knew I was tremendously in love and I think the brutes were flattered.

I was in love with the doorman of the large department store. . . . I am sure maman was quite pleased with me for wanting to be so helpful in going for errands, and that is probably when I started to acquire the reputation for being very kind. The thing is that I was in love with the doorman. He was so handsome and he smiled at me so sweetly. It did not occur to me that he was paid to do just that, and that probably he also was very much amused at seeing me so often and so reluctant to go past him, going or coming. The fact that I invariably forgot something was explained by my desire, according to Freud, to see him again, and my sub-conscious did the rest. . . .

Then, I was in love with my English teacher. . . .

Maman decided that I needed a little more English and she arranged for a handsome (is it possible that they were all really handsome?) young man boarding in the neighbourhood to come three times a week and give me lessons in English conversation.. . .

I don't know how much he charged maman for those painful hours but whatever he got he earned. After school every one of these three times a week found me looking my best and all a flutter waiting for that door bell. Maman would leave us alone in the living room and the conversation would start. He would try very hard by asking me questions in English. I understood every-thing, but the sight of a handsome man focusing all his attention on me, and smiling besides, was too much for me and I could not talk, so I would just either nod or shake my head to indicate yes or no to his questions. He explained to me that I would never learn the language that way and that I must express myself, so to his next questions I said a little yes or a little no according to what seemed demanded, and of course I had that Pepsodent smile and my eyes were glued on him. To me it was heavenly — again — but to him it was torture and after a few lessons he found an easier way of earning a few dollars and explained that he could not come any more. Maman was quite disgusted with me and seemed to think I was hopeless, and I myself had a sense of failure, but try as I might, I had not been able to do my share and express myself. A foreign language and a man's attention, and love, and shyness, all wrapped up together had been too much for me. In fact, it was almost a relief not to have to cope with that any longer.

I kept on attending the private school taught by an old man. He was probably thirty-five. The class was quite small but he had me by myself in a small room and would come and bend over my work and just about put his arms around me. Well! There I was again. He was very nice to me and somehow I was not shy with him but that love was cut very short because right after All Saints Day holiday his school was automatically closed. The teacher had disappeared, and so had a young girl. There is something I must tell you right now. It was not at all made clear to me then why the school had closed, or that the teacher had run away, and even if maman had told me that the man had run away with a young girl I would not have known what for. And I was sixteen! I was sixteen and I was guessing.

It was at about that time that I came home one day and an-nounced that Annette, my girl friend, was going to get an Alsatian for her bitch so that they would have thoroughbred puppies. I will never forget what a sensation that announcement caused. Papa and maman were stunned for a moment, a very short moment, and then papa flew into a rage (he was very quick tempered) and maman scolded me and said I was never to go with that girl again and that was what came from associating with older girls. I had announced that in all innocence, merely repeating what I had heard, but this storm made me think that there must be something to getting two dogs together. I was terribly ignorant and had not the faintest notion of where babies came from. I had never seen a little baby closely and had never been allowed to play with a little boy. I was just beginning to wonder though how babies came. When I was little I had asked the nuns but always they had looked shy and turned away, so I had stopped asking. And never would I have asked maman or papa. So that by the time I was fifteen or sixteen I had just taken it for granted that when people got married something happened in church — of all places — and that at intervals babies were delivered to such people. I had never given the matter very much thought except that I would have liked to know exactly how they came. I figured the stork story did not make sense, so as time went on I became more and more curious. I had overheard maman say to papa that So and So was going to have a baby. I knew So and So, and she was not married, so that shattered my something-must-happen-in-church theory; and also how did maman know that girl was going to have a baby? Well, I would have died rather than ask maman. When I had reached puberty I was told it was a big sin to talk to other little girls about such things, so I never asked anyone. Besides, in my conceit, it never occurred to me that the other girls knew any more about it than I did, and being a good little girl I just dismissed the whole thing and kept right on with my loves. Well, I was sent back to the convent. I guess maman had had enough of male teachers. . . .

Paul Hiebert has distinguished himself in widely separated fields, winning the Governor General's Medal for Science in 1924 and the Leacock Medal for Humour in 1948. Sarah Binks is an unusually funny book and may be the finest of its kind ever written. It is the only extended piece of parody to win the Leacock medal. It is so well done that sometimes even the most knowledgeable reader has to be reminded that there is no such poet as Sarah Binks. She and her delightfully atrocious poetry are all from the inventive mind of Paul Hiebert.

PAUL HIEBERT
from Sarah Binks

A plain shaft of composition stone with the simple inscription:

HERE LIES
SARAH BINKS

marks the last resting place of the Sweet Songstress of Saskatch-ewan. Below the inscription at the base of the shaft in smaller letters is carved the motto: ALONE, and above it in larger type:

THIS MONUMENT WAS ERECTED BY THE
CITIZENS OF THE MUNICIPALITY
OF NORTH WILLOWS
AND WAS UNVEILED ON JULY 1, 1931
BY
THE HON. AUGUSTUS E. WINDHEAVER
IN THE PRESENCE OF
THE REEVE AND COUNCIL

Here follow the names of the reeve and councillors together with the names of a number of outstanding statesmen of the day. Truly a fitting tribute to so great a woman. And it is no less a tribute to the Province of Saskatchewan that on the occasion of the unveiling of this monument the register of names at the Commercial House at Willows should be at the same time the roster of the greatest of Saskatchewan's sons. The Hon. A.E. Windheaver writes of that occasion in a letter[1] to his committee:

[1] Private letter, now in possession of the Author.

49

It was hot as hell! There was no making it by road and we could have arranged for a hot box to hold the 4:46 for half an hour, but it was no use. We had to stick it until everybody was through. I think I was wise to leave out the tariff in my speech. This Sarah seems to be something of a tin god around here.

Something of a god! The tribute of a great statesman to a great artist and a great woman.

Halfway between Oak Bluff and Quagmire in Saskatchewan lies the little town of North Willows. Its public buildings are unpretentious but pure in architectural style. A post office, two general stores, Charley Wong's restaurant and billiard parlour, two United churches, the Commercial House (Lib.), the Clarendon Hotel (Cons.), a drug store, a consolidated school, and eighteen filling stations, make up the east side of Railway Avenue, its chief commercial street. On the west side Railway Avenue is taken up by the depot, the lumber yard and four elevators. At right angles to Railway Avenue runs Post Office Street, so called because the post office was on this street before the last provincial election. It is, however, generally known simply as the Correction Line.

Business in Willows is not what it used to be. The Board of Trade meets every Thursday night above Charley Wong's, and the younger set of the town is beginning to give up auction bridge in favour of contract, but in spite of these signs of progress there has been little real growth for several years. The town is now in what is known as the dry belt. Once it boasted seven elevators; one was torn down and two were destroyed by fire and have not been rebuilt. But Willows has little need for commercial greatness. It lives in its glorious past, and to its shrine every year come hundreds who pause for a brief moment at the Clarendon Hotel or the Commercial House, or buy gasoline at the "Sarah Filling Station."

If we follow Post Office Street, or the Correction Line, due east for half a mile to where it corrects we come to Willow View Cemetery where Sarah Binks's monument stands. From a distance it appears to rise in lonely grandeur. If we follow Post Office Street due west for a mile and a quarter from the town, we come to the North East Quarter of Section 37, Township 21, Range 9, West, the former home of Sarah Binks herself. Little remains of the old homestead. The house itself has been torn down by souvenir hunters, one of the barns leans drunkenly and the other is about to fall. Gophers play on the site of the little corral where Sarah kept the calf, wild roses grow where once were beans and potatoes. In the coulee, now dry, that ran behind the house, a meadowlark has built its nest. It may have been that Sarah, with the prophetic eye of the poetess, visualized this scene when, in her later years, she wrote those famous lines, now inscribed in bronze over the gateway of St. Midget's, entitled *Ode to a Deserted Farm*:

> How changed and bleak the meadows lie
> And overgrown with hay,
> The fields of oats and barley
> Where the binder twined its way!
>
> With doors ajar the cottage stands
> Deserted on the hill —
> No welcome bark, no thudding hoof,
> And the voice of the pig is still.

The west was still the West in the days when Jacob and Agathea Binks first homesteaded the N.E. ¼ Sec. 37, Township 21, R. 9, W. To the east lay Oak Bluff, the end of the steel. To the west stretched the boundless prairies of the North West Territories, in which, to quote Sarah's own words, "The hand of man hath never trod." Here was the home of the coyote and the gopher, the antelope still flaunted his lack of tail to the western wind, and the pensive mosquito wandered unafraid. A region rich in historical interests and traditions, of tales of Indian fights with their squaws, of squaws with the Mounted Police. Willows was then Wallows, and the very name, Oak Bluff, was derived from an old Indian word, or combination of words, indicating that at that spot the white man had been frightened or, to use the Indian term, "bluffed" at a conference between Chief Buffalo Chip and Colonel MacSqueamish, the outcome being described by the chief in the Cree dialect as being "oke," meaning very good, or excellent.

Into this free and untrammelled country came Jacob Binks and his wife Agathea (née Agathea Thurnow), the parents of Sarah. It is not known exactly from where they came but, from a report of a conversation in front of the post office, and from the fact that Sarah was often wont to refer to herself proudly as a daughter of the Old South, it is now generally accepted that they came from South Dakota. Beyond this fact we know little of the Binks antecedents. The Thurnows, however, are said to have traced their family back to Confederation. The parish records in Quoddykodiac in New Brunswick show that a daughter Agathea was born to one Abram Turnip and that the Turnips later moved to South Dakota. The name Turnip may have been Americanized to Thurnip and later to Thurnow.

Prosperity smiled upon Jacob and Agathea Binks. The original sod house of the homesteader was replaced by a more pretentious frame building faced with best quality tarpaper and having an outside stairs leading to the guest room over the kitchen roof. One entered the "lean-to" or antechamber before reaching the main body of the house and living quarters. This antechamber served the purpose of receiving and storage room. In it was kept the fuel, the churn, the harnesses undergoing repair, here the chickens were plucked, the eggs collected, and here slept Rover, the dog, and Ole, the hired man. Through the antechamber one passed into the kitchen and from there into the parlour which in turn led into the bedrooms.

The birthplace of Sarah has been described as having been furnished with some taste. Around the walls of the parlour were hung in pairs the ancestral portraits; Jacob and Agathea Binks in bevelled glass and gilt frames occupied the south wall. A crayon enlargement of Grandfather Thadeus T. Thurnow, together with a black-and-white steel engraving of a prize sheep which bore a remarkable resemblance to the old gentleman, occupied the north wall. The gaze of all four was thoughtfully concentrated upon the Quebec heater which stood in the mathematical centre of the room. This heater, when glowing with fire, not only served the purpose of heating the room, but acted during the night as a species of navigating light from the bedrooms to the outdoors via the kitchen when the occasion required. The keynote of severely artistic, almost geometrical simplicity, marked the arrangement of the three chairs and sideboard which completed the appointments.

The parlour was used only on great occasions. Rover and Ole were never allowed to use this room if we except the one occasion when, according to Dr. Taj Mahal, who claims to have examined the floor, the former made a complete circuit of the freshly

painted surface, paused for a moment at one of the chairs and
departed through the north window.

The kitchen, too, was not without its artistic touches, but here a
lighter and more imaginative motif prevails, the influence of the
Thurnows to which Sarah's artistic and imaginative qualities may
always be referred. Two calendars in particular mark the aesthetic
discrimination of the home. One shows a vessel in full sail in
dangerous proximity to the Eddystone Light, and the other, of
more idyllic theme, shows in an orchard a young woman of beautiful proportions offering a cherry to a young man of her acquaintance. One of these calendars is said by experts to be an original.
(Both are preserved in the Binksian collection.) But quite apart
from the cultural influence which these two great pictures must
have had upon the susceptible mind of the young Sarah, they bear
a great significance in that they enable us to fix with considerable
certainty the dates of several of her early poems. Professor R.
Ambush has called attention to the fact that the date of April 1st
bears the entry "caff," and that this refers to the date on which
Sarah's pet calf was born and that those poignant lines of *Calf*
could not have been written before this date and were probably
written soon after since it had not yet received a name:

> Oh calf, that gambolled by my door,
> Who made me rich who now am poor,
> That licked my hand with milk bespread,
> Oh calf, calf! Art dead, art dead?

> Oh calf, I sit and languish, calf,
> With sombre face, I cannot laugh,
> Can I forget thy playful bunts?
> Oh calf, calf, that loved me once!

> With mildewed optics, deathlike, still,
> My nights are damp, my days are chill,
> I weep again with doleful sniff,
> Oh, calf, calf, so dead, so stiff.

Sarah was the second or possibly the third child of Agathea and
Jacob Binks. None of the other children survived their infancy,
and Agathea Binks either died or abdicated while Sarah was still a
child. But there is no evidence that Sarah was lonesome. She

seems to have loved solitude and although some of her later work, notably that of her early Post Regina period, displays a touch of the morbid whose origin psychologists could undoubtedly trace to her childhood, there seems to be no doubt that her early girlhood was spent like that of other children of her day. She was a happy and a healthy child. She assisted in the simple household chores of weeding the garden, gathering the eggs, and picking the potato bugs.[1] During the summer months the little Sarah, her lunch pail under her arm, trudged the mile and a quarter to the one-roomed school at Willows. Her education was sporadic at best. More often than not, especially as she grew older, she was obliged to stay at home and help around the farm. Moreover Jacob Binks was opposed to much education. "There ain't no dam' sense in all this booklearning" was the frequent expression of his inner conviction and his public policy, as a result of which he was elected and invariably re-elected to the School Board.

But if Sarah's formal education was neglected, if her acquaintance with the great authors was a mere nodding acquaintance, she learned all the more from the big school of nature. Nature to her was something alive, and the life of the farm, wild as well as domestic, acquired in her eyes a character and a personality. The lowly blade of grass and the stately horse were equally objects of her sympathetic speculations. She understood the grasshoppers and held them in contempt, whereas the gophers, whose inclusion in the primordial curse had, according to Jacob Binks, been omitted only through some oversight on the part of the Creator, were to Sarah a constant source of humorous amusement. For the perennial calf she had a womanly affection, and its stupidity enthralled her. She was keenly aware of the beauty of sky and field. She loved the hot sunlight of the afternoon and the feel of the wind on her cheek. One need only read *My Garden* and *The Bug* to realize how deep is Sarah's sympathetic understanding of nature.

[1] Miss Iguana Binks-Barkingwell, of St. Olafs-Down-the-Drain, Hants, Hurts, Harts, England, who claims to be a distant kinswoman of Sarah Binks, has recently made a presentation to the Saskatchewan Zoological Society of a mounted collection of potato bugs from all parts of the Empire, to be known as the Binksian Collection. Dr. Termite of Toronto has raised the question, and with it a storm of controversy, as to whether the so-called "young potato bugs" in this collection are not actually lady-bugs. It is unfortunate, in the Author's opinion, that this controversy should have arisen over a collection of potato bugs which was originally conceived to do honour to a great poetess.

MY GARDEN

A little blade of grass I see,
Its banner waving wild and free,
And I wonder if in time to come
'Twill be a great big onion;
We cannot tell, we do not know,
For oft we reap and didn't sow;
We plant the hairy coconut,
With hope serene and sturdy — but
We cannot tell, for who can say,
We plant the oats and reap the hay,
We sow the apple, reap the worm,
We tread the worm and reap the turn:
Too much, too much for us this thought,
With much too much exertion fraught;
In faith we get the garden dug —
And what do we reap — we reap the bug,
In goodly faith we plant the seed,
Tomorrow morn we reap the weed.

THE BUG

In a little nook, a nooklet,
There beside a babbling brooklet,
Sits a little bug, a beetle,
Browsing in a little volume,
Reading in a brand new booklet,
Studying the spinal column,
Learning where to put his needle,
Get me with his little hooklet.

But not only is Sarah's understanding of nature a sympathetic
one but her love for the animal life is deep and abiding. One need
only recall *The Goose*, or *The Apple*, or the ever popular *Song to the
Cow*, songs which Bishop Puddy[1] of Bingobingoland places in the
very first rank.

---

[1] Rev. Beckus Puddy, *A Comparative Study of the Literature of Saskatchewan with that
of Easter Island. The Sunday Sleep. Vol. I, No. I.* (Out of Print.)

THE GOOSE

The goose, a noisome bird to chatter,
But handsome on a garnished platter,
A loathsome brute to toil among,
But caught and killed and cooked and hung,
Before a crackling fire,
A songster to admire.

THE APPLE

Today as I an apple mulched
A worm I fain did bite in twain,
'Twas curled up in its little world
Where it in peace had lain;
So ruthlessly did I disturb
The little worm, helpless, infirm,
Yet no remorse did shake my soul,
No pricks of conscience make me squirm.

SONG TO THE COW

I'll take no cow that fails to sing,
Or throstle with its horn,
Her milk must stimulate like tea,
Her tail stretch to infinity,
And her nose be plush-like and warm
Amorous of optic, mild but quick
To perceive where the grass is pale,
A rhomboid snout, a mellow lick,
And a breath like ale —
These attributes in a cow, I deem,
Are the best to be had and win my esteem.

" 'Amorous of optic . . . breath like ale!' What imagery! It is in lines like these," says Miss Rosalind Drool, "with their haunting cadence that Miss Binks expresses the great soul of Saskatchewan. One wonders how she does it." . . .

One may trace many influences which affected Sarah's work, influences great and small which touched her here and there; Ole, Rover, William Greenglow, Henry Welkin, Grandfather Thurnow, strong, masculine influences which affected her outlook, touching her mind, and leaving their light and sometimes their shadow upon her poetry. But to Ole, cheerful hard-working Ole, big of heart and feet, must go the honour of having been the first to put the young Sarah upon the path of poesy. It is significant, even symbolical, that just as years ago on the morning after Dominion Day, Ole himself was traced for miles across the alkali flats that lie north of Willows, so today one traces his splendid footprints across the dazzling pages of Saskatchewan literature.

Ole's other name is not known, or if it ever was known it has been forgotten. He answered simply to the name of Ole. When, on the rare occasions a more formal address became necessary as when the extra mail-order catalogue arrived, it became, Ole, c/o J. Binks. Professor Ambush has suggested that the name Ole may be a diminutive of Olafur or perhaps of Oleander, but no diminutive can possibly apply. He was above all a big man such as the West is fond of producing. His feet found their way with difficulty through the trousers of his store suit, his shoulders were of gnarled oak, and his two hands swung at his sides like slabs of teak. He was noted for his great strength. He could haul the stoneboat with its two full water barrels from the coulee to the house, and when, as sometimes happened, a horse would straddle the barbed wire fence, he would assist it from its predicament by lifting one end or another as the circumstances required. He had an equine playfulness and would toss Mathilda, even when eighteen and already large for her age, from the ground to the hayloft with great ease and to her infinite delight.

But if Ole's strength was great, his good nature and cheerfulness were even greater. No one is known ever to have offended Ole. His mind had that simplicity and directness and that acceptance of the world which one associates with his race and occupation. He and Rover were inseparable; Ole shared his lunches in the field with Rover, and the latter shared his fleas at night with Ole. Both had a deep and abiding affection for Sarah.

Neither Rover nor Ole actually wrote any poetry, at least none has come down to us unless we accept the terse verses, often fragmentary and sometimes illustrated, which Ole was fond of writing upon the granaries and other small buildings with a piece of coal. (Two of these boards, one of doubtful authenticity, are known to exist in private collections of Binksiana.) But where both Ole's and Rover's chief influence upon Sarah's poetic talent lay, was that it was they who first taught her the singing quality of verse. Rover's voice had a deep and throbbing cadence with which he tended to experiment in metrical forms especially on moonlight nights. Grandfather Thurnow's remark, that "At least he cuts it up into stove lengths," was at once a recognition of Rover's success and an appreciation of his talent. Ole's voice, on the other hand, was a high falsetto and tended to break. When it broke it took on a certain screeching quality, not altogether pleasant in itself, but particularly well adapted to the old Norse ballads and folksongs which he rendered with full pedal and with an abandon which aroused Sarah's boundless admiration. He translated these songs freely — almost too freely. But he planted the seeds of poesy in Sarah's heart, nor could Jacob Binks's frequent admonition to "Shut up, you dam' squarehead!" prevent the seeds from sprouting.

Between Ole and Sarah there was a bond which was never broken. She leaned heavily on him throughout her life, both in the matter of chores and in the matter of inspiration; "My staff and my stick, my Pole and my prop," she says of him in a fragment of verse in which she reveals a rather hazy conception of the geography of northern Europe but acknowledges her debt. Ole was her slave and her dependable friend. It was he who first taught her the satisfaction of the occasional pipe, he taught her to swim in the dugout, he taught her all he knew about handling a calf, about farm machinery, and about Mathilda.

For Sarah, poetry was ever the expression of the soul, whether it was her own soul or somebody else's or simply that of Saskatchewan. In *The Hired Man on Saturday Night* she expresses Ole's soul and in its moment of greatest elation.

THE HIRED MAN ON SATURDAY NIGHT

A horse! A horse! Give me a horse,
To dash across the frozen north,
And wallow in the mire,
A noble barb with cloven hoof,

With brazen wings and blatant snoof,
And molten eyes of fire.

I'll carve a furlong through the snow,
And bring the bastard she-cat low,
And bind her to a tree,
That ding-bat dire, shall put her sire,
Out of the frying pan into the fire,
Where e'er she be.

With gathered rage of many an age,
I'll blot the boar from off the page,
And twist his face;
I'll smite the rooster in the snow,
And crafty Rover, dumb with woe,
Shall curse his race.

I'll tie a reef knot in the tail
Of Barney's bull — with tooth and nail
I'll fill his day with gloom;
The calf shall wail, the cow shall quail,
The horse shall totter and grow pale —
Give me room!

It would appear that on Ole's one free evening of the week he developed a sense of aloofness from farm animals which excluded even Rover. The poem does not approximate the high standard which Sarah usually sets for herself. However it has a swing and rhythm and Professor Marrowfat rates it very highly. He says, "Sarah has hit it on the nose. I don't know much about farm animals, my line being literature. But I know just the feeling that Ole has. I have it myself almost every Saturday night." Nevertheless, in the opinion of the Author, Sarah expresses the feeling more accurately in *Steeds*. Here the sense of elation is combined with the rush and sweep of horses. The occasion of this poem was the time when Ole returned from Willows on the late afternoon of election day, 1911. On that occasion he is alleged to have disappeared with two demijohns of linseed oil which he was transporting with his team from the Liberal to the Conservative Committee rooms. (The incident is recalled in the memoirs of the Hon. Grafton Tabernackel, at that time Administrator of the Farm Implement Oiling and Greasing Act.)

STEEDS

I have two dashing, prancing steeds,
Buttercup and Dairy Queen,
What for spirit, what for speed,
Matches this amazing team?
One is roan and one is plaid,
One a mare, and one a lad,
One a pacer, one a trotter,
One a son, and one a daughter:
When they're fastened side by side,
Yoked together in the traces,
Joyfully prepare to ride
O'er the big and open spaces;
Whoopee! Swift across the stubble,
Over boulders, banks and rubble,
Up the hill and down the glen,
Cross the county — back again,
Through the fence and greenhouse go,
Pumpkin garden — to and fro,
Pounding, puffing, like a dragon,
Kill the calf and smash the wagon,
Through the hayloft, dust and smother,
In one end and out the other —
Zowie! When their spirit's up!
Dairy Queen and Buttercup!

On an even higher level is the short poem, *The Cursed Duck*, a poem in which Sarah reveals her sympathetic nature and essential womanhood following the loss of one of Ole's ears one Sunday morning. The ducks on the Bink's farm had a passion for vegetables to which Sarah's garden bore mute testimony every fall, and it is supposed that Ole had inadvertently fallen asleep in or near the vegetable patch.

THE CURSED DUCK

A cursed duck pecked off his ear,
And his face grew peaked and pale;
"Oh, how can a woman love me now?"

Was his constant and lonely wail;
But a woman came, and she loved the man,
With a love serene and clear —
She loved him as only a woman can love
A man with only one ear.

It is undoubtedly to Ole's influence that we owe the *Song of the Sea*, characterized by Professor Dumplin[1] as " . . . the finest sea song ever to come out of the dry belt." Sarah had never seen the sea, in fact it was not until years later that she saw Lake Wascana, but the blood of the Vikings flowed in Ole's veins, and from Ole's veins to Sarah's verse was but a step:

SONG OF THE SEA

All hail, all hail, to the shriek of the gale,
Huzzah, huzzah, to the boat,
  As with mainsail rent,
  And the keel all bent,
  The mainfore gallant sail split like a tent,
  The captain dead,
  And the mate in bed,
The ship's carpenter downstairs sounding the lead,
She runs amuck, and she runs amoke,
O'er the rollicking, frolicking, bounding main.

Rear Admiral R. N. Saltspit, retired, in a letter to the *Times* calls attention to a technical error in this poem in that the duties of the ship's carpenter are not to sound the lead but to swing it, but he adds in commendation, "The colonies are doing some remarkable things. Miss Binks charts her way through the shoals and intricacies of metre in a way that makes us all feel four sheets in the wind. Our Laureate may have to look to his laurels."

Sarah's greatest poem to Ole is undoubtedly *Where Shall I Find*. As in so many other of her greatest lines the spirit of the West breathes through and through it. Here she not only extols Ole's virtues as a man, but also pays splendid tribute to that manhood in a hired capacity.

[1] Bootlick and Dumplin, *Some Observations on the Marine Life of the South Saskatchewan River and Its Beaches.* Trans. Proc. Lit. Phil. Sci. Soc. Agric. Sask. (7) 11, 1937.

WHERE SHALL I FIND

Where shall I find a hired man
For homely destiny to toil,
To mend harnesses,
And shovel cement,
And boil oil.

Where shall I find a hired man,
To gather rocks and do the chores,
To harrow wide,
And plough deep,
The big outdoors.

Where shall I find a hired man
With a single passion for his job,
With thoughts of work,
And nothing else,
Within his knob.

Where shall I search for a hired man,
With corded arms and knotted knees,
With beamed shoulders,
And feet
Like Hercules'.

At a recent joint meeting of The Ladies' Literary League of Quagmire, and The Former Friends of Ole, Willows Chapter, it was decided to have this poem carved upon Ole's tombstone when he returns from Bear Lake, if ever. In rising to propose a raffle to defray the expenses of this monument, Mrs. Pete Cattalo, F.F.O., paid a tribute to Ole as well as to Sarah when she said, "It is a big poem. It's going to cost us money to have this done. But then Ole was a big man, big in every way, you can take it from me."

From St. John, New Brunswick, Stuart Trueman was the first winner from the Maritimes. A superb collection of his newspaper writings, You're Only as Old as You Act, *won the Leacock Medal in 1969.*

STUART TRUEMAN

from You're Only as Old as You Act

"I thought of having a birthday party for Charlene," a woman said to another on a bus, "but I decided to wait — she's hardly the right age yet."

I don't know how old Charlene is. It doesn't matter. The lady was making a great mistake. *Any* age is the right age to invite children to a party — the younger the better! Putting it off only invites disillusionment.

For sheer uninhibited party fun, you just can't beat the littlest ones — the three-year-old boys and girls. You may want to, but you can't, not when all their mothers come too.

How heart-warming it is to see the joy they get out of the simplest pleasures! — climbing on the dining-room table, running over the dishes, pouring chocolate milk into the ferns, writing with a ballpoint pen on the piano bench. (This convulses the mothers because, as they laughingly point out, the little mischiefs haven't been to school and can't really write one word!)

Even if the mothers are sipping coffee, don't think they're unaware of what their rollicking gamins are up to. I'll say that for modern mothers — they watch all the time; they don't miss a thing. Why, no sooner does little Lola-Lee hoist a kitten high over her head, leaning back as if going to throw it at me, when her mother sharply rebukes her:

"*Darling!* What did Mother say about stretching up and showing your panties? My goodness!" — she laughs — "I think, girls, I'm going to have a delinquent daughter!"

They all scream with merriment at the very thought. Personally, I'm sure she is, as I snatch back the kitten in mid-air.

Then the glowing birthday cake. How the little tots squeal! How they love it! Of course, they don't eat it. Only a fool would think a birthday cake is for eating when there are valuable prizes in it. It's for digging into. This is best done with the fingers, so you can feel the wax paper and the tin whistle inside it. If you don't feel anything there's only one thing to do: Knock the stupid old piece of cake off the table and howl, "*I* didn't get any prize!" This is a signal for the host to come running with another slice, into which he has hurriedly thrust two dimes from his pocket, as he couldn't find any arsenic.

Due to the inexplicable way trinkets creep around in birthday cakes, this slice will, when properly gouged and crumbled, yield up one whistle, one lead wedding ring, one plastic charm in the shape of a horse, and two sticky paper-covered dimes.

A secret of party-giving, I learned, is to have plenty of trinkets (also extra paper hats, horns, candy and balloons), as every child expects to carry home all his favours, even if he has already burst his balloon, wolfed down his candy, shoved his horn into the canary's cage and flushed his paper hat down the toilet to see it go.

Even after every kid is re-stocked, however, a sudden tearful "WAAAAAAW-W-W!" rends the air.

Coaxing an answer through the sobs, the child's mother looks up, laughing.

"Isn't this just *awful*! He wants to take his present back home again. He's heartbroken — I don't know *what* to tell him!"

I could tell her what to tell him: "It's not yours, you little brat; you gave it away. Now start hiking to blazes out."

But I say, "Oh, let him take it! Yes, we insist. We *want* him to have it. Poor little tyke!" And I push my own little boy behind me, hoping his mother will have sense enough to propel him into the kitchen before he finds out what's up.

The woman, backing out the front door, expostulates, "This is *terrible* — I shouldn't *do* it! But I'll send the bunny back very first thing tomorrow."

She's lying, of course. But so was I.

There's one wonderful feature about a three-year-old party: Somehow, eventually, mercifully, it comes to an end. Then you bask in a blissful thought: You won't need to have another until all the forty-four other kids have had parties. As birthdays fortunately come only once a year, your own child will then be all of forty-seven years old!

This is a common delusion. To your amazement, by the time your child is six, it's his turn again. No one knows why this is.

"Thank heavens anyway," you tell yourself, "they've outgrown their babyishness. Why, they're almost mature."

They are, too: They weigh a hefty sixty pounds. When one shrills, "I wanta drink of water!" they all stampede kitchenwards with such velocity you'd better not risk getting in the way unless you're playing regularly against the Winnipeg Blue Bombers.

There's one worse crisis, however. It's when a young guest is seized with the inspiration, "I wanta go to the bathroom!" This is infectious. Instantly they all want to. A host with any presence of mind will leap for his life off the stairs, before they swarm all over him and trample him. Then he must race up after them to haul back the boys or the girls, respectively, depending on whether it's a boy or a girl who got into the bathroom first and is now breathlessly bracing the door against the others, having momentarily forgotten, in the excitement of holding the fort, what he (or she) went there for.

It's a real job to drag them down the stairs. They bite and kick; nobody wants to give up a hard-won place in such a dire emergency. You have a vague uncomfortable notion they're all going to report when they get home, "That awful old man at the party wouldn't even let me go to the bathroom!"

The surprising thing is, at six they still burrow in the cake for prizes. Now, however, they don't thoughtlessly brush broken pieces off the table, like little kids, littering the carpet with cake, icing and candles. Instead, they gleefully throw them at each other, plastering the sunny floral wallpaper with sticky marshmallow frosting giving it a winter landscape effect.

But eight years old — ah, this is different! The sexes have separate parties.

The guest of honour is now really grown up. He knows what birthday parties are for: They're to get presents. He closely inspects each arriving guest, staring not at the guest, which would be impolite, but at what he's got under his arm. If he hasn't conspicuously got a present, he may not even get in.

And the heartiness of their fun! They immediately pile on the guest of honour and pummel him until he is bawling. This is in honour of his birthday. He will then, alternatively: (a) reappear from his room in a moment, grinning sheepishly, and rejoin the gang; (*b*) lock himself in and refuse to be coaxed out; or (*c*) with blind rage and shame welling up within, come flying out and start kicking everybody and screaming swear words (which he could only have picked up at school or at Camp Happy Chief last summer) and order them all out of the house.

A resourceful adult will immediately suggest Pin the Tail on the Donkey. This relieves the tension. No wonder it's the favourite party pastime — it harmlessly works off the competitive spirit in boys. They all compete to see how fast they can, with blindfolds slightly raised, stick the pins into the buttocks of their playmates.

Then, implored to take a rest from the game, they dutifully do so, wrestling, getting headlocks and refusing to let go, sprawling over the hi-fi, and working up a wonderful appetite.

Comes the birthday cake and they all dig feverishly for prizes. But happily at this age there are always one or two Sanitary Boys, who won't touch the cake because the honour guest, in blowing out all the candles at once, has blown a wad of gum right into the frosting. And there is always one Fat Boy who eats what the others leave, so there is less cleaning up.

I was afraid, when we held a party for our older son at fifteen, that all the fun had gone out of the bunch, that the reappearance of girls might put a damper on their ebullient nature.

How merrily I was surprised! They were as full of high spirits as ever, except now each weighed one hundred and fifty pounds and could hurl an entire armchair across the room.

But I was ready. I stacked records for a dance, knowing the magic of the girls would quickly make itself felt.

"Paul Jones!" I cried. "Boys march around the girls!"

The Under the Double Eagle March blared. The girls tittered. I looked around. Not a boy in sight.

It took ten minutes to find them.

Four had secreted themselves in the bathroom, where they were putting aspirins in their pop, having heard it would give them a kick. I wished I could, but the door was locked.

Two were in a bedroom, putting bullets in a .22 rifle. I disarmed them and ordered them downstairs.

Five were huddled in the old coal bin in the cellar, evidently determined to stay out the winter if necessary.

I discovered the last two pairs of boys' legs protruding from under the dining-room table, where their owners were avidly reading, with a flashlight, a book from my library about the Gaza patrol, Trouble On The Strip, — hoping it would expose what really went on in burlesque houses.

I will say for all these lads that when I pointed out how they were spoiling the party, they apologized profusely and promised to behave.

So I triumphantly strode back, started Under the Double Eagle again, and turned around expectantly:

Only those silly asinine girls, still giggling.

Distraught, I seized on an idea.

"This is a *Sadie Hawkins* Paul Jones," I told the girls.

Well, you never saw boys reappear so fast, dragged by ear lobes and Chinese finger-locks! They clung together while the girl marchers went around; then they danced. They had no choice.

If I do say it, this was my greatest party. The evening was a complete success. Oh, the boys *did* show off a little, naturally, in intermissions; they piled up on each other's knees, and it just happened that our antique sofa's legs buckled.

And it's true that in the general confusion several ornaments somehow detached themselves from the mantel and soared through the air. An empty dinner plate, I remember, hit me in the solar plexus, but it was only cardboard — and this possibly wasn't the boys' fault at all. I've read that a phenomenon called poltergeist can cause objects to fly around mysteriously if an adolescent girl is present, and we had seventeen of them.

It was such a good party we didn't have another for six years. My older son was then twenty-one. Realizing his friends were now seven feet tall — a conservative estimate, as several habitually placed their palms on the kitchen ceiling and leaned forward comfortably to talk, and weighed 225, or was it 325? — I prepared the house like a brigantine captain clearing the decks for action.

Ornaments were removed. The canary was entrusted to a neighbour.

They came to supper, forty-four of them, in a progressive New Year's party. In despondency I was thinking I could always unpack the .22 rifle if I had to act as town marshal.

They sat around quietly at first, as if they thought they were grown-ups. This didn't fool me.

The girls, in shimmering dresses, were sedate. The boys hastened to offer fresh linen handkerchiefs whenever even a small crumb dared to fall on the organdie and nylon.

I put my ear to the living-room door and listened. Any moment now they would be planning to blow the roof off!

It was strange.

Fragments of conversation drifted out. They were talking about showers and weddings.

When they finished dinner, every single couple carried the cardboard plates out to the kitchen and warmly thanked us for our hospitality. They really meant it. That was the most disheartening thing.

I waited, but not one hit me in the solar plexus. I couldn't believe it. I was suddenly tempted to throw a plate myself, to get things going; but then I realized to my dismay it was too late. These were old people.

So take my word for it:

If you want to have real fun at a party for children, hold it while they still are.

Earle Birney was the son of a Western pioneer family, working as a labourer in the Kootenay region of British Columbia to enable him to enter the University of British Columbia. An academic like Stephen Leacock, he received his Ph.D. in English at the University of Toronto. Having taught there as well as California and Utah, he was appointed professor at the University of British Columbia. His poetry won the Governor General's award twice, in 1942 and 1945. Readers of World War II vintage may be particularly enamoured of his inept Turvey in this 1950 medal winner.

EARLE BIRNEY

from Turvey

The afternoon before Christmas a sudden sun spread ankle-deep slush over the camp. Turvey, with Ballard and their corporal, sat cramped in a small unheated guard post by the canal bank. The other two in their group were out trudging the gooey snow; soon Turvey would have to relieve one of them. He was bored. The sergeant had crossed him up somehow on Christmas leave; the best he could hope for now was New Year's Day. Meanwhile he was perfunctorily responding to the latest rumour retailed by the corporal, a laconic Nova Scotian with asthma.

"Sykes — the Stores Corp, you know — was sayin the quarter-master's goin ta catch it from NDHQ account a Landis."

"Landis?" asked Ballard, "the silly bugger fell in the canal we had a miltry funeral fer in the summer?"

"Yeah. They buried him with his boots on," said the corporal.

"So what?"

"So Ottawa wants em. Demand come through from Ordnance, Sykes sayin. Boots, moist leather, issue, black, one pair; laces, one pair. Improper burial. Should a took em off, returned em to Stores."

"The QM have to pay for em, eh?"

"Mebbe. I figger he oughta work on the padre to dig up Landis an get the boots back. They'd still be good enough to turn back in Stores."

Turvey was about to remark that he could do with a new pair himself, when there was a sudden rip . . . ping . . . smack . . . plop; chips flew, and a little jagged hole appeared just above head-level in the door-top.

71

"Well I'll be dammed," said the corporal, only mildly per-
turbed, "was a bullet." Stepping over the prostrate bodies of Turvey and Ballard — who had made the floor in a dead heat — he
examined the hole and, turning about, hunted and found a paral-
lel splotch on the cement of the back wall. He was trying to pick
up the hot lead slug from the floor when rip . . . ping . . . smack
. . . plop, there was another hole in the door, an inch away and at
the same level.

"It's the Jerries!" shouted Turvey. "Paratroops, I bet! Let's
charge em!" He was scrambling to his feet, one arm reaching for
his rifle stacked in a corner, when Ballard pulled him down. For a
tough guy, Turvey thought Ballard looked surprisingly pale and
worried. His voice was shaking.

"Stay put, yuh mug. They got us cornered, see, aint they corp?
We gotta surrender."

Just then an unintelligible shout floated across the canal. The
corporal, despite blasphemous protests from Ballard, edged to
their tiny window and peered gingerly through its barred pane.
"McKelvie," he announced, after a breathless pause. "Wonder
what's up."

"That jerk! He'd do anythin fer a laugh. Dont show or he'll pot
yuh. I'll bet he's stinkin."

But the corporal had already pushed open the door. McKelvie
could be seen standing outside another guard house identical with
theirs, sixty yards down on the other side of the canal. His melton
cap was cocked drunkenly on his head and he held his rifle in
both hands. His voice carried easily across the steep banks.

"How's that for shootin, corp? Jest wanted to wake you christers
up. Wotcha doin anyway?" His tone was sober and cheery, as if he
had just rung them on the telephone.

The corporal peered at him biliously. "You mighta hit somebody, you know. Where's your corporal? Aint he there?"

"Nah," shouted McKelvie offhandedly, "he and the rest of them
hightailed it downtown for beer. They left me in charge! How
about a shootin match? Come on, jest fer the hell of it, they aint
nothin to do."

"The bucker's gone screwy!" said Ballard anxiously. "You better go arrest him, corp."

"You feelin all right?" shouted the corporal. "Better walk
around by the bridge and come over here. . . . Leave your rifle,"

he added.

But McKelvie was not to be persuaded, and hoisted his gun. The corporal decided, wisely, to retire. During the next few minutes McKelvie demonstrated his really admirable and sober marksmanship by drilling an almost straight line of holes across the top of their wooden door. The three besieged lay smelling the mould on the cold cement floor and cursing. Ballard easily led in this form of retaliation both in the speed and variety of his responses. "Rip . . . ping . . . smack," went the bullets; "#$/$*§⅞," went Ballard, before the pellet had plopped to the floor. "We coulda been in Bufflo now, Turvey," he whined reproachfully, after the fifth bullet struck. "Yuh see what happens wen you stick around the — — — — — army. I dint join up ta git drilled by some buckin stir-crazy Scotchman."

"He's only got fifteen rounds," the corporal murmured soothingly. "Somebody'll hear the shootin and stop him."

Rip . . . ping . . . smack-smack.

"Ow, jezus, I'm shot!" yelled Ballard, clutching his left wrist. But it was only a glancing burn from the seventh slug, which had ricocheted.

"*We* heard him but he didnt stop for us, you know," said Turvey mildly. "Maybe we better wing him. He's a nawful good shot."

"Holy cow! Now he's startin a lower set. He'll be pickin us off right here on the friggin floor," cried Ballard, whose face had turned the colour of grey goat-cheese. "I'm gittin out a here." The twelfth and thirteenth bullets had started a new line several inches lower on the doorframe. But since his only exit would have been directly into McKelvie's line of fire Ballard didnt actually move.

After the fifteenth bullet there was a long pause, some confused shouting, and a new voice yelled, "All Clear!" Squinting cautiously through the window Turvey saw McKelvie, still surprisingly nonchalant, being led off by an impressive posse of NCO'S and guards, under close arrest. It looked as if the posse also had been waiting for McKelvie to expend his fifteen rounds.

Whether it was the indignity of being shot at, however playfully, by his own side, or whether it was Christmas Eve without a pass, or the frustration of not being allowed to shoot back, or just the milder weather, Turvey wasnt sure; but when, after supper, Ballard again raised the topic of going on the loose Turvey found himself listening with more interest. Ballard this time drew a detailed picture of the charms of his two Buffalo friends, the softness of their beds, the comparative variety and abundance of American food, and the bliss of lying-in till midday unattended by corporals, sergeants or their betters. By nine that evening they were both on the Niagara Falls road, their cap-badges gleaming in the auto headlights, their right arms twisted out from them, thumbs wistfully curved. . . .

The sun was a colourless wafer in a steely sky, and the January cold, invisible but bitter, filtered efficiently through the cracks in the little wooden nests of Number Two Security Regiment. In the feeble afternoon sunlight four soldiers stood shivering and stamping their feet on the bare porch of a square hut known somewhat grandiosely as the YMCA Hostel. A casual observer would have been puzzled to know why a sergeant, a corporal, and two privates continued to linger in such a cold spot for no apparent military purpose, and without the benefit of greatcoats. They made an oddly chummy and idle foursome; one of the privates was even smoking, in full view of the midday camp and of possible prowling officers.

Turvey would have enjoyed the cigarette more if the sergeant, in permitting it, had not added, "It's the last you'll smoke for a month of Sundays, my boy. Nothing like that where you're going. They got a real brassballs from Ottawa running the courts this week. Colonel Sloggin, Old Fishface, they call him. You wont pull your panties over *his* eyes."

The frost-rimmed door behind them abruptly screeched and opened. A little bald soldier peered out, winked heavily at the sergeant and jerked his thumb inwards. "O.K."

"Chuck cigarettes," the sergeant hissed quickly, then instantly transformed himself into a stiffbacked loudspeaker. "Escort-n-prisner ten-HOWN," he bellowed and, suddenly *sotto voce* again, "allri, allri, corpral in front, prisner, then you, Davis." Then the loudspeaker blared. "RrriiiTUN, weeeeeek MATCH." The little procession clomped briskly into the blessed warmth of a square room, past stacks of upturned chairs and tables, and a handful of officers and men standing at attention beside benches. Turvey heard the sergeant behind hissing something about "headdress" and somebody neatly whipped his melton skull cap from his head. Clump, clomp, clump, clomp they went toward a ruddy Winnipeg heater and a low platform against the far wall, on which three officers were perched behind a table spread with papers.

" 'Scortnprisner, HALLT! . . . Riii TUN . . . 'Scort two pacestep-back MATCH." Turvey felt his companions vanish from beside him, and began absorbing the stare of the three sets of officer eyes on the dais. The middle ones were especially formidable; they were steel blue and glittering beneath an impressive redbanded officer's hat, and above two red neck-tabs and the brassy shoulder adornments of a Full Colonel.

Turvey reached his hand up to smooth his hair, and stopped, his arm paralysed by the Full Colonel's eyes. They seemed to be saying that, however solidly the officers of the court might squat on their chairs, he, Turvey, the prisoner, was to stand at attention.

The sergeant was right, Turvey thought; the colonel's eyes, behind thick rimless spectacles, looked remarkably like those of a trout, and Turvey unaccountably remembered what Calvin Busby had said about the army being a fish hatchery. This colonel looked about the room with the calm unwinking orb of the fish that knows itself several sizes bigger than any other in his tank. A big plump Dolly Varden swimming in a pool of documents, Tur-vey decided, with a Sam Browne belt and a bright row of buttons for belly stripes; the two redtabs were his gills. The way his cheeks sloped into a tiny chinless mouth was fish-like too.

The Big Trout stared down at a paper one of his two flanking troutlings slid in front of him, stared up at Turvey, opened his puckery mouth as if about to gulp air, and, miraculously, spoke:

"Are you B-08654732 Private Turvey, Thomas Leadbeater?" The voice was cold and clear and utterly colourless.

"B-086547 TWO 2, Private Turvey, sir, yessir," said Turvey brightly.

There was a small stir in the papery pool above him until it was discovered that the mistake was the colonel's, not the documents. The colonel sucked air again: "Take your place beside your Defending Officer, Turvey. The court will now be sworn in."

"I swear by Almighty God," the Great Trout said expression-lessly and paused; all the minnows throughout the stuffy little room opened their mouths in unison and echoed the words and the tonelessness: "swearbymightygad. . . . To tell the truth. . . ."

He was glad to feel that he was still within warming distance of the stove. His toes and fingers throbbed slowly into life. Then the Orderly Sergeant sat Turvey on a bench on the left of the court and for the first time he was able to look around. Opposite him sat a solemn private with a long nose like a badger's and a lap full of files; next to him was a captain, a newcomer to the unit, remarkable for a large fierce moustache, RAF pattern, set in the middle of a small baby-face. Behind them he identified his old Hut Corporal and Platoon Sergeant, and the provost who had brought him back from the border. He stole a glance behind him and spotted the RAP Sergeant, the MO, and the Nut Doctor who had visited him in the guard house this morning.

And, beside him, breathing a most exciting odour of whiskey into his right ear, was Lieutenant Sanderson, the paymaster, a devil-may-care character with a literary turn of mind who had been sent back from England officially as over-age; he was popularly rumoured to have been returned because he paid off the same regiment twice in one week in a burst of alcoholic benevolence; he was also said to be the author of some plain-spoken ballads of army life circulating in the camp. It was this gentleman who, Turvey had been surprised to learn yesterday, was defending him. . . .

And now the swearing was over and the president had swivelled his eyes to the opposite side of the room from Turvey, bringing them to rest on the equally expressionless face of the long-nosed private that Turvey had noticed sitting with a thick file of papers. "The Clerk of the Court will now read the charge against the accused."

The clerk rose instantly, released by some secret spring, holding the wad of papers in front of him like a choir soloist. He began to recite the charge in a shrill nasal monotone, running the clichés together.

"The accused, B-08654722, Private-Turvey-Thomas-Leadbeater, on-a-strength-of Number-Two-Skewerty-Regiment, Cam-Byngtario, soldier – Canain – Active – Army – s – charged – with – w'en'n Active-Service," here he took his first breath and his voice rose another notch, gaining speed, "SENTING-SELF-THOUT-FICIAL-LEAVE in-that-he . . . did-sent-self-from twenty-two-hundred-hours. Friday cember-twenty-four-nin'n-hundred forty-two . . . un'l apprehen'd-an-return-barracks steen-hunr-sen-

hours Saday-Janwy-fteen-nin-hun-for-three. . . ." The clerk's
voice shifted into an even higher gear and raced dizzily through
a computation of the exact number of hours and minutes Private
Turvey had deprived the Canadian Active Army of his activity,
and the precise clauses and provisions of the Army Act which
had anticipated such conduct and laid down the appropriate
punishments.

"Do you plead guilty or not guilty?" It was the Big Trout again,
the clerk having subsided as abruptly as he had arisen.

Turvey suddenly couldnt remember how the RAP Sergeant had
told him to plead. But he could see they had everything down
exactly and no argument, and he was about to acknowledge his
guilt, a little surprised that the president should think it debata-
ble, when the paymaster came to life and stood up. His leathery,
whiskey-veined face dimpled in a great mock-hearty smile, rakish
with a gold molar. He announced to the colonel, as if it were the
most natural thing in the world:

"He pleads not guilty, sir."

The glassy vision of the President of the Court-Martial rested
briefly on the paymaster.

"You have been appointed, Lieutenant, uh-er."

"Sanderson," whispered the Righthand Troutling.

"Lieutenant Sanson," the president went on majestically, "to
defend the prisoner, not to plead for him. Private Turvey, are you
guilty or not guilty of the charge as read?"

Turvey shifted the weight on his feet; he was really stumped.
Had the president given a peculiar emphasis to the last two
words? Perhaps there was a loophole somewhere. And yet, come
to think of it, nothing the president had said really had any emphasis to it at all. The paymaster was now elbowing him in the ribs
most energetically, and had screwed his mouth up into an elaborate almost-silent "Not Guilty," shaking his head, and winking all
at the same time.

"Whatever you gentlemen like." He paused. There was silence,
except for a smothered whisper from the paymaster. The
president's face for the first time betrayed impatience and even
some anxiety. Turvey groped in his mind for something that
might please everybody and suddenly though of what Ballard
had said about a nice compromise in Scottish law. "Not Proven,"
he said, louder than he intended.

"Write down Not Guilty," said the president crisply. "You have not sufficiently instructed the defendant, Mr-uh-Sansom," he added; even the president's voice was beginning to betray emphasis; there was a sharkish edge to it which did not bode well either for defendant or his counsel. After some general remarks on court-martial procedure, he held a whispered consultation with his two supporting judges, and announced that in view of the inclemency of the weather, witnesses would remain in the courtroom until their testimony had been given. "The prosecution will commence."

Up stood the captain with the moustaches. He had been nervously twirling the ends; now one was curled jauntily up and the other hooked villainously down; but the rest of his face looked as childlike as ever. His voice was a jittery imitation of the president's; that is, it would have sounded impartial if it had not quavered slightly. While Turvey listened with interest, the prosecution proceeded to establish the undisputed fact that Turvey had been absent on the dates set down. Turvey's Hut Corporal gave the greasy Bible a gingerly peck and swore, with the clerk's prodding, "by mighty-Gad-tell trut-whole trut-nottin buta-trut." He testified that Turvey was not in his hut at bed-check 2300 hours Christmas Eve. Then Turvey's Platoon Sergeant plodded through the same ceremony to assert that Turvey had not responded to rollcalls since 1400 hrs December 24th, and produced his roll-books in proof. They were duly accepted as exhibits for the evidence of the court.

As the trial droned on, Turvey got the feeling they were talking about someone else; the facts fitted him, but they had all ceased paying him any attention. All, that is, except the paymaster, who kept up a succession of sighs and soothing murmurs beside Turvey's right ear, a kind of punctuating rebuttal to each damning sentence of evidence. Turvey would have been quite comforted if the lieutenant's aromatic gusts had not blown into him a growing longing for a good stiff drink.

Then came a beefy provost corporal, circumstantial and bored. He testified to having received into his care the body of one Turvey, Thomas Leadbeater (whom he also identified as the prisoner) from the custody of a United States Police Officer at the International Border, Niagara Falls, N.Y. He produced signed documents to prove it, and to prove also that he had delivered the same body later the same day to the corporal in charge of the guard house, Number Two Security Regiment.

A slight hitch developed here when the president's lefthand Troutling discovered that the guard house corporal had signed for Turvey on the wrong line. The president reproved both the corporal and the provost for this carelessness, and offered the paymaster an opportunity to enter an objection. But the latter cheerfully waived his rights, as he had waived all suggestions up to now that he cross-examine or in any other way enter the proceedings except by quiet wheezes and grunts to Turvey. The president thereupon decided that the document could be entered as evidence, together with a special emendatory form which the clerk had been rapidly making out in quadruplicate.

Then the clerk, who continued throughout the proceedings to be by far the busiest man in the room, released the secret spring in his knees and bounced up to intone a long series of reports which had been delivered up to the provost along with Turvey's sinful body. Although, from the point of view of an intimate chronicler, these documents revealed disappointing gaps, they nevertheless proved to be the most interesting of the day.

They informed all who might be concerned that the said person, giving his name as Thomas Leadbeater Turvey and admitting to being a Canadian citizen and a soldier in the Canadian Army, had been taken into custody in the bedroom of number nine Paradise Apartments, Raintree St., in the City of Buffalo, N.Y. The apartment, the report went on to specify, was legally and jointly tenanted by a Miss Ruby O'Reilly and a Miss Helga Bolinski, employees of the Earthquake Aircraft Corporation. The soldier had been apprehended in the course of a routine investigation arising out of a complaint by a tenant in the next apartment — who objected to the noise of night parties emanating from the windows of number nine. The soldier had been unable to produce evidence that he had legally entered the United States or that he was on official leave from his unit, and he had therefore been taken into custody as a potential deserter.

This somewhat tantalizing report was duly passed to the clerk, and then passed to the paymaster at the latter's request. Turvey was somewhat startled to gather from Lieutenant Sanderson's chuckles and admiring wheezes that his Defending Officer had not previously examined this document at any leisure, if indeed at all. The lieutenant's tsst-chah's finally became so audible that the president sent a freezing ray from his eye over Turvey's right shoulder, the chuckles ceased, and the document was returned to the clerk.

The Prosecuting Officer, both horns of his moustache now sagging piratically, indicated that his case had been presented. The paymaster again airily declined to cross-examine, and the president called upon him to begin the defence.

With a great odorous wheeze Lieutenant Sanderson arose beside Turvey and beamed at the president. "Well, Your Honour — "

"The President of a Court-Martial is addressed as 'sir'," said the Great Trout coldly.

Lieutenant Sanderson's cheeks purpled a little more but otherwise he seemed unperturbed. "Sir," he said, "our first witness is Sergeant Sawyer here."

The RAP Sergeant, his face a somewhat rosier reflection of the lieutenant's, stumped noisily from a side bench and was sworn in. Turvey thought his expression looked a little unnatural and then realized that for the first time he was seeing the sergeant when he was not chewing snuff.

"Tell His Hon — tell the court, sarge, about the pitiful condition of the prisoner when he was brought into camp."

"At sixtin-fittin hours on January fiftint," the sergeant rattled on at once, obviously well-rehearsed. "I 'as called from the regmentl aid post to guard hut t'attend a prisner here, Priv' Turvey, wh'ad jus been brought in. I foun him na highly nervous nweakened condition. Hands tremblin. Pulse slow. Eyes bloodshot. Very, uh-tired." He paused, his green eyes darting over the impassive faces of the judges as if to measure his effect.

"Was he drunk?" asked the president casually.

"Nassir. Very sober. Well, had a hangover, mebbe. Walked kinda splay-legged, but," the sergeant chuckled bronchially, "I'll bet tha was just a case a lover's n —"

"Kahumph," the paymaster intervened with a breezy cough. "Tell us what you did for the prisoner."

"Objection," said the moustachioed captain suddenly. "All this is irrelevant to the charge."

"What are you seeking to prove by this testimony, lieutenant?" asked the president.

"Ah, sir, many things, many things." The paymaster made a

large vague gesture with one arm. "This lad here, he's a good lad, sir, but nervous, very nervous. We shall present expert testimony to prove this. Impulsive, you know. And penitent, penitent too. Like the Ancient Mariner, sir. 'This man hath penance done and —' uh. Coleridge, sir. The, uh, the sergeant here is giving you first-hand evidence of this, this really pitiable nervousness."

The president looked skeptically at his watch. "The witness may proceed. But make it short."

The sergeant began rasping away at once. "He ast me fer a drink, a drink a — water." He pronounced the last word with a long twist of his great mouth as if the word itself proved Turvey's strange and heart-rending condition. "When he took the glass, sir, his hand shook so much he spilled it." The sergeant paused for the full effect of this to penetrate his hearers. "Had to give him a bit a brandy to pull him to."

"Is that all your testimony?" asked the president with some bewilderment, as the sergeant stood silent.

The paymaster and the sergeant beamed common assent. The president shifted his glittering eyepieces to the Prosecuting Officer. "Do you wish to cross-examine?"

"One question, sir. Sergeant Sawyer, you handed a glass of brandy to the accused after his ah — poor trembling hands had spilled the water?"

"Yassir."

"Did he spill the brandy, too?"

"Nassir."

"That's all, sir," said the captain, his moustache tips quivering triumphantly. The sergeant stood down.

"My next witness," said the paymaster, seemingly as confident as ever, "is not available. He is Private Horatio Ballard who was reported absent without leave at the same time as the prisoner and who has not yet returned. I hope to show that it was Private Ballard who planned this unfortunate uh-expedition and prevailed upon this poor lad to accompany him. He was the brains, gentlemen, the Mephistopheles, and young Turvey here was the uh — was the victim. I now ask for an adjournment of these proceedings until such time as Private Ballard is available as a witness."

Even the president's equanimity was upset by this barefaced bid to derail his trial. He stared glassily, sucked air, wriggled in his seat almost as if he were flicking a great tail-fin, and denied the lieutenant the support of Private Ballard.

The paymaster looked, for the first time, really put out. He licked his lips abstractedly. Then he nodded to himself, bent over and whispered to Turvey: "It's all right, old boy, we'll finagle a little break." He put on his most winning gold-toothed smile:

"With the court's permission, sir, the prisoner asks for a five-minute recess. He has to attend to the duties of nature."

Turvey was startled, since he had made no such request, but the interruption was welcome.

The president agreeing, none too graciously, Turvey was duly marched out and around to the latrine on the side of the Hostel. While his guards were standing shivering outside its partly open door, Turvey was surprised to see the paymaster brush between them into his privacy. Without a word the lieutenant closed the door, reached over Turvey's dutifully seated figure to a dark recess between the roof braces, and drew forth a half-empty bottle of Haig & Haig.

"After you, my boy. And make it snappy. We've just time to finish it. 'Freedom and whiskey go together.' Robbie Burns. The Immortal Memory. Hope you dont mind drinking out of the crock." Turvey didnt mind at all.

When the court had reassembled, the paymaster called briefly on the MO to corroborate Sergeant Sawyer's impression that Turvey was of a nervous temperament. The MO seemed to have little of any consequence to say, however, and that little was immediately objected to by opposing counsel. He was stood down, to give place to another officer.

Captain Norton Montague, Temporary-Acting-Neuropsychiatric-Consultant, was a tall, elegant young man — surprisingly young, Turvey had thought when the captain interviewed him in the camp brig last night. Following a fashion popular among officers in combatant arms he had extracted the wire framework from his peaked cap and wore the shapeless residue at a rakish yachtsman's angle. His buttons shone more brightly even than the president's and he was adorned with the neatest black pencil-line of a moustache Turvey had ever seen. After the clerk had droned the oath Captain Montague took the Bible in a gloved hand and casually kissed the air in front of it.

Under the breezy promptings of the paymaster, who had recovered marvellously his normal magenta hue and his confidence, the captain testified that he had indeed examined the prisoner on the previous evening.

"Just give us your report, doctor." Lieutenant Sanderson beamed expansively around the roon as if there could be no doubt what the good young doctor would say.

Captain Montague drew a neat sheaf of papers from a shining briefcase, and flaired horn-rims from a leather pouch in his pocket. He seemed to be in no hurry and he managed to smile in a way that suggested he thought the proceedings, however necessary, a trifle quaint. But the Great Fish wasnt intimidated: "We havent time for you to read all that, you know," he remarked testily. "This case is taking far too long anyway." He glittered briefly in the paymaster's direction.

The young doctor bowed slightly but charmingly to the president. "I will endeavour to be brief, sir. But I must claim the privileges of what this court calls, I believe, an Expert Witness." He began to read in a most professional voice, skimming his papers. "Umm, yes, Turvey, Thomas Leadbeater. Private. Let me see. No admitted history of veneral disease, mental illness, fits. No present symptoms. . . . No apparent addiction to drugs or alcohol." He raised his eyes. "For purposes of this court, addiction may be taken to mean a habit marked enough to interfere with, ah, ordinary duties." He flipped another page. "Memory and concentration normal. No certain mental deficiency. No vertigo, tinnitus, parasthesiae, incontinence, nystagmus, diplopia or rombergism. Normal stereognosis and two-part discrimination. Orientation for time and place probably ah, normal. Examination of glands, joints — "

"For God's sake, captain, was this an autopsy? This man is accused of being absent without leave! What's all this gibberish got to do with it?" The president had, for the first time, quite lost his temper. His little mouth puckered in and out and he bounced up and down on his seat.

The paymaster hastily interposed. "What we most want to know, doctor, is about this lad's nerves, you know. Now dont you think he's pretty high-strung, eh?"

"Objection!" shrieked the Prosecuting Captain, twirling his moustaches, and dropping a paper.

"Sustained!" boomed the president. "This is your last warning, Lieutenant, uh, Samson. If you ask another leading question, the witness will be stood down."

"No signs of organic nervous or mental disease," Captain Montague went on blandly, as if no interruption had taken place. "I rather think, however," and here he paused professorially, "that the subject's personality *tends* towards that of the, ah, constitutional psychopath."

"Constitutional what?" barked the president.

"Constitutional psychopath, sir. Probably of the inadequate type."

"What's that?" the president asked grudgingly.

"Ah, this is a classification sometimes used in psychiatry" — Captain Montague's manner had gradually become that of a somewhat sophisticated professor speaking to an unusually callow freshman class — "to denote a personality which, though apparently not suffering from any of the psychoses which might respond to treatment, nor classifiable legally as insane, ah, nevertheless presents a settled pattern of marked instability. This type — and of course I am venturing only the most tentative of diagnoses, and suggesting in the case of the prisoner merely an approximation to a type — this type is, for example, likely to be reckless with himself and with others, to come into conflict with the law and the, ah, social mores — "

"Come, come, captain. Cut it short! You mean the fellow's immoral?"

"Let us say," the captain permitted himself a worldly smile and an arch of the eyebrows, "the type (to which he *may* belong) is often in trouble over women, ah, is fond of liquor (without necessarily being an addict) and gambling, the usual things. A large percentage of our civilian jail population is made up of such psychopaths. Unfortunately there is still considerable disagreement as to whether the pattern is acquired or congenital. In either case," he finished brightly, "they are generally considered incurable." He was about to sit down when the president made a sound as if he were strangling and then found breath:

"What *has* all this to do with it? What *are* you trying to tell us? That this man is crazy? Or, or what?"

"O dear no, sir. It is my opinion that he is and has been, for all legal purposes, civil and military, in his, ah, right mind."

"But — ," the paymaster jumped up. He had been winking agonizingly without effect at Captain Norton Montague and looking very much like a boy whose pet hamster had suddenly taken to gnawing the leg of a valued visitor, "but you wouldnt say, now would you, that — " he stopped and looked apprehensively at the president. "Well, would you say that he was fully aware of the nature of his act when he — when he went on the loose?"

"Perfectly aware," said Captain Montague calmly. Then, as if to assure the paymaster he hadnt entirely deserted him, he added, "though to what extent he has a normal understanding of whether it is right or wrong to do such a thing, I couldnt really say. *Or* to what extent — " here the young doctor cast a professional eye on Turvey who happened at that moment to be wearing his fatal nervous grin — "to what extent he actually experiences such common feelings as guilt, penitence, pity or even, ah, fear."

"Have you *quite* finished, captain?" the president enquired with savage politeness.

"Unless there are any more questions?" The captain looked about him with elegant disinterest. The Prosecuting Captain stood up and opened the little pink mouth under his great moustaches, but before he could speak Captain Montague added: "I understand, of course, that the report of an Expert Witness is not subject to cross-examination." The prosecutor sat down, his mouth still ajar. Captain Montague bowed once more to the president.

"Quite, sir," he said and sat down.

The president sucked his thin lips in until they disappeared.

"And have *you* quite finished?" He flashed his spectacles at the paymaster. But the latter, though punch drunk, was not yet on the canvas.

"I claim the time-honoured right, sir, to introduce this poor boy, the — the prisoner, into the stand in his own defence."

The president glared, gulped air, and seemed to be expanding silently. But there was no explosion. The paymaster had him.

Turvey was alarmed. The RAP Sergeant had been so confident Turvey would get off easily he hadnt coached him for rising to his own defence. But there was not time to brood. The paymaster, with one of his large easy gestures, was already wafting Turvey to the stand. The clerk bobbed up in the same instant.

"Ye-swear-a-might-gad-tell-tru-nothin-but-a-trut?

"Sure," said Turvey, "yes, sir," taking care to implant an especially firm smack between two grease spots on the black Book.

"Say 'I do'," said the clerk unappeased.

"I do."

"Now, Turvey," said the paymaster affably, "suppose you just tell us your story, the one you told Sergeant Sawyer yesterday, you know. How you lost out on your leave, and then didnt like being shot at by McKelvie; and how Ballard, your, uh, evil genius so to speak, how he talked you into going — "

"Objection," yelped the Prosecuting Captain. "The witness is being led!"

"Objection sustained," said the president effortlessly. "Just tell your story, Private Turvey, without further promptings. And," he looked at his wrist watch again, "you are warned that you must be brief."

Turvey obliged. He gave some account of McKelvie's shooting prowess, his own disappointment at loss of Christmas leave, his conversations with Ballard, and their faring-forth on Christmas Eve. They had been lucky enough to get a lift with an American trucker on his way back from a Buffalo — Toronto run. The trucker, it appeared, had somewhat anticipated the Christmas festivities and had been in the proper mood to smuggle them, under a pile of sacks and empty crates, across the border. Once over, they found that their uniforms and the season together created a passport to free food and a surprising number of drinks all the way to Buffalo. The trucker had by this time grown so enthusiastic about Canada's role in the war that he brought them to his home for the night and for most of Christmas Day. They had then proceeded to an address known to Ballard, the address at which Turvey was later discovered.

"May we presume you had settled down there for the duration?" the president asked, with acidity.

"O, no, sir," said Turvey, round-eyed and earnest. "We were goin to come back next, uh, that night, but the girls wanted, well, that is, it was Christmas and we got hoistin a few and we thought we might just as well hang around another day."

"Tomorrow and tomorrow and tomorrow, creeps in this petty pace from day to day." It was the paymaster, suddenly, beaming with pride at his own literary wit. "He just put if off, sir, a human — "

"Has the defendant anything more to say?" the president cut in grimly.

"Well, sir, only this, sir," said Turvey, stumbling desperately. "I woulda come back right away except I was, I was waitin for Ballard. The day after Christmas he started off to hitchhike to Cleveland. Said he had a nant there he was going to hit up for a loan and I wasnt to go back till he come. He said it'd be better for me if we come back together on our own steam; then he could explain I was, I just went along with him for the ride."

The president sniffed faintly. "How long did you intend to wait for Ballard?"

"O, of course, I was goin to nip back anyhow before my 28 days was up. Ballard told me we hadda do that, or else we'd be charged with desertion and not just bein AW Loose."

"Do you realize," the president retorted implacably, "that the charge against you may still be altered to one of desertion? No evidence has been presented in this court that you were still in uniform when apprehended. *Were* you in uniform, by the way? Remember you are under oath." There was an ominous smile about the president's lips, a thin, icicled smile.

"No, sir," said Turvey, faltering and hanging his head.

"Hah," said the president shortly, "so you admit to being apprehended in civilian clothes."

There was a pause. Turvey ran his finder under the collar of his battleblouse.

"No, sir," he said bashfully.

"Come, come" — the president was irritated — "you must have been in one or the other, you know, unless — " He paused, struck apparently by an interesting new idea.

"I was in the bed, sir," said Turvey blushing now. "I didnt think to take my pajamas when we went over the line."

There was a snicker, which quickly died under the president's revolving stare. "*The* bed?" the president could not quite conceal a note of salacious curiosity. "Was there only *one* in the apartment?"

"Yes, sir." Turvey's voice had faded to a shy whisper.

"Do you mean to say you were sleeping with both these women?"

"Well, not exactly," said Turvey, as one who didnt wish to boast. "You see, sir, one of them was on day-shift at the airplane plant, and the other was on nights." Turvey paused, and added in a burst of honesty, "They did change shifts the second week I was there. Ruby went on nights and took over shoppin and keepin up the uh — liquor supply — I didnt go out, a course, cause I mighta got picked up by a Namerican MP or somebody. I always kept my uniform hung over a chair, though, O, gosh, no, I wouldnt put on any civvies" — Turvey seized on the thought with horror.

This time the president allowed the court-room reaction to go unreproved. For a long space he peered at Turvey, as if seeing him for the first time. Then he trained his little glassy headlamps on the empurpled paymaster.

"Lieutenant," he asked with his most precise and military accents, "do you consider yourself a nervous type?"

"Me, sir?" The paymaster was definitely caught off base. "O, dear no, sir. Average, uh — sta-stability, I should say, sir. Hic! At least average."

"Hah! And do you suppose, lieutenant, that if you had spent the previous fortnight taking alternate shifts with two ladies in the same bed, and indulging in apparently alcoholic parties of sufficient, umm, exuberance to prompt complaints to the police from a neighbouring apartment house — do you suppose, lieutenant, that your hand would not have trembled when you were suddenly transported to one of His Majesty's guard rooms and handed a glass of water?"

It was the president's moment; the paymaster had no reply. The Great Trout, having clearly established his greatness, stilled the little commotion his coup had wrought with a funny flick of his hand, and looked left and right to his silent admiring Troutlings. "Does either of my colleagues wish to question the defendant?" But they shook their heads quickly; any question from them would be an anticlimax, if not actually a piece of insubordination, at this moment. Turvey was stood down, and his somewhat deflated counsel began the hopeless task of summing up for the defence. When that was over, the bristled captain had merely to ask tartly for a conviction on the evidence given, and the court-room was cleared, leaving the three large fish to decide on the fate of Turvey the minnow. Fortunately (it seemed colder than ever outside, and there was no shelter) the judges took almost no time to confer. The court was reassembled and Turvey informed that the findings would be promulgated.

"It means you're guilty," whispered the paymaster cheerfully, behind his ear again, "but don't worry, you wont get much."

Turvey wondered how much was much to the paymaster. The length of the sentence had something to do, he knew, with the state of his "crime sheet," his MFM 6. This the Clerk of the Court now proceeded to chant, much like a minister with a reading from the Scriptures. It wasnt too bad, Turvey thought with relief. "Three days' CB for being improperly dressed, in that he did appear without anklets in the streets of. . . . Two days' CB and one day's Field Punishment for. . . ." His little catalogue of sins having been read without comment, Turvey was informed that they would be weighed in considering his present sentence. His Majesty's Court-Martial was over.

"ULLLef . . . ry . . . lef . . . eye. . . ."

Next day Turvey had to disrupt some newly formed friendships in the camp brig and betake himself to the much larger and grimmer District Detention Barracks, there to consider, for the next forty-five days, the wickedness of his life.

Eric Nicol's third winner was in 1958. Like his first, Girdle Me a Globe *is a travel book.*

ERIC NICOL
from Girdle Me a Globe

The only real reward of travelling east-to-west about the globe is that you can make Britain your last port of call before coming home, so that you have not only travelled in space, from South Pacific islands to these of the North Atlantic, but also travelled in time, from primitive man to the most enlightened.

The minute you land in Dover, from the Continent and all points east, you know you have come to more than an island in a cold sea.

You know you have found the rare refuge of sanity and civilization, in a world-wide ocean of monkey business.

This is the sanctuary, the tiny, sea-bound asylum for that rare bird — a gentleman. This is the home of fair play, of respect for justice, of the rule of law divorced from use of force.

This is where man has learned to live as a social animal to whom respect for his neighbour's rights is second nature. This is where he behaves himself without the intimidation of religion or revolver-toting cops. This is Britain.

And how we take it for granted!

Until a person has travelled through those exotic countries whose natives look so charming in the tourist posters — spearing fish and pitting olives — he doesn't realize how numerous the primitives are, nor how ready to spear each other and pit riot against reason.

These are the exotic people of the world, these English. Only fifty million of them on a globe alive with billions, they never think of becoming part of a mob, of stoning to death, of burning, lynching or otherwise participating in the normal practices of men from Bombay to Montgomery, Alabama.

Incredibly, these people live completely cut off from hysteria and all the more elaborate forms of superstition, a veritable lost continency.

When you talk to one of the natives of this strange island, you find that he has no hatred for anybody. Fantastic, isn't it? Here is a world rich in grudges of all sizes and shapes, made to match every colour of skin, of politics and of religion, yet these Britons somehow get along happily without any of them.

What a find for *The National Geographic!*

Other peoples have created great works of art, but none to match the masterpiece that is the British Character. This creation is as artificial as any baroque temple, since it subdues the natural impulses of self-interest under the elaborate structure of what isn't cricket.

Nothing the Greeks and Romans ever invented in the way of architecture has been as useful to mankind as the arch of the British eyebrow.

True, in many parts of the world it no longer supports the colonial attitude. In Asia, in the Middle East, it is now the popular pastime to boot a stuffed lion in the behind and call it Britain.

But these new states and republics that are intoxicated with over-indulgence in freedom are nowhere near kicking the actual animal, the real, genuine lion that lives in a den of bumbling and spluttering and only appears when thoroughly aroused.

You know you are getting close to the lion country when you smell his spoor, the acrid stench of English pipe tobacco in the boat-train from Paris to Calais.

You know you are even closer, on the ferry to Dover, when the old lady in the deck chair asks a sailor what time we leave and he bends over her with genial solicitude, consulting his watch and saying:

"Why, I don't know, dear. What time would you *like* to leave?"

And you know you've arrived when the trim, green fields of Kent fly past your carriage window, Kent that is full of hops and black-faced lambs, disciplined by hedgerows and houses ranged in regiments, plumes of chimney smoke proudly waving.

I recommend rounding the globe east-to-west.

In 1962 W. O. Mitchell was a highly popular choice for the Leacock Medal. Like many struggling writers Mitchell supported himself in different ways while he wrote, including, he says, jobs as "a high diver" and "an organ grinder's assistant." His 1962 recognition came when he translated into a novel his very popular radio show Jake and the Kid *starring, among others, the late John Drainie who gave so much joy to Leacock fans. The sympathetic treatment of the relationship between Jake, the hired man, and the country boy remains a kind of Canadian classic.*

W.O. MITCHELL
from Jake and the Kid

Miss Henchbaw she got up, and she stood there with her hands folded together across her stomach; her mouth was sort of turned up at the corners, like when she's got something to tell us and it's good. Jake he claims she always looks like a hungry goshawk, only he isn't fussy about her, not with her all the time saying he didn't capture Looie Riel and Chief Poundmaker singlehanded.

Miss Henchbaw she looked down at us; her grey hair, that's piled up like one of those round loaves of bread, was under the writing on the board:

"The girl plays with the dog. It is fun to play."

She waited for Una to quit whispering to Violet, and the pencils to stop their dotting sounds, and Fat to finish grinding on the pencil sharpener. Fat he's always sharpening a pencil.

Steve Kiziw, that sits in front of me, he was leaning back lazy in his seat, twirling his ruler on the point of his pencil. Steve has two brothers in the Air Force. Me I got my dad that's in the South Saskatchewans. Steve and me have our trap line together; skunk and weasel been running good since the last of October.

"Children!" Her voice all the time goes up at the end.

Steve's ruler clattered to the top of his desk.

"Just three weeks till Christmas." She smiled and you could hear the Grade Ones and Twos sighing all over the room. "Time we were getting to work on our Christmas concert." The Grade Ones and Twos sort of all squealed together. "Now I've — Steve, sit up in your seat!"

Steve he sat up.

"I've been thinking that we — instead of getting a play already

94

made for us, we'd do something new this year." Everybody was looking up at her. Beside her you could see the orange flames flickering to beat anything in the school stove. "We're going to make up our own play this year. And — yes, Una?"

Una took down her hand. " 'Bout the Babe in the manger, Miss Henchbaw?"

Miss Henchbaw sort of pulled her mouth up together. "Why, I think that — "

"Er — thuh Three Wise Men." That was Fat by the pencil sharpener.

"Them sheepherders," piped up Ike. His dad raises a lot of sheep. "Where they wuz watchin' their herda sheep an' they saw thuh northern lights — "

"The Star of the East, Harry — were watching — Sit down, Willis." She meant Fat. She turned to the board. On one side she wrote "Babe-manger", on the other "Three Wise Men". She turned around again. "We'll vote."

"Didn't put down no sheepherders," Ike muttered under his breath.

It turned out 11 to 10 for the Three Wise Men. We got 10 girls in Rabbit Hill. Ike he didn't put up his hand for either one.

Ike he got picked for one of the Wise Men along with Fat and Steve. Miss Henchblaw she made Steve in charge of all the stuff we needed for the concert: broomsticks for the camels' heads to go on, red tissue paper and a light bulb for the campfire, candles for all the Grade Ones for when they were all dressed up in green tissue paper to make a Christmas tree out of themselves.

I got to be the Wise Men's hired man, only Miss Henchbaw she suggested they better call me a camel driver.

We made up a pretty good play, all about where the Three Wise Men are figuring out what presents they're going to bring, and they end up where Fat brings gold and Steve some perfume called frankincents and Ike he was going to bring meer, whatever that is. Fat had the most to say.

After four Steve and me kicked our way through the schoolyard. She'd been snowing most the afternoon, so the yard was spread white and the prairie had lost her edge. You could only see a glowey place where the sun was supposed to be low down in the sky. By our forts we built in the corner of the yard where the buck brush had its black arms held out, Steve burped.

He can burp whenever he wants to by taking down the air first. When he burps he can talk at the same time. Once he said five words and only used up one burp. You ought to hear him pretend to sneeze too.

"You gotta pelt thuh next one," Steve said.

I didn't say anything. In our trap line we'd got 11 weasel and three skunks; Steve meant she was my turn to skin the next skunk. I didn't say anything.

We walked down Government Road, with the snow sort of squealing under our feet.

"Wonder if we got a badger this time, Steve?"

"Dunno — Oughta be a good play."

"Yeah. I didn't want to be in it much."

Steve said he didn't either, but he didn't mean it any more than what I did.

"Guess we ain't gonna have Henchbaw teachin' us next year," Steve said.

I stopped right in the middle of Government Road.

"Huh?"

"They're gonna git Miss Ricky that's at Broomhead — Old Man Ricky he's gittin' her."

Mr. Ricky he's down the road from us and he's tight. The last three years he's been chairman of the school board. I never heard about Miss Henchbaw leaving Rabbit Hill. I said:

"I never heard about her leavin', Steve."

"I heard my dad talkin' to Ma — he says Old Man Ricky's after the $15 a month board he'll git outa Louella. If she comes here to teach she'll hafta stay with her dad."

"What'll Miss Henchbaw do?"

"I dunno," Steve said. "Git her another school."

"Wonder if Ricky's daughter's like he is."

"Can't be no worsen Miss Henchbaw."

"No," I said, "guess she can't."

But I wasn't so sure. Jake and me we're not very fussy about Mr. Ricky. Take the way we can't even get a softball for the school out of him, and the way he's all the time kicking about us using up the chalk. He claims Miss Henchbaw lets us waste it, throwing it around all over. I never threw any. Every time he gets a chance he hints about Miss Henchbaw not being so good a teacher; Jake he sort of agrees with Mr. Ricky on that; he claims her history's shaky.

When I told Ma what Steve said she blew up. "Why, that's a shame! Miss Henchbaw's been at Rabbit Hill 20 years!"

"Twenty years too long," Jake said.

"She's been a very good teacher," Ma said.

Jake he muttered something under his breath.

"I don't think the people around here want to see her go."

"Well, I knowa one that ain't enny too — "

"This is her home," Ma said. "She — why I've never heard of anything like that in my life!"

"Ricky he's thuh whole school board," Jake said. "Got his own hired man, Art, on. Old Man Gatenby he ain't much good, him bein' deef. Ricky he jist runs that there school board."

"That isn't democracy," Ma said.

"Miss Henchbaw she isn't so democratic, Ma. The way she — "

"That'll do, son!"

Sometimes Ma isn't so democratic either.

The next week I sort of forgot about Miss Henchbaw getting fired. She didn't act any different in school that I could see. Steve and me were pretty busy with our trap line: two weasels, no skunks, one of Tincher's chickens.

Friday I went back to the school to get my Health book I forgot, and I was almost to my seat before I noticed. Miss Henchbaw's head was resting bent forward on her desk, with her hands made into fists and them by her ears. I stopped. I didn't know what to do.

I scuffled some with my feet.

Her head came up. A hunk of her grey hair had come out and it was hanging down by her ear. Her face was streaky. Her eyes were just as red as the Santa Clauses sort of marching along the top of the side blackboard.

Old people look awful when they've been crying.

I got out of there without my Health book.

When I got home I looked for Jake.

"Jake."

"Yeah?"

"I — I'm not so fussy about — about the way Miss Henchbaw —"

"I ain't fussy about her either."

"No — I mean — about Mr. Ricky gettin' rid of her."

"No skin offa my knuckles."

"Jake — I got to thinkin' — everybody makes fun of old maids, don't they?"

"Uh-huh."

"It isn't funny, Jake."

"Whut ain't?"

"Bein' an old maid."

" 'Tain't likely — "

"It must be awful lonely, Jake — she's lonely — "

"So's a goshawk."

"But he wants to be — she hasn't got anybody, Jake — she hasn't even got anybody in this war — she — once Ma told me she had a fella she — "

"Who? Her?"

"The last war — he was at Vimy."

Jake's mouth came open and it stayed there. Jake he was at Vimy Ridge too.

"She's always askin' about Dad or about Aunt Margaret's baby."

"Is she?" Jake he's fussy about our baby.

"Gettin' old and not having anybody give a whoop about you — Jake, that's worse than hail or rust — something you can't do anything about."

Jake he nodded his head slow. He isn't so young.

"An' if Ricky he — Jake — she was bawlin'!"

That night Jake went over to see Mr. Tincher. The next day they started the paper around for people to sign saying they didn't want Miss Henchbaw to leave. It stirred up a lot of talk, all about how Mr. Ricky he was getting his hired man to tend the school stove and not paying him any extra wages but charging for a janitor all the same. Everybody signed.

In school we went right on like there was nothing wrong. We had our play all memorized. Ike he'd forgot all about the northern lights. Steve and Miss Henchbaw they had an argument and it was about chickens.

Steve he figured she'd be nice to have some chickens around the Wise Men's bonfire in our play. Miss Henchbaw she said no. Steve he kept bringing her up and Miss Henchbaw kept right on saying no.

It was about a week after we made up our Christmas play that Mr. Ricky came into the schoolyard. If he wasn't all the time coming around to snoop he wouldn't have got Steve's snowball in the back of his neck, the one with the special centre Steve meant for Ike.

Mr. Ricky he got Miss Henchbaw to line all us kids up and he started in giving us a talking to about running wilder than hooty owls, and how we needed somebody to really give us some discipline. Every few words he'd say, "Section so and so, paragraph so and so of thuh School Act." He said he didn't blame us so much as he blamed the teacher that would let us get out of hand the way we were, and Miss Henchbaw she was blushing real red.

Steve he sneezed the way he can do.

Mr. Ricky, standing there with his hat still on and the flaps down so he looks like a goshawk with blinkers on, he said:

"An' I wanta know who threw that there snowball?"

Steve he went, "AAAaaah — whooooo!"

"I'm agonna keep yuh all here till I find out which one a yuh."

"AAaaaaa — whuhiiich!"

Mr. Ricky looked sort of startled at Steve. He began to say something, but Steve looked like butter wouldn't melt in his mouth. "Ain't no use in tryin' tuh git outa her — I'll find out ef we gotta stay here all night."

"AAAaaaaaah — huh-huh-hu-night."

"Say — " Mr. Ricky took a step toward Steve. "You ain't tryin' tuh — " "Aaaaaaay — huh — ho — noooooo!" She was a wet one.

Mr. Ricky leapt back and reached into his hip pocket for a handkerchief. "That's him!" His voice sort of cracked. "That's thuh boy that done it!" He reached out and lifted Steve up by the collar of his jacket. Steve's face started in working again. Mr. Ricky let him go quick. Steve's face straightened right out again.

Mr. Ricky he said likely the teacher wouldn't do anything about making sure it wouldn't happen again.

Mr. Ricky was wrong. I saw Steve's hands afterward.

After that Mr. Ricky spread all over about how bad us kids were, and he said seeing the teacher couldn't keep any control over us he had no way of doing his duty as chairman of the school board except by getting somebody else to take her place the next school year. He said he felt the paper everybody signed didn't change things a bit; the folks didn't know how bad things were in the school and it was time something was done about it.

Ma blew up again.

She said, "Something has to be done, Jake!"

"Ain't nothin' a fella kin do," Jake said.

"But — can't — "

"Ed Tincher he said somethin' 'bout holdin' a ratepayers' meetin' — tellin' thuh board how they — "

"Then why — "

"Ricky'd run her — soon as thuh notices wuz posted he'd git her all figgered out how tuh throw a monkey wrench intuh her — all thuh time talkin' about that there School Act nobody knows about — fella feels like a fool ef he gits up tuh argue with him — can't open your mouth but whut she's wrong by section so an' so, paragraft such an' such."

"Why doesn't — can't somebody get a School Act and — "

"Why — I'spose — "

"Does Mr. Ricky have to know about the meeting ahead of time?"

"There's somethin' about yuh gotta have her up three places — I remember when — how kin yuh hold a meetin' ef folks don't know about her — an' ef they know, Ricky he'll know too. He — say! Kid! When's that there Christmas concert?"

"Week from Thursday, Jake."

"That's whut we kin do — folks'll all be tuhgether — hold our meetin' right after thuh concert — good time too right after a entertainment she got up — kinda softens folks up toward her."

All that week the weasels were running good. The night before the concert Steve and me took a badger out; his hair was real long and thick.

It was the night of the Christmas concert we got the skunk.

Steve he came over to our place for supper, and he helped me with my chores. He brought over his sheet for being a Wise Man all wrapped up in paper. Ma and Jake went over to Tinchers early so they could go to the concert with them. Steve helped me hitch up Baldy to the bobsleigh when she was about time to go. He threw his parcel into the back of the box. I went back to the house to get my Little Daisy .22; our trap line lies right on the way to the new Community Hall and we figured we might find something in her to shoot.

When I came back outside, Steve he had a gunny sack in his hand and he was tying the neck up and there were some squawks coming out of it.

"What you doin', Steve?"

"Jist borra'd a couple of your chickens for that there play."

"But — "

"Ain't nothin gonna happen — "

"Miss Henchbaw she said you couldn't."

"It'll make it a lot realer to have some chickens up on the stage."

"But what'll Ma — "

"We'll bring 'em right back after the concert. They'll be all right."

I didn't argue any more. How'd I know he'd caught the barred Rock and the Wyandotte? They bust loose every time they catch sight of each other. They're roosters.

When we got to the fourth trap there was a skunk in her. Steve shot it and he took it out. He threw it into the box of the sleigh. We went on to the hall, and the smell of skunk came right along with us.

Because he had to fix up the light bulb with red tissue paper and sticks for the Wise Men's bonfire, Steve went in the hall ahead of me. He took the sack with the chickens, said he was keeping them in the kitchen till it was time to use them. He told me to bring his other parcel.

I tied Baldy up to the fence then went to get Steve's Wise Man sheet.

The Skunk was lying right on top of it.

The smell of skunk followed me to the hall real strong.

For a good 15 minutes before our play came on the folks out front could smell Steve's sheet, not so strong at first, Jake told me after, but when the curtain came apart she just leapt out at the audience. I know when I came onto the stage I could see the folks looking around sort of sidewise at each other, like they were wondering whether the skunk was somewhere in the hall or just outside.

Two of the Wise Men knew — Ike and Fat; when they came out on their camels there was a lot of distance between Steve and the other Wise Men. Even the two roosters Steve had turned loose just stood there on the stage, looking dazed. When I came up to take the camels away the smell sort of caught at my breath.

The way he was supposed to Steve sat up close to the bonfire; on the other side Fat and Ike were just as far away as they could get without looking as though something was wrong.

"What are we going to give, O Wise Men?" Ike's voice came out sort of muffled. He was holding his sheet up over his nose.

"We must bring the best presents that can be brung." Miss

Henchbaw had told him not to say "brung".

"And what are you — goin' — to — what — uh." Ike choked.

Steve got up and started around the fire the way he was supposed to. "Thuh bee-you-teeous perfume of thuh East. Frankincents."

"I-will-bring-the-gifta-meer." Fat ripped it out; he was way ahead of himself, but it was the speech he was to make before he went off. He left.

"Me, I better throw down a bundle to them camels." That was real smart of Ike; it wasn't what was written in the play at all, but with Steve coming for him Ike had to think quick. He turned and ran. The light cord for the bonfire caught his foot; he took off and lit flat on his face.

The barred Rock rooster let out a crow and leaped at the Wyandotte, his feathers up around his neck. Then they were going at it, just like a couple of balls you throw up in the air and catch and throw up again.

Smell or no smell I rushed out on to the stage to help Steve get those roosters. He'd got one, was holding it squawking under his arm whilst he tried to get the other. Just as we got the Wyandotte chased off into Fat's arms, the barred Rock got away again, and we had to go through her all over again.

We'd sure messed her up for Miss Henchbaw getting back again as teacher in Rabbit Hill. I told Steve that whilst we were out getting rid of his sheet and helping to open all the doors to air out the hall. It didn't seem to bother Steve; he had his mind on the Christmas candy and pop they were going to hand out.

When we came back in the front of the hall Jake and Mr. Tincher were up on the stage. Mr. Ricky was standing out in the audience.

" 'Tain't legal!" he was yelling. "Can't hold her unless yuh got yer three notices posted!"

"We posted 'em!" Jake yelled back at him.

"Where? I ain't see 'em. Where was they posted?"

"Backa our cow barn," Jake said. "One on Totcoal's windmill — 'nother on Ed's granary in his East forty."

"But that ain't — I didn't — "

"We're here tuhnight," Jake said, "tuh make sure thuh folks in this district get thuh teacher they want teachin' their kids. So we have — "

"Section fifty-three — paragraph five says — "

"We have met tuh direct our school board tuh — "

" — only ratepayers kin — "

"Will Mr. Ricky set down an' shet up!" That was Bent Matthews.

"No, he won't," said Mr. Ricky. "I've set here tuhnight an' seen thuh most disgraceful display I ever — "

"Fine concert — what I saw," said Mr. Tincher.

"Them roosters!" shouted Old Man Gatenby. "Most comical thing I ever seen!"

"Ain't bin so much excitement sence thuh Fenian raids," yelled Phadrig Connor.

Then they were all yelling what a good concert it had been, and they meant it. When they had quieted down Jake said:

"We're gonna take vote — "

"Section fifty-three — paragraph five — "

"Johnny — Bent!" Jake called out. Mr. Totcoal and Mr. Matthews stood up on either side of Mr. Ricky.

"Kindly lead out thuh school board chairman — in — uh — accordance with section two hundred an' — uh — sixty — paragraft ten — which says — ennybuddy don't shet up when they're told three times, jist take 'em outa thuh hall."

"But there ain't enny such — "

I guess Mr. Ricky finished up outside.

I don't understand so well how they worked it, but Ma says Miss Henchbaw's staying. After the folks voted they asked Mr. Ricky to quit being chairman. He did. Even Mr. Ricky, Jake says, hadn't got the nerve to hang on after that meeting.

Harry Boyle first made his mark on the world in radio, serving the CBC as commentator, director and executive producer for twenty-six years. He is now Chairman of the Canadian Radio-Television Commission. Shortly after his warm Homebrew and Patches *won the Leacock Medal in 1964, he was acclaimed the Mayor of Leacock's mythical Mariposa, an office which he has upheld with dignity and delight. His second medal came in 1976.*

HARRY J. BOYLE

from Hombrew and Patches

Our town was really only a village, but it held many delights for a small farm-boy. This was especially true on a spring afternoon when I was allowed to go "in" with Father and take a load of grist to the mill.

A greenish tint suffused the brown waste of the fields and hills. Shoots were showing up like green whiskers, and pussy willows popped their "kittens" on slender stems over the creek, swollen by melting ice and run-off water. Cattle stood around in barn-yards, while dogs nosed on sandy hillsides anticipating groundhogs. Other dogs yapped their joy down laneways, as if they couldn't contain their spirits on such a bright day. Here and there, a late maple-syrup shanty sent stray rings of gray smoke filtering up through trees to vanish into the void of blue sky.

There was one ritual that had to be observed during the drive. We knew it really was spring when Hector Macpherson appeared on his front veranda. Long past retirement, he lived in a tiny house on a small plot on the corner of the homestead now farmed by his two boys. As we went by, the old man on the veranda would raise a hand in fluttered greeting, while his old hound would half raise his head and then nuzzle back into his paws for more sleep.

I never ceased to wonder about the old man. It seemed strange that this was the "lumber-camp hero" of brawls and fist fights, the strong man of legendary stories who could, as they said, "dance all night and work all day." Now, wrapped in a faded sweater, he passed the time alone, content to sit on the sidelines and watch the active world that he had once enjoyed pass by.

Spring was the time when Mr. Jenkins worked in his bee-yard. It was a small, fenced field with a shack in the middle of the hives and the gnarled, old apple trees of what was once a prosperous orchard. Mr. Jenkins, a retired railwayman, had fifty hives of bees and supplied our township with honey, except those of us fortunate enough to find a wild-bee tree when cutting wood during the winter.

Clotheslines fluttered with clothes of all kinds and colours. These were not lines of washing, but quilts, linen and good clothes put out for their annual spring "airing." From drawers smelling of camphor, mothballs or cedar boughs, the heirlooms of patch quilts, bed spreads and winter coats had been taken out for an antiseptic cleaning by spring sunshine and air. Men, shanghaied into service, beat carpets and rag rugs and studiously avoided looking toward the road as we passed by. They were only too aware of the joshing that awaited them at the grist mill, store or social.

As we approached town, we saw a congregation of boys around the stream that provided power for the grist mill. What was a trickle by summer had mighty proportions in spring. It flooded over the flats where some monuments of dirty ice still perched, slowly vanishing under the rays of the sun. Some boys were fishing rather fruitlessly with lines. Others were trying to net suckers down by the abutments of the bridge or beside the mill race where the sturdy cedar piling provided for the fish a quiet nook in the powerful waters.

While the men leaned against wagons or sat on the edge of the mill platform and talked, we escaped uptown. The village had an air in spring different from that of any other season.

A minister, looking frail, with a duster disguising his clerical garb, was wrestling with storm-windows. Shiny, painted farm machinery, in contrast with battered, dirty, used equipment, was lined up beside the implement dealer's. Men stood around and enviously eyed the new machines while waiting for repairs. In the dim depths of the blacksmith shop, the forge flared orange and red, and the measured blows on the anvil beat out a tempo fitting for the spring season.

A fragrant smell came from the open barber shop, mingling with a yeasty odour from the little bake shop. Jimmy Medd, the diminutive tailor, wearing a green eyeshade on his forehead, perched on a table inside the open door of his shop. Gossipers congregated in the double warmth behind the big window of the post office, as if afraid to leave their winter vantage point for the spring sunshine. The chairs on the veranda of the Commercial Hotel were filled with mumbling talkers, their low talk contrasting with the hearty sounds of laughter that spilled out from within the hotel.

Men stood around reading the auction-sale bills in the window of the print shop or else turned to watch the women and girls venturing out with only jackets over bright dresses, having shed their bulky winter coats. The hardware store and the harness shop had merchandise spread out on boxes and barrels on the sidewalk. There were racks of seeds in gaily coloured packets, bottles of formaldehyde, garden tools, tall racks of buggy whips with bright tassels, and red wheelbarrows. In front of Murphy's general store a salt-encrusted barrel signified a special price on the remainder of his Lenten salt herrings.

It was a fine spring day. With ten cents I could crown it with an ice-cream soda at Lee's Café. If my treasure horde was only five cents or some pennies, I could, by judicious spending, purchase an assortment of jaw-breaker candies or licorice for delicious pleasure on the trip home.

In the country spring was the time for the bride hunters. Bachelors, who had spent all winter huddled in lonely seclusion, feeling the stirring of spring, yielded to the lure. They made a trip to town to purchase a new suit and hat, oiled and polished harness until it was supple and bright, and varnished the buggy up until it shone. The bridles got new ornaments, pompons were stuck on the horse collars and, with new red and white tasseled whips stuck in the dashboards, the bachelors set out "bride hunting."

Late on a Sunday afternoon we would see all the bachelors and widowers in the township coming along side roads and concessions, heading for the village. By the time the churches let their parishioners out Sunday night, the main street looked the way it did on a fall fair day, because the villagers also came down to the oiled strip, known as the "Main Drag," to watch the fun.

There was a pleasant fiction among families in the village that everything was under control when two girls went walking on Sunday night. Few questioned this fiction. J.A. Hopkins took a different view. As a boy, I knew him only as Preacher or "J.A." He sold insurance and passed for a "jack-knife lawyer" — one who could draw up a will or witness a document. He was a short, fussy little man, with a fringe of white hair on a bald, shiny, turnip head, who always wore a checkered vest. He was always seen either posting letters at the post office or else taking mail away. He was a lay-preacher and filled in at various churches when the regular preachers were sick or away. Also, he wrote letters to the town newspaper and, when they were printed, cut them out and pasted them up on the bulletin board in front of the village library.

Mr. Hopkins conducted a one-man campaign against the Sunday night procession of bride hunters. When the regular Baptist minister took his holidays in the spring to go and preach in J.A.'s brother's church in the city, J.A. took over the pulpit and thundered against the immoral young men who stood around ogling girls on Sunday nights on the main street.

Wally McEwan had a good farm. It was probably the best hundred acres on the Sixth Concession. Unfortunately, although Wally was a good farmer, he was also one of the Black Scotch. In our community this name meant that, along with the Black Irish, Wally had certain characteristics. He could work all day and play all night, and had, as well, an amazing capacity for almost any form of intoxicating beverage.

There were four girls in the Hopkins family. The youngest three were dumpy like their father, but the oldest, Margaret, was surely a throw-back, because she was tall, dark and probably the most attractive girl in the village. Wally and Margaret were naturally attracted to each other, but they couldn't do much about it because the eagle eye of J.A. was always upon his daughter.

One Sunday J.A. went away to preach in the next county. On the following Sunday, the village really had something to talk about. Margaret had gone riding with Wally. Three days later, the little man accosted Wally on the street, calling him all the names he could think of. The Black Scot simply reached over, picked up the moralist and dumped him in the watering trough in front of the Commercial Hotel.

The odds were laid then that Wally had queered himself for good. The resourceful Wally, however, waited for three weeks and then appeared at the Sunday evening Baptist service. He was smart. He merely nodded to the Hopkins family for two Sundays and then, on the third Sunday, drove around to their house, apologized to Mr. Hopkins and asked in a straight-forward manner if Margaret might go for a buggy ride. Hopkins was taken off base completely but rallied and agreed. He then proceeded to go with them, sitting squeezed in the centre of the sea between the couple.

Margaret, who was taking a correspondence course in book-keeping, was supposedly too busy to see Wally. Then the community stepped in. The grist-mill owner, a distant cousin of Wally, had her in to do his books. She was hired one day a week to operate the telephone switchboard, and the librarian, Wally's great-aunt, brought her in to help catalogue books. Wally was in town a lot during that month, even though it was seeding time.

Hopkins went around beaming at his own cleverness in making Margaret take the book-keeping course. One day by chance he went to see the grist-mill owner about the renewal of his insurance, and found the McEwan buggy vanishing across the bridge with Margaret in it.

This was the end of Margaret's business career. J.A., however, had overlooked two things: the village was on the side of the lovers, and Margaret had turned twenty-one. On the day after the grist-mill incident, Margaret vanished.

Hopkins laid a complaint of kidnapping with the township constable, and, since that worthy officer had never had a case like it before, he took the advice of the community on it. Hopkins was on the verge of going to the county sheriff when he received a wire from Margaret saying that she would be in that afternoon on the four o'clock train from the city.

Hopkins was at the station. So was practically the whole village and half the township. When the train arrived, Wally and his bride stepped off. There wasn't much Hopkins could do when he saw her ring, and especially when he found out that his own brother had officiated at the wedding.

After that, Hopkins never again mentioned the bride hunters. In fact, he even let his three daughters walk uptown every Sunday night unchaperoned. It didn't do them any good. They were the three who looked like him.

Country women scheme all the time, trying to ensnare eligible bachelors and widowers into matrimony, but only when these belong to another family. The women sing a different song when it comes to their own brothers, fathers or uncles. I guess that's why everyone in our family took it so hard when Grandfather started courting the widow Marshall.

Mrs. Marshall was a tidy-looking woman with a sort of pouter-pigeon look. She was puffed up around the top and front and tapered off into neat legs and tiny feet. She wasn't young, but she had a youthful appearance, because her eyes sparkled and her hair always looked freshly marcelled. She owned a gift shop next to Lee's Café.

The first sign of the affair came when my grandfather dressed up one night and took the Model T to the Odd Fellows Hall for the euchre game. It was unusual for him to drive the car in the day-time, let alone at night. It was also unusual to find him in a celluloid collar and tie. Most of the time, he considered himself dressed up when he wore a white shirt and gold collar button. The morning after the game, the party line was buzzing. Grandpa had taken first prize in the euchre tournament and had celebrated by escorting Mrs. Marshall to Lee's Café.

Next day he was in a rare old humour. He joshed Mother, gave me ten cents and hummed all during the chores. When I heard a buggy leathering up from the front gate, I knew it was bringing one of my aunts. When two of them stepped out, I knew it meant a council of war. They handed me the reins and stomped into the kitchen.

"Him almost seventy, and they say she's over sixty."

"It's indecent."

Mother was partially loyal.

"I don't think there's anything to it. He's not feeble-minded."

Another aunt squelched her: "At his age, all men are feeble-minded about women like that."

Grandfather gallantly welcomed his daughters to supper. Mother and my aunts hovered over him, trying to get him to talk. Father was making my mother angry, because he was grinning and refused to co-operate. Grandpa was in fine fettle, and the three sisters were afraid of him. It wasn't until later, when he came down all dressed up, that one of them said, "Pa, where are you going?"

"Out to do the chores," he said jauntily.

He took the Model T again, whanging the front fender as he tried to short-cut the gate post.

In later trips to the village, Grandfather smashed the other fender and lost a headlight. Mother was certain he was going to kill himself. When they heard he had danced the fox trot at an Orange Lodge dance, the women started worrying that he would lose his faith. Indignity piled on indignity: he had taken the widow to dinner at the Commercial Hotel; he had left the Model T at the livery stable and taken Mrs. Marshall to see Keebushkin Falls with a rented horse and rig.

I don't think Mrs. Marshall's gift shop was a success. A lot of people went in there out of curiosity and bought envelopes or writing paper. Most people thought that her stock was "cute" but impractical for a village like ours.

Grandfather came home one night with a present for Mother. It was a cuckoo clock, and, for once, Mother was beside herself.

"A coo-coo!"

At first she almost screamed, and then she started to laugh. This completely unnerved Grandfather and he grew anxious.

"What's the matter?"

Mother just waved him away and afterwards confessed to Father that she hadn't the heart to tell Grandfather that buying the clock was the first sensible thing he had done in weeks. Then we heard the news. Mrs. Marshall had sold her stock to the druggist and gone back to the city after another dinner at the Commercial. Grandfather had even seen her off on the train.

When my aunts arrived for dinner on the following Sunday, they were bursting to know all the details. They buzzed in the pantry but were quiet at the dinner table. Grandfather knew what they wanted. He stood up after dinner and went to the window ledge for his pipe. Slowly he tamped the tobacco, lit the pipe and reached for the screen door. Then one of my aunts exploded: "Well Pa, what happened? For heaven's sake, can't you tell us?"

Grandfather squinted at them through a wreath of tobacco smoke. He stroked his beard, which had been transformed into a Van Dyke during courtship and then gave an answer that delights me to this day.

"We broke up. She wouldn't agree to bring up the children in my faith."

We could hear him laughing all the way to the barn.

When Lawrence Earl won the Leacock Medal in 1953 with The Battle of Baltinglass, *the world had not yet heard of "New Journalism," but this remarkable and true story of the conflict between a culture and a government may have been the first of that much acclaimed new genre. When Helen Cooke was denied the Irish postmaster's position, held in her family for four generations, everyone in the village of Baltinglass, and presently everyone in Ireland, chose sides.*

LAWRENCE EARL
from The Battle of Baltinglass

Mr. Costello, the Prime Minister, was not at once aware of it, but that Friday was a black one for him (though certainly not as black as he was yet to face), for it was on that very day Paddy Cogan sat himself down in his home in Tullow, not many miles from the village of Baltinglass, and composed a letter.

"Dear Mr. Costello," he wrote, taking his own time and making sure of his words,

> Now that it is clear from the statement of Mr. Everett in Dáil Éireann that the Government are supporting his action in depriving without justification a public servant of her only means of livelihood —

Mr. Cogan lifted his pen and paused to think —

> I have decided, till this wrong is righted, that I will never again enter the division lobby on the Government side.

Mr. Cogan chewed the end of his pen, and stared through the wall of the room and through the snowy-sloped Wicklow Mountains into the infinite distance towards Dublin.

> I feel that it is my duty as one of the Independent Deputies who supported your election to the office of Taoiseach to inform you of this decision, and to express the hope that a means shall be speedily found to undo this grave injustice.
>
> I well appreciate that there are bigger issues involved than the filling of a minor post-office position. The civic conscience of plain people has been aroused by this grave injustice and the fight can go on. . . .
>
> The Battle of Baltinglass is everybody's battle. It is a battle for clean administration and decent public life. It is a fight for justice

113

for the weak and defenceless, and in particular in the exercise by a Minister of his executive functions.

I take this opportunity of thanking you for your unfailing courtesy and kindness to me, and sincerely hope you will find it possible to right this grave wrong.

Yours,

P. COGAN, T.D.

The Deputy read his letter over carefully, and then, satisfied, made copies of it to be sent to the daily Dublin newspapers so that there would be others, in addition to the Prime Minister, who would know exactly how Paddy Cogan stood in the matter of his vote in the Dáil and in the matter of Helen Cooke.

But, indeed, that was not the only message sent to Mr. Costello that day in connection with the Baltinglass affair. When the Reverend J. B. Fisher, the Rector of Kiltegan, a parish about four miles from Baltinglass, heard about how Father Doyle had sent a letter of protest to the Taoiseach he sat right down and wrote one himself, addressed to that same important personage.

"I have lived in the near vicinity of Baltinglass," said the reverend gentleman,

> for a number of years and have always found Miss Helen Cooke a very efficient postmistress. I would like to voice my strongest indignation at the action of the Minister for Posts and Telegraphs in changing the office without any apparent reason.
>
> In the interests of justice and good will I would appeal to you to effect an honourable settlement to this dispute, even at this late hour, and request the Minister himself to reconsider his decision.

Still another blow was struck that day (indirectly) against the Prime Minister and (directly) against the Prime Minister's Government.

At an evening meeting of the Helen Cooke Protest Committee — it was sometimes called the Baltinglass Protest Committee, but the Farrells objected to this all-embracing name — Bernie Sheridan suggested that the committee call off the picketing after Saturday. "Because," the husky, earnest young man said, "the Government could wear us out, having a considerable advantage in manpower. . . ."

Yes, it was unanimously agreed that the picketing would have to stop. But, on the other hand, they could not take the risk that the Government forces should attack and catch them wholly unprepared. What could be done? How to protect their businesses and the unprotected flank at the same time?

"I may be having an idea," Sheridan suggested diffidently, "which will get us out of this fix; and I would be glad to carry it through myself." He looked remarkably boyish as he continued, "I suggest an air-raid siren to be set up to warn the town."

"Eh?" said Felix O'Neill. "And what would we be needing with an air-raid signal?"

"I mean we could set up a couple of hooters and sound them off to warn the whole town if the Gardai come. Then we would be ready to meet any kind of an attack."

It was agreed, without further argument or discussion, that this — combined with their espionage service — would be as effective a first line of defence as the picketing had been. Then the Committee moved on to other business, and finally the representatives of the Press were called into the meeting — and eagerly anxious they were to be in on the news — so that a formal statement could be read out to them.

It was General Dennis who read the communiqué.

"We, the people of Baltinglass," the farmer-soldier said, "are now satisfied that we have established beyond all reasonable shadow of doubt that a grave injustice, which by now must be common knowledge, has been done by the Minister for Posts and Telegraphs. We deeply regret that the Government has endorsed the Minister's action.

"The matter now rests with those members of the Dáil who stand for integrity and clean administration. Baltinglass is one of many small towns, and what has happened to it may happen to your town to-morrow."

Thus, in the span of one day, the Prime Minister was attacked from three sides; but at the time it must have seemed to the great man like the attack of three mosquitoes, and ineffectual, stingless mosquitoes at that. For, in the high and secret places of Dublin, it had now been decided how to dispose of this awkward and embarrassing situation in Baltinglass — where there was a newly appointed sub-postmaster with his unused post-office, and, just down the street, a post-office which was still being used though it had no postmistress in it.

And there was no doubt at all — in the high and secret places, that is — that very shortly Mr. Michael Farrell would be in and

Miss Helen Cooke would be out, which would end the matter.

On Saturday morning (Sheridan said) I went to Patrick Dunne's garage at about half-past eleven.

"Pat," I says, "have you got a couple of heavy hooters so I can put them up as an air-raid siren?"

"Yes," Pat says, "I think I have just the thing." He went to the back of his garage and dug around in a greasy pile of cogs and axles and things like that. There was the banging and the scraping of metal against metal, and the smell of stale oil was stirred through the air. Soon he says, "Ah!" and came up out of the mess with the hooters and handed them to me. Pat had been a picket for Miss Cooke, and he was glad to lend the hooters for the purpose I had in mind.

I took them home, and then I got to thinking. These hooters will be loud enough to warn the Main Street, I thought, but what about the rest of Baltinglass?

I walked down to Joe Morrin's place and found Joe there and say to him, "Joe," I say, pointing to the bell on top of his mill, the one that was once used for calling the mill workers to their jobs, "what about that old mill bell there? Can we ring it to warn the people in case of an attack?"

Joe says, "Oh, that bell? That bell is dangerous, Bernie; it may pull down the gable and all if we use it. The gable is very weak, and that is why we stopped using it."

"Oh," I say, disappointed. I looked at Joe, and then I looked up at the bell and the rope hanging down, and then I looked back at Joe Morrin. We stood there. He thought about it for a while, rubbing his chin. From the other side of the mill we could hear the water sliding over the millrace.

"I'll tell you what we'll do," Joe says finally, not rubbing his chin any more.

"Well, what?"

"We'll use it, and to hell with the danger of it and the gable coming down."

"Thanks, Joe," I say, slapping him on the shoulder, and I went off quickly to tell the Press about the new arrangements: Joe Morrin's old mill bell would warn the Mill Street and the air-raid siren made out of Pat Dunne's hooters would alarm the Main Street. And, after I told the Press, Jim McCann helped me put two hooters up, outside my bedroom window, and I fastened them to two twelve-volt batteries. Then we tested them. They worked fine, sounding sad and mournful, but fairly loud.

So the pickets were withdrawn, according to our plan, at seven o'clock that night. But, just to make certain that we wouldn't be taken by surprise in the meantime, Paddy O'Grady posted himself again in the office of Morrin's mill until ten that evening, with the coal fire flickering behind him and the telephone at his side, and with nothing to do except watch out of the window across the Mill Street to Cooke's Post Office. . . .

That night I undressed for bed early, not much after eleven o'clock in the evening. It was about midnight when I heard a knock which came to the downstairs door. Our maid, Susie Byrne, a dark and pretty youngster, answered. She came up and tapped at our bedroom door and says, through it: "There's a man at the door to see you, Mr. Sheridan. He says it's important."

I went down, pulling a blue woollen dressing-gown on, and it was a friend of mine, a young man whose name I won't mention at this time. I can't say even now who he is because he was part of our secret service. "They're coming in the morning at 7.30," he says, his voice shaking a little.

"*Who's* coming?" I say.

"The post-office engineers are coming, and the Gardai with them."

"Oh!" I say, with a funny feeling running through me like quicksilver, for the moment was at hand. This was the news from Dublin we had prepared for and were waiting for. "We'll have to hold a council of war," I say.

I dressed so fast it was amazing I didn't finish with both feet through the same trousers leg, and I went to call on Mr. Hooper, the headmaster of the Technical School, who lives just across the Main Street from me, and from him I called on Patrick O'Grady and then James McCann and then Felix O'Neill. I tried to wake up Paul Kehoe by knocking on his door, but Paul is a man who sleeps far from this world, and I had no luck.

"D-Day is in the morning at 7.30," I say to each of the others. "We're holding an emergency meeting right away at my place. Tell the others."

All of them, excepting, of course, Paul Kehoe, got dressed and arrived at my place at 12.45 in the morning, and we met in the tap-room. I sent Patrick O'Grady to the post-office to awake Miss Cooke and to take over the switchboard and to connect all the switches — there was no night service then as there is now — and to give me a line to each subscriber as I asked for them. First I called John A. Doyle. It took five minutes for the ringing of the bell to waken him.

"It's to-morrow, John," I say. "They're coming at 7.30."

"Oh, my God, Bernie, are you sure?" he says, sounding very wide awake for a man who was so recently asleep. He got dressed and came up here right away.

I phoned Mrs. Boreslaw Gaj — who is an Irishwoman, though married to a Pole — Mrs. Mellamy, Major George Anderson, Michael Patterson, Mrs. Joe O'Neill — in fact, all the subscribers in turn — and gave them the message to be in town and on hand for duty at 7.30. "The Gardai and the linesmen are coming to disconnect the telephone cables from Miss Cooke's in the morning," I say. "They're coming in force. Be in town for it."

They all said they would be on hand at 7.30.

Major Anderson lives five and a half miles out of town, to the north-east. He was half asleep or more when he answered the phone. He says, "When shall I be there, Mr. Sheridan?"

"About a quarter past seven, just to be certain sure," I say.

"He looked down at his wrist-watch, which was pointing to twenty-five minutes to two. In his sleepy state he thought it was 7.10. It gave him quite a start, and he jumped into his clothes and into his car and hurried to my place as if the banshees were at his heels, and knocked at my door. I answered it, and, surprised at the quick sight of him, say, "Good morning, Major! I didn't mean for you to come right away."

"Why," he says, a little taken aback, "you said a quarter past seven." The major is a tall, middle-aged man with sandy hair and a red face.

"That's right," I say, "but that's to-morrow morning. It's not yet two."

He looked like a man with a puzzle on his mind. "Well," he says, "it was ten past seven when I left." Then he says, "Or at least I thought it was." A peculiar expression crept over his face, and he examined his watch closely.

"Oh, good Lord," he says, "I read the damn thing wrong!"

We had a drink together and he went home, his complexion healthier than when he came. . . .

The meeting was adjourned at three or a little after. I had no trouble falling asleep.

At 6.30 I woke up. I had some corn-flakes and a cup of tea. I didn't feel hungry, and my stomach felt nervy. Maureen says to me, putting a soft hand on my shoulder, "Be careful, Bernie. Don't get hurt."

"All right," I say.

As I was finishing my cup of tea Felix O'Neill, Jim McCann, and Paddy O'Grady came to pick me up, and I shoved the cup aside and left with them. O'Grady says, "What time will we set off the siren, Bernie?"

"At 7.15," I says. "That gives the people a quarter of an hour to get out of bed and dress."

At this point Paddy had an idea of his own, and he went to put it into action. He went to E. P. O'Kelly's place — O'Kelly is a grocer and auctioneer — with the intention of borrowing the bell O'Kelly uses for calling an auction. A big hand-bell it is. Mary O'Kelly was up and around when Paddy got there, and gave the bell to him after he told her why he wanted it. Then, since she was up and getting impatient, she went to the post-office to be on hand when the Gardai and the engineers arrived.

The minutes were the slowest minutes I had ever waited for. At last 7.15 came, and I went back to my place and threw the switch, and the siren started to wail, a mournful, drawn-out sound, like a dog bemoaning the moon. As soon as he heard it Paddy O'Grady started running around the town, clanging O'Kelly's hand-bell; a very good thing, too, because we couldn't get Joe Morrin out of bed to ring the bell in the mill, the way we had arranged it. Mr. Morrin is a very sound sleeper, and the mill bell was never used after all, but even at that it seems unlikely that the town of Baltinglass had ever before been awakened under similar circumstances or in such a clamour.

Oh, indeed, and the town woke up! When the siren died away and Paddy O'Grady stopped clanging at the hand-bell you could hear the sharp morning voices — excited voices — everywhere around. A baby cried somewhere near, and youngsters were shouting to one another as if it was Christmas morning, and I heard a woman's voice calling, "Don't get into any trouble now, Joe. Remember!" I couldn't make out which Joe it was or what he said in reply. I hurried down the Main Street and turned right along the Mill Street to Miss Cooke's.

Perhaps it was only a special awareness in me, but it seemed as if the whole town was as taut as the highest fiddlestring. The minutes dragged. A crowd was beginning to gather. When Major Anderson arrived he grinned at me.

"This time," he says, "I got it right; eh, Mr. Sheridan?"

"Yes," I say, but I was watching the road for the Gardai and the engineers. I was keeping my eyes on the bend they would have to come round, and I was tuning my ears in for the slightest sound of a motor coming from that direction.

By 7.40 they had not come. About eighty people of the town were packed in the road in front of Miss Cooke's, and others were arriving every minute in cars and vans from the outlying districts. Soon there were more than a hundred. It was bitter, freezing cold. There was a driving sleet slanting into our faces. Some of the people stamped their feet hard on the ground and pulled up their coat collars. When the picketing had started I had borrowed a street brazier from Carlow, about twelve miles away, and now it was filled with orange-glowing coke, with the sleet spluttering and arguing into it, and a circle of men and women were huddled around it borrowing a little of its warmth.

"Where are the Gardai, then?" somebody muttered. "This is just a dress rehearsal that Bernie's having."

I raised my voice. "Now, listen," I say, "I don't want any of you people to think this is only a dress rehearsal. The enemy may be late, but he will be here shortly."

Meanwhile newcomers were arriving every minute. The General and Mrs. Dennis came at 7.47, followed by Ben Hooper and Father O'Mahoney, another Baltinglass curate. The General, and, indeed, all of the Protest Committee, were afraid that, if tempers flared up and fists flew — and maybe a few stones with them — the people of Baltinglass might get themselves badly hurt. The original idea, of course, had been to get some one arrested on the slab for the publicity it would bring. But now we were getting the publicity without the arrest, and there was no need to take chances.

General Dennis stood up on the pavement in front of the crowd. "Ladies and gentlemen," he says, "the Government have decided to enforce the Minister's decision. They are sending Gardai to Baltinglass, but we will have no violence. If they are determined to change the cable they'll succeed in doing it. We don't want any serious clash with authority."

There was a murmur running through the crowd, like a complaining wind, and I didn't care for the sound of it. Somebody made a funny, disbelieving snort. Miss Cooke and her sister, who had come from Roscommon to visit, began handing out cups of hot tea.

I kept watching the road, waiting, with a tight feeling in my throat. I was sure now that I heard motors in the distance, but getting louder. At five minutes to eight somebody says in a high voice, "Here they come!"

It was the first of the police: two car-loads of them and one radio car.

I forgot about the sleet and the cold, and, by the tense looks on their faces, so did everybody else. A moment later two lorries and more cars followed.

"Good God," a voice said behind me, "they're sending an entire army of men to do their job."

There were about seventy Gardai in all. The local superintendent of the Gardai, Tom Heavey, had gone up the road to meet them and came in with them. Chief Superintendent W. P. Quinn, from Bray, the head of the Gardai for all of County Wicklow, got out of the leading car, a big, stout, weather-beaten man, wearing a look of combined disappointment and surprise. He had good reason for this, and I could guess what was troubling him. He was wondering how it was that there should be a Baltinglass crowd to meet him and his army of men when the whole operation had been planned as a deep secret behind locked doors, and, indeed, he had expected to find all of Baltinglass still snoring away in bed.

The crowd watched the Gardai, suspicious in their turn, and restless and waiting for action. It could not have been better timed if it had been planned when, at that precise moment, Soup Doyle charged into the crowd, waving a rusty old gun in his hands, a relic of the bad Troubles of 1798. There wasn't any shadow of a doubt now regarding his participation in the battle, and certainly none about the temper of the crowd. They were ready, and, in fact, some of them were anxious, to fight.

This, at last, was the showdown.

Don Bell has been more interested in music than literature, having studied and sung in Vancouver, London, Berlin, Düsseldorf, Lausanne, and Tanglewood. But a collection of his writings about Montreal, Saturday Night at the Bagel Factory, *winner of the Leacock Medal for Humour in 1973, clearly indicates he has an ear for words as well as melody.*

DON BELL

from Saturday Night at the Bagel Factory

With apologies to Stephen Leacock, whose story "My Financial Career" may have inspired the following. . . .

You've already read about the Anti-Serious Society, and how a Polish-born journalist named Stash Pruszynski marched during the McGill riot, holding up a sign announcing: "After the Riot, Eat at Joe's." For his bravado role in that story, I paid my friend Stash the sum of fifty dollars. And so began the financial careers of two most interesting individuals.

Stash was timid about accepting the fee. "You're the one who wrote the story," he said "All I did was — "

"Since you insist," I said, withdrawing the cheque.

But Stash reached out and grabbed it from my hand. "On the other hand, I can use the money," he said. "I'm going to give you one share in Stash's Flea Market."

"That's wonderful," I said. "By the way, what the hell is Stash's Flea Market?"

Stash then explained his concept to me: What this country needed was an authentic flea market, in the style of Marché aux Puces in Paris, or Portobello Road in London, where a colourful atmosphere was provided for artisans to sell their wares. They would set up outdoor stalls and work and haggle out in the open. The public would love it.

We had many talks about the flea market. As a shareholder, I wanted to underline that there would be no decisions made without my approval. Even though Stash conceived the idea and

123

owned the other ninety-nine shares, I felt it was my duty to help in the growth of the company. It was the first time I have ever been an important executive, and I wished to be right where the action was.

Realizing that our agreement wasn't down on paper, I invited Stash to Dinner at the Club des Moustaches in back of the Bistro. After plying Stash with wine and boeuf bourguignon, I delicately brought up the subject of a contract. Stash agreed that it should be written, and scribbled his commitment on the paper tablecloth: "This is to certify that Don Bell has one share, or one per cent of the Marché au Trésor enterprise and is entitled to one per cent of the firm's profits as long as the Marché exists. Signed: Stash the Manager."

I folded the tablecloth, which had a few broccoli sauté stains on it, and carefully put it in my pocket. Later, I locked it in a metal strongbox that also contains my birth certificate, marriage contract, passport, vaccination certificate, and will.

In the spring, Stash found a site for the flea market on St. Paul Street opposite Bonsecours Market. Frankly, I had a few reservations about the site, but I finally gave my seal of approval — I wouldn't try to stand in Stash's way as long as my dividends were to come in regularly.

Stash set up about twenty-five stalls, and in the summer Stash's Flea Market was one of the most thriving enterprises in Old Montreal. Stash was interviewed by countless radio and TV stations. Hundreds of tourists visited the market; even the mayor and the Governor General dropped by.

With delight, I watched the value of my stock rise. By August, Stash estimated that it was worth $100 — twice its original value — but he advised me not to sell just yet. I would be a fool not to hold on to the stock, he said. No doubt, the profits alone would soon cover my capital outlay. I tried to bug Stash about the profits, but he said he wasn't in a position yet to pay off fat returns. For one thing, there was still the question of his rent, which was not the least of his debts: he convinced me that the wisest course just now was to sink all the profits back into the enterprise.

Every Sunday I visited the open-air market to make sure that all was running smoothly. I felt that my presence was needed. You can never tell when the charcoal portrait painter, for instance, would give vent to cubist impulses. Or the Pakistani trinket vendors would fight over stall privileges. A shareholder on the premises would have a cooling influence.

Stash introduced me to the resident artisans. They all looked at me with awe because they knew I was a bigshot, some Mafia wheel who had his fingers in the pie. I was called Sir and Mr. Big and other names. Stash introduced me to customers as "one of the shareholders." I smoked cigars and wore loud ties. Everyone was really impressed.

Stash may have had all the dynamism and energy, but I was the silent partner behind the scenes with the brains. One day, near the end of summer, Stash came up to me and said: "We're going to have to find another site."

"Why?" I asked.

"No lease. We're being kicked out."

"The dirty rats. We'll have to find another site," I announced.

The decision was made. Stash agreed we'd have to find another site.

Stash found a building with a large courtyard nearby on Notre Dame Street opposite City Hall. I gave him my blessings — luckily for the concern; this was no time for bickering at the top executive level. Stash signed the papers and we moved to our new premises, which is where the flea market is now located.

Stash did most of the physical work, painting signs, sweeping up, paying the rent and so on, but anyone who has a plug of intelligence can see that the flea market wouldn't be the same without my genius.

I must say, I was proud of the market. During lunch hour, I'd walk to Notre Dame Street and see how Stash was coming along in his chores. Sometimes, he would foist a paint brush or a broom upon me. After a while, I decided to go by car and admire the market from the outside instead as I didn't want to be in Stash's way. Often I would point out the market to friends.

"You see that building?"

"What?"

"That building on your right."

"Stash's Flea Market?"

"Yup."

"What about it?"

"I'm a part-owner. I have shares in it."

"Oh — you've left journalism? Gone into business?"

"Not quite. It's one of my holdings on the side. The share is worth a fortune."

"*The* share? One?"

"Well, there are not too many shares. Outside of Stash and myself, I can't think of anyone else who has a share."

"How much is it worth?"

"I'd rather not divulge the figure," I said, sneaking a little smile. "Tax reasons."

In December, Stash had an Anti-Serious Society party at the Flea Market. Admission at the door, 75 cents. I arrived with several out-of-town guests.

"That will be 75 cents," said the girl selling tickets.

"That's all right," I told her. "Let them pass."

"Let them pass nothing," she growled. "Admission 75 cents."

I took her to the side. My voice sounded threatening. "Do you realize who you're talking to?" I asked.

"I don't give a damn if you're the prime minister," she said.

"I'm one of the owners of this market. In a sense, I'm your employer."

She kind of jumped back and looked at me aghast. Her face turned a greenish shade. "Oh, I'm sorry," she gulped "You should have explained."

"You were doing your duty," I told her. "I'll see that you get a bonus at the end of the year."

A group of people was just then coming out of the door. "Don't bother going in," said one collegiate type, with a girl strapped to his arm. "Great flea market but lousy party. Save your money."

"We have to go in," I said smiling. "I happen to be one of the owners."

"Then you're just the guy we want to see," said the girl. "What can you do about getting us our money back?"

"That's right," said the boyfriend, who looked like a bruiser on the college football team.

"Any complaints should be addressed to Stash," I said loudly. Then, quieter: "I'm only a small shareholder."

At that same party, Stash spoke to me for the first time about dividends.

"Dividends," he said.

"What?"

"You'll be getting a $10 dividend shortly," he said. "But can you hold on for a few weeks? I'm strapped for funds now."

"Yes, whenever you have it," I said, giving Stash a way out.

During the party, I did nothing but think of the dividend. How should I spend it? Should I just let all my dividends pile up in the bank? No, that was selfish. Besides, I'd have to claim them when making out my income tax. The tax question was something I hadn't thought of before; I didn't want government people hanging around with a lot of queries. I decided that the only loophole was to re-invest it in the flea market.

The next day I called Stash. "That dividend," I said, keeping my voice low. "I've made my decision: you can plow it back into the company."

"I'm glad you made that decision," Stash said. "Here's what we'll do for you. We'll regard it as a long term loan bearing you 8¾% interest."

I looked at the phone, awed. It was such a simple expedient. Why hadn't I thought of dividend re-investment months ago? "You're on," I told Stash, with genuine feeling.

The secret of most successful financiers is that they know when to buy and sell. Choosing the ripe time is practically a question of intuition.

I realized that the time might be ripe to sell my share in Stash's flea market. No one knows what the future augurs for Stash or the fleas. But how could I break such news to my friend Stash without hurting his feelings?

It so happened that it was Stash himself who made the first move. Recently, the phone rang. Stash's voice at the other end. Did I detect a note of urgency?

"Listen," Stash said. "This may be a surprise, but I know someone who wants to buy your share."

"Me sell?" I said, playing difficult. "Never."

"A Polish friend of mine is willing to pay $200 for your share," Stash went on. "That's four times your original investment."

I did some elementary arithmetic in my head. He was right. It was four times my original investment. I'd make a killing.

"All right," I said. "I'll sell, but there's one condition." I paused for effect. You could feel the tension over the phone. "I would like to reserve the option," I said, choosing my words very carefully, "Of buying one of *your* shares at the market price at my convenience."

There was a long silence at the other end. It was all or nothing. I knew my strategy had to work, though, and I could almost hear Stash's mental calculation. Finally, his voice, low but firm: "You're on," he said. "It's a deal."

Through clever planning and careful manipulation of my stocks, I'd become an overnight financial phenomenon. I heard that Bay Street and St. James Street got wind of the deal and all money was tight. The reverberations would be felt on Wall Street and as far away as the Bourse in Paris and the Taj Mahal in India.

However, there was a hitch. And there's a lesson to be gleaned from all this: Never — I repeat, never count your financial chickens until the transaction is down on paper, until the deal is signed and you've got the dough safely tucked into your pocket.

You see, at the last minute Stash phoned me with the news that the prospective buyer of my share got cold feet and decided to put the money in the bank instead, even though his returns would be only a fraction of what he'd get if he invested in Stash's Flea Market. Anyway, Stash said, I shouldn't be too disappointed because even had the share been bought it would have taken at least a year before I saw the money. Stash, who was acting as middleman in the deal, was planning to use the money to pay off some more of his back rent — but he intended to pay me 8¾% on the loan, which would have amounted to $17.50.

"By next year, your share may be worth double its present value," Stash hinted.

"Yes, I think I *will* hold on to it," I agreed. "With any luck, they'll be standing four deep by next year to get their hands on that share."

"I don't suppose," Stash said, "you know of anyone who would like to float a loan of $200 that will yield high interest?"

"How high?"

"Say fifteen per cent," Stash said.

"I can ask around," I told Stash. "I can't help you myself, but there must be dozens of others just dying to start a business career."

In a sense, I'm glad I didn't sell out, because beneath the hard facade of most businessmen is a tender spot. I'm a sentimentalist at heart. It would have been sad to have passed by Stash's Flea Market and to have felt like a stranger.

Now, I drive by several times every week, and each time I get a kind of sinking feeling, and it's not without tears in my eyes that I've been known to boast: "This is mine — almost all mine."

With any luck, Stash will give me another share in the market once this gets printed. I don't call myself a pusher, but I figure if I play it right, gradually I can manoeuvre my friend Stash to a position where he has no choice but to cough up the whole flea market, fleas included.

Volume II of "The Bandy Papers" won the Leacock Medal in 1974.
That's Me in the Middle *established Donald Jack's hero as one to be*
reckoned with in Canadian humour.

DONALD JACK
from That's Me in the Middle

We spent the first night of our honeymoon sitting up in the train
to Scotland after a modest white wedding (Katherine's gown, my
face) in a small country church, followed by a gay reception at the
Lewises' ancestral home — and mine, now, too — where Miles-
tone, who'd come over from his new squadron near Croydon to
be my best man, became tight and unsentimental. The Lewises —
Mr. Lewis had been granted a week's leave from the F.O. for the
occasion — were charming, and even the groom contrived to look
happy.

   We had been invited by the Lewises' Scottish friends Sir Angus
and Lady McIntock to spend our honeymoon at their place in
Ayrshire, which was why we were sitting up all night, holding
hands and coughing. Although the train windows seemed to be
hermetically sealed, gritty smoke somehow managed to coil its
way into our lungs.

   McIntock was Lord Lieutenant of the County, I think it was
called, and owned a large sandstone house on the Ayrshire coast.
He was a large, genial man of sixty with unruly white hair and a
kilt. His wife was a Highland lassie of about 220 pounds, also with
unruly white hair, except that in her case she was growing bald on
top. They were the most tactful of hosts, and after an enormous
breakfast of pease brose, porridge, kippers, ham and eggs, Scottish rolls, strawberry jam, and more tea than could be poured into
the gravity tank of a Sopwith Camel, they announced that the
following days were entirely ours to do with as we pleased. They
even, with straight faces and semi-incomprehensible dialect, gave

131

us to understand (except that I *didn't* understand until it was too late) that we could go up to bed there and then at ten in the morning ("Tae sleep off the jurrney") if we so desired. But as I said, by the time I had it all worked out it was too late, so we went for a walk instead. Katherine was quite short with me for the first half mile or so.

She had changed a lot since I'd first met her; or perhaps I had simply gotten to know her. She had been hard to get to know well, but the weeks of companionship leading to our marriage had finally broken her down, revealing depths of levity I had never suspected in her. Even the abruptness of her speech had smoothed itself out. She had become almost self-assured.

We stood on a hilltop and admired the view. The sea glittered in the distance and the air was balmy. We were not unhappy.

"Isn't it wonderful?"

"M'yes," I said, but thinking that it wasn't as wonderful as Burma Park.

"Bart?"

"What, my love?"

"What are you thinking about?" she asked, squeezing my arm.

"Oh . . ."

"You have almost an ecstatic look on your face."

"How can you tell?"

"You're thinking the same thing I'm thinking, aren't you?" she said, blushing a little.

So she was thinking of Burma Park, too. "Yes," I said, and squeezed her arm warmly. "It won't be long now," I murmured. In another week we would be going home.

"Oh, Bart," she said, breathing faster.

A half mile from the house she said, with a rush: "Have you ever — you know — done it before?"

"Done what?"

"You know."

I glanced at her, but she was looking at her feet. "No," I said.

"Haven't you?"

"No."

As we neared the house ten minutes later she said, somewhat crossly, I thought, "Then, how will we know how to?"

"How to what?" I asked.

She looked up at the sky for a moment; then, "But of course," she said acidly, "I was forgetting: you've read all about it in *Pride and Prejudice.*"

As we entered the house she said, "Well, I suppose I should be grateful it wasn't just the *Boys' Own Paper*, or we'd probably spend our wedding night over a tuck hamper saying, 'Ouch,' 'yaroo,' and 'cave, you chaps.' "

"And 'leggo, you cad,' " I murmured.

Over luncheon Sir Angus insisted on talking about his own wedding night.

"Shush," Lady McIntock said.

"I will not shush, woman, for it is one of my treasured memories."

"Why?" I asked, interestedly. "Ouch," I added. Katherine had kicked me painfully in the shins.

"I beg your pardon, Lieutenant?"

"I said, 'Ouch,' " I said.

"Aye," Sir Angus said, nodding and drifting back forty years. "There we were, alone at last in the bedroom. It was a wee farm cottage up in the Isle of Skye. It had a terribly low ceiling, with great black beams."

Lady McIntock laughed heartily, then cut it off and frowned.

"Shush, Angus," she said.

"So as I said, there we were, alone at last," Sir Angus went on reminiscently, "in our wee nightiegowns. And I clapped my hands the gether and I said, 'Well, Margaret,' I said, 'let's not be wasting any time.' "

"Shush," Lady McIntock said.

"So the next thing I knew, Margaret here said, 'Whee,' or something like that, and bounded into bed — "

"I was that nervous," Lady McIntock said.

" — but unfortunately she bounded so high she hit her head on one of the oaken beams and knocked herself silly. And," McIntock said, "I spend the rest of the night cycling round in a howling gale looking for a doctor."

"I still have the stitches," Lady McIntock said, inclining her head toward me. "Look, you can just see them if you search carefully."

"But it wasn't as bad, Katherine, as what happened to your mother and father. Shall I tell her, Margaret?"

"Look, Bart," Katherine said quickly, "isn't that a lovely tartan

Sir Angus is wearing."

"This?" McIntock said, plucking at his kilt. "Yes, this is the Lamont tartan. An ancestor of ours once traced the Lamont line back as far as the twelfth century."

I looked suitably impressed; Katherine looked relieved.

Lady McIntock said, "With a gap in the line here and there, of course. Three hundred years here, a hundred there. But still."

"Yes," McIntock said imperturbably, "my ancestor was trying to prove we were descended from King Malcolm the Second, but he soon gave it up when he found that practically all our forebears were either sheepstealers busy being done in by hangmen or hangmen busy doing in sheepstealers. That explains why there's so many missing branches in the genealogical tree, you see. But I was talking about Mr. and Mrs. Lewises' wedding night. Like us, they couldn't wait to occupy the bedroom of their new house. And then afterward, feeling a bit peckish, they came galloping down the stairs for something to eat, riding piggyback, stark naked, with Mrs. Lewis shouting 'Yoicks,' 'Tallyho,' and similar expressions; and then all of a sudden all their friends and relatives, us included, jumped out from behind the curtains and the furniture shouting, 'Surprise, surprise!' It was indeed. Har har har."

Katherine didn't look at all amused.

"Well," McIntock said, putting his big red hands on the table and forcing himself up, "I'm off to have my nap. Why don't you two up and have a wee lie-down yourselves?"

Katherine was still looking down at her coffee cup.

"Well," I said.

"That's right," Lady McIntock said kindly. "You know where your room is, children."

As they went off down the corridor I heard Lady McIntock saying, "Yon's a peculiar chap, is he no, Angus? Does he not understand us, or is that his normal expression?"

There was silence for a minute or so in the dining room.

"Well," I said, stretching.

"Yes," Katherine said quickly. "I think I will, too. I'm feeling just a little bit tired."

"Oh," I said. "I was just going to suggest we stretch our legs. Go for a walk."

"Oh," she said.

"It's such a fine day."

"Yes," she said.

"But of course, if you — "

"No, no," she said.

After dinner we withdrew to the withdrawing room.

"Would you like to play the piano for us Bartholomew?" Lady McIntock asked.

"Are you — are you sure we're not keeping you up or anything?" Katherine said quickly. "I mean — "

"I remember you saying, Katherine, that Bartholomew here was a fine pianist."

"Oh, I was just boasting," Katherine said. "You were asking what he was like, and that was the only thing I could think of in his favor."

McIntock laughed, as Katherine had meant him to. I think. She was saying curious things more and more of late. Mrs. Lewis had commented on this a few days before, intimating that the girl was coming too much under my influence; but I couldn't see that at all.

"Aye, play us something lively," McIntock said, slapping his Dundreary, or whatever that leather handbag was called that he wore in front of his kilt. "Something with a tune to it. None of this modern stuff, Waggner and Mendel, and the like. I've no time for it at all."

So I played them a medley of Scottish melodies, roving by means of a variety of florid *arpeggi* from the banks of Loch Lomond to the braes of bonny Doon. Ending with a triumphant flourish, I turned, smirking, to McIntock. He was nodding interestedly.

"Aye," he said. "Those'll be some of they Canadian square dances of yours, I expect." Lady McIntock was nodding, too; she'd fallen asleep.

"Canadian square dances?" I said.

Of course, I knew that I was not exactly a Paderewski or a Liszt or a Rubinstein or an Ian Smythe, but . . . Canadian square dances?

I suppose subconsciously the truth had been dawning on me for some time. The suspicion now fused into a flaring certainty. There exploded in me a blinding flash of revelation, a Moment of Truth so overwhelming as to make the matador's insight, just before the bull gores him, seem by comparison a mere idle thought or passing fancy. It had finally, irrevocably, unequivocally become clear: *I was not a very good pianist.*

"Well, that's it," I said, almost inaudibly. "That's it."

"That's what?" McIntock asked.

Deep inside me, of course, I'd always known. But I'd refused to face the fact, the truth that I was lacking in something: coordination, imagination, technique, sensitivity, musical ability, knowledge of the keyboard — call it what you will, I was lacking in it.

I took a deep breath and closed the piano lid with an air of marked deliberation befitting the end of an era.

My air of marked deliberation, however, went unnoticed, so I had time to plumb the depths of the revelation. At the bottom was the fact that I'd never liked playing the piano.

Right from the start, when I'd had the hair at my temples tweaked for faltering over the introduction of a mediant triad into an F minor progression, or been rapped on the knuckles for stumbling over some clay-footed melody, I'd never really enjoyed playing. It was simply that the piano had become a nasty habit.

But I was free now. Free. And I announced to the company that I would never play the piano again.

The finality of my tones startled even me.

Katherine looked up slowly with an unreadable expression on her face.

"Do you — " she said; then stopped, overcome. "Do you," she began again, "do you really, truly mean it?"

"Absolutely," I said.

"Oh, Bart," she said, and again was unable to speak for a moment. Then: "But perhaps you shouldn't give up so easily."

"Why?" McIntock asked. "How long have you been trying?"

"Twenty years," I said.

I turned back to Katherine. "But," I said, "if you don't think I really ought to give it up, I — "

"Oh, no, no. You've made up your mind, I can see that," she said. She turned to McIntock. "Once he's made up his mind, *nothing* can budge him."

"M'well," I said, "I've given it up. Definitely."

Katherine clasped her hands together and bit her knuckles.

"I believe," I said, "I'll take up the oboe instead. Or perhaps the bagpipes."

After a long silence McIntock said, "Aye. Well. . . ." He looked at his watch. "Nine o'clock. It's bedtime, I suppose."

Katherine sat up straight. McIntock gave her an encouraging smile, then turned and shook his wife. "Wake up, Margaret," he said, "It's time for bed, is it not? It's after nine o'clock."

But Lady McIntock seemed to be taken off guard. "What are you talking about, Archie?" she said sleepily. "You know we never go to bed before ten."

"Aye. That's right," McIntock said, somewhat heavily.

Katherine slumped back again, squinting.

There was a silence. Lady McIntock seemed to be concentrating hard.

"But surely it's past nine o'clock," she said at length, brightly. "Are you sure your watch is right, Angus?"

McIntock brightened. So did Katherine. "By Jupiter, you're right," he exclaimed. "It's stopped." Then he looked at his watch. "Aye, so it has," he added.

Katherine started to yawn daintily.

"No, my watch says nine o'clock too," I said. I listened to it. Yes, it was ticking. "Yes, it's ticking," I said.

Katherine's mouth slowly closed, and a slight film spread over Lady McIntock's eyes. They all looked at me in a strange fashion. I was forced to point to the mantle clock in self-defense, which clearly registered two minutes past nine.

Katherine looked away. Then I saw her stiffen, so I followed her eyes to a grandfather clock in the corner. *It* clearly registered twenty minutes past ten. Katherine was just about to say something when the grandfather clock started to rattle alarmingly; then chimes announcing the three-quarter hour were heard; then there was a breathless pause and the clock struck nineteen times in rapid succession, then hesitated, then struck twice more. Then it settled back into an irregular ticking.

There was a brief silence.

"It's broken," McIntock said.

We all nodded.

There was another silence.

"Do you care for cards?" Lady McIntock asked me.

"That's a good idea," Katherine said. "Give him a pack of cards. He could play patience."

"Aye," McIntock said.

About nine-thirty Lady McIntock heaved herself up. "Well, I don't know about you young people," she said, "but I'm feeling terrible tired, so I'm off to my bed."

We all got to our feet. Katherine said, "Yes, and I'd better have a bath." Then she stopped and went on a little defensively, "I always have a bath beforehand." We all nodded. "I mean, every night, regardless of what — " then stopped again and hurried out of the room.

"Well, Bartholomew, would you care for a nightcap?" McIntock asked me with revived joviality.

"No, I — I've never worn one," I said. For some reason I was suddenly feeling nervous.

"I'm talking about a wee dram," McIntock said.

"Oh," I said with an englightened expression, and laughed heartily. So did McIntock. "A what?" I asked blankly.

McIntock's eyes glazed. "A drink, man," he said. "A drink."

"Oh," I said. "Oh. Yes. Och aye." I laughed again. "A wee dram. Of course. Yes, I — yes, I'll, I'd like a wee dram."

When McIntock said a wee dram he meant a wee dram. He poured about half an inch of Scotch into two huge tumblers; that is, a quarter inch in each. We drank and nodded at each other. There was another of those frequent pauses with which the evening had been strewn. McIntock seemed to be waiting for something.

At last he said, "I must say you're — you're one of the most patient fellows I've ever come across." He squinted at me. "When you consider the circumstances," he began, then halted, looking lost. Then: "Are you sure — are you *quite* sure you wouldn't like a nice game of chess? You know, to while away the time?"

I hesitated. I didn't really feel like playing chess at the moment, but he had been so pleasant I thought it was the least I could do in return if he really wanted to play at this late hour. "Well," I said, "if you'd really like a game, I — "

McIntock almost dropped his whisky glass. "Great thundering McGubbins, man!" he shouted. Then he sighed and helped himself to another wee dram, except that this time he filled the tumbler about half full.

Finally we went upstairs. I was about to barge into the bedroom; then hesitated, and knocked.

"Who is it?" Katherine said from within.

"It's me," I said.

"Who?"

"Bandy," I said.

"Bandy?"

"Yes," I said. "Don't you remember?"

"Oh," she said in a muffled voice. "You mean *Lieutenant* Bandy?"

"That's right," I said through the door. What on earth was wrong with the girl?

"What do you want?" she asked.

I didn't quite know how to answer this. I was beginning to feel somewhat foolish, lurking about in the hall talking through a closed door. "Can I come in?" I asked.

There was no answer; so I took a firm grasp of the doorknob and pulled.

"It's locked," I said in surprise. "Why have you locked it?" There was no answer. "Katherine?" I said.

Katherine pulled the door inward, and without a word went back to combing her hair at the dressing table. The door hadn't been locked at all. I'd become so used to doors that opened outward, and. . . . Well, the Nissen hut doors opened outward, and so did the doors of the Spartan Hotel.

Our room was frilly with lace, flowery pelmet, ornamental fireplace, patterned antimacassar, and fussy lamp, and had a tiny adjoining room, presumably for the ladies because it contained only a dresser, chair, and a large mirror for powdering the nose, and so on; and it was this little room that Katherine went back to. She was wearing a blue silk nightgown that trailed around her ankles and the awful quilted dressing gown I'd seen her in at Burma Park. She didn't say anything, so I shuffled around the bedroom for a while, picking things up and putting them down. Then I gazed out the windows. Then I realized the curtains were drawn, so I pulled them back, which enabled me to gaze out the window. But not being able to see anything, it being quite dark outside, I took up my towel and my little toilet bag and went to the door.

"I'm going to the bathroom," I said.

There was no answer, so I went and had a bath, brushed my teeth and cut my toenails, and when I got back Katherine was reading in bed. I wandered about the room for a bit, tidying my clothes and so on. Finally I got into bed.

Katherine went on reading. I sat there for a while, having a little stretch. It was a huge bed, and there was a considerable acreage between us.

After some time I got up on my hands and knees and crawled across to Katherine and leaned over to look at the book. "What are you reading?" I inquired.

She showed me the cover, then went back to her reading. It was *Quentin Durward*.

"Oh, yes," I said. "Walter Scott."

Five minutes later I said, "Is it any good?"

"It's not bad when you get into it."

A couple of minutes later I said, "I see."

Katherine had been sitting bolt upright, very stiffly. She now lay back on the pillows. This outlined her bosom. It pouted very prettily against the silk nightdress.

"Well," I said, feeling short of breath. "It must be getting late."

"It's only half-past ten," she said. "I forgot to tell you: I always read until dawn. Then I like to go for a long walk."

"Mm," I said.

She turned a page. I took a deep breath, drawing it in as unobtrusively as possible, and put my arm round her shoulders.

"It's been a long day," I remarked conversationally.

There was another of those damned pauses; then she put the book aside and looked at me. She had long since lost any self-consciousness about her slight strabismus; I'd told her so often it made her look all the more desirable. It did now. My face was fiery.

"Yes," she said. "It's been a damned long day." And laughed a bit shrilly.

I started to put my other arm around her. She was apparently wearing nothing beneath the blue silk, and as my fingertips brushed her stomach she twitched and hid her face against me. "Put the light out," she whispered. Her breath tickled my neck, and I started twitching too.

The frilly lamp was on her side of the bed. I didn't want to kneel up and lean over because my pajamas were noticeably bunched, so I got up and walked around the bed, sideways.

With the light out, the room was pitch dark, and walking back to my side of the bed I smashed my toe against the bedpost.

"What's the matter?"

"I hit my toe."

It was all the more painful because it was the same toe I'd broken when I kicked that rock in France. However, the thobbing soon died down, and I groped my way back, but all that hopping around had set my compass spinning, and I went in the wrong direction. There was a tremendous clatter as I fell over some fire irons.

"What on earth's the matter now?" Katherine asked in a despairing tone of voice, and switched on the lamp again to find me in the fireplace about twenty feet away. Fortunately the fire wasn't lit, but one of my hands was black with soot and I had to go back to the bathroom to wash it. I met McIntock in the corridor. He stopped and looked at my hand.

"I expect," he said, "you were trying to get away up the chimney. Is that it?"

"Of course not," I said coldly. "I was on my way to bed but walked into the fireplace instead, that's all."

"Aye," McIntock said.

When I got back, the lamp was still on and Katherine was all covered up in bed, pretending to be asleep. I switched off the lamp once more, being careful to take my bearings properly this time, and I managed to navigate back to bed successfully.

There was silence for some time. Katherine didn't stir.

I reached over inch by inch, my heart pounding.

It certainly was a large bed. I couldn't locate her at all. I moved, over three or four feet and reached out again, but even though my arm was stretched to its limit I still wasn't making contact. I felt around. I was damned if I could find her.

After a moment I whispered hoarsely, "Where on earth *are* you?"

She didn't answer. I expect the poor girl was suddenly a mass of nerves, and, making allowances for this, I moved over another foot or two and whispered tenderly, "Where the hell are you, Kath?" But again drew a blank. My hand was swishing over the sheets, searching for her. "I can't find you," I complained. Really, this was a bit much. There *was* such a thing as excessive modesty. I moved again, a trifle impatiently, and fell out of bed.

Feeling myself fall, I naturally tried to grasp for some support, and in so doing grabbed the tasseled cloth covering the bedside table, and the next moment there was a shocking din as the table, the tasseled cloth, the frilly lamp, two or three ornaments, and I crashed to the wooden floor. I got a splinter in my behind. The door to the little powder room was flung open and Katherine appeared, outlined against the light.

"I fell out of bed," I explained.

She leaned against the wall for support.

I got up and trod on some glass from the shattered lamp.

When Katherine had pulled herself together, she said, "You'll have to ask McIntock for some first aid for that foot."

I knocked at McIntock's door. He emerged, blinking, to find me smiling ingratiatingly, balanced on one leg in my pajamas, which now had blood as well as soot on them.

"Sorry to disturb you," I whinnied, "but would you happen to have anything that might be helpful in stopping the flow of blood?"

McIntock looked terribly concerned. "You rotten beast," he said. "Oh, the puir wee girl," and started to rush along the corridor.

"Come back," I said. "It's not Katherine; it's me."

"Great thundering McGubbins," he said. "It's the first time I ever heard of — "

"I trod on some glass," I said.

There was quite a long silence.

"I fell out of bed, you see," I went on, but then dried up, possibly because of his expression.

Lady McIntock came out. "What's up?" she asked.

"Nothing yet," McIntock said. "It seems Bartholomew has fallen out of bed now, and cut his foot on the lamp. I did not dare ask him what the lamp was doing on the floor, of course."

"No," Lady McIntock said. She stared at me balanced on one leg and similing fatuously, looked as if she was going to say something, but apparently decided against it and fetched the first-aid kit instead, and fixed up my foot there in the hall.

When I got back to the bedroom once again, Katherine had just finished clearing up the mess and was talking to herself. She soon stopped, however, and switched off the light in the adjoining room and we got into bed once more. I gave a grunt and got up again.

"*Now* what's the matter?" she said.

"Oh, it's nothing."

She got up and switched on the powder-room light again. "What *is* it?" she said, shaking me. "Come on, tell me. Out with it; it's something *else* now, isn't it? Tell me, tell me!" She sounded just a trifle hysterical and was shaking me so hard my answer was a tremolo.

"I have a splinter," I quavered.

A couple of minutes later there was a knock at the door and McIntock and his wife came in with a bottle of iodine for my foot and found me lying face down on the bed, and Katherine holding a large safety pin poised over my right buttock.

The McIntocks stood transfixed for a moment, then slowly began to back out, obviously fearing that they'd interrupted some dreadful perversion culled from the pages of the Marquis de Sade's *Philosophie dans le boudoir*, or *Les Crimes de l'amour*.

"It's all right," Katherine said, almost inaudibly. "It's only a splinter."

"Aye," McIntock said.

"We forgot to put iodine on his foot," Lady McIntock faltered.

They gathered around. By this time I wouldn't have cared if they'd brought in the butler, half a dozen upstairs maids, and a poacher or two. I just shut my eyes and tried to think of other things. They took turns trying to pry the splinter out. Lady McIntock won.

Finally we were alone once more, and in the light of the powder room — by this time Katherine didn't dare switch it off — we snuggled up, our two faces jammed together like workmen's braziers. I was rather inept, I'm afraid, for though I knew the technique in theory, in practice it didn't seem to be quite so simple. Still, Katherine appeared to be happy enough at the end of it, and I was reminded of what Queen Victoria was supposed to have said to Albert: "Do you mean to say," she was supposed to have said, imagining, I suppose, that supreme bliss was somehow a royal prerogative, "Do you mean to say that the common people enjoy this just as much?"

I mentioned this to Katherine, but she was not amused.

Pierre Berton was born in the Yukon and has stood slightly aside from the mainstream ever since. The pieces in Just Add Water and Stir, *from which this 1960 selection is taken, were written while he was listed as an associate editor and "controversial columnist" for the* Toronto Daily Star. *Winner of Governor General's awards in 1956 and 1958, Berton seems to have almost inexhaustable energy. Besides authoring a number of best-selling books, he is a distinguished panel member of TV's popular* Front Page Challenge *and moderator of* The Great Debate.

PIERRE BERTON
from Just Add Water and Stir

A lot of my friends seem to be getting divorced these days. Ten years ago a lot of my friends seem to have been getting married and I served my time as usher, best man, toastmaster and so on. But that has all changed now and at this stage more of my friends are getting divorced than are getting married. It is the fashionable thing to do.

Yet I cannot help feeling that all these divorces are handled untidily. Half the time I don't know which of my friends is getting divorced. Or I hear they are getting divorced but I never know exactly when the divorce occurs. And sometimes they don't get divorced after all and as a result they never speak to me again because I told someone they were.

What I mean is, there is no proper ritual, no sensible code of behaviour for people getting divorced as there is for people getting married. Well, why not? Why shouldn't there be a divorce ceremony laid down in the Book of Common Prayer? The idea has considerable merit and should appeal to florists, department stores, telegraph offices, social editors, caterers and Syd Silver's Tuxedo Rentals. Formalize divorces as we formalize weddings, I say! Send out engraved invitations in double envelopes. Invite your friends and enemies.

The ritual, in my opinion, should be held in a church and it ought to be presided over, whenever possible, by the same minister who forged the original bonds of matrimony. We will have ushers, of course, wearing white carnations in their buttonholes and conducting friends of the husband and friends of the wife

145

down the aisle, and seating them, balefully, on opposite sides. (You'll remember that she never could abide his friends).

The divorce itself will have been handled by the new divorce counselling service of the Robert Simpson Company. There was a bit of trouble over that. At one point *he* swore that if he had to wear formal clothes there wouldn't be a divorce, and *she* went off and had a good cry and said she just couldn't go through with it, there were too many details. But finally they patched it up and here he is, entering from a side door with the Worst Man (sometimes known as the Other Man). It is the job of the Worst Man to snatch the wedding ring from the little woman's hand at the appropriate moment and to fling it on the floor and stamp on it.

Now the church doors swing open and the wife comes down the aisle on the arm of her father who once gave her away and is now, somewhat reluctantly, taking her back. The bridal procession may also include a Matron of Honour (sometimes known as the Other Woman) and several flower girls (the children of the divorced couple), whose custody is still in doubt.

The ceremony itself should be simple and dignified. A few simple "I do's" in answer to the minister's question as to whether he or she rejects him or her as each other's wedded spouse, never again to have, hold, love, or cherish. Then the usual rhetorical remark: "If any here present know cause as to why these two should not be separated, ye are to declare it." It is to be hoped that there will be no sloppy speeches at this point and that the ceremony can continue with dispatch.

Time now for the newly-divorced couple to go into the vestry and scratch their names off the marriage register. Meanwhile a local tenor sings some appropriate song such as "Brokenhearted." The department store service includes photographers, not only for the social pages, but also for the Divorce Albums which are permanent mementos of the occasion. A divorce, unlike a wedding, requires two photographers for it will be traditional that the couple leave by two separate exits. The guests throw confetti and old shoes — those shoes that he was leaving around the house, to her annoyance.

A reception follows and there is the usual receiving line, congratulations from friends, a mildly intoxicating punch, and, of course, a toast to the new divorcee by her mother who says how glad she is that her little girl has finally got rid of that monster.

The ex-groom replies with a few graceful remarks of his own about in-laws. Some telegrams are read, mainly salutations from old girl friends to the ex-groom, inviting him up to the family's place for a steak dinner Saturday night.

And now we cut the cake, while the photographers stand by. The two figures atop the divorce cake are, of course, facing resolutely away from each other. There may be a tendency for one or other of the happy pair to want to slice the head off one of these little figures, but this ought to be discouraged.

After the cake cutting (the guests each get a piece to keep under their pillows), it's time for the little woman to toss away her bouquet. All the young matrons vie for it, because there's a charming legend going the rounds that she who catches the flowers will be the next in line at Reno.

Did I mention the wedding gifts? They're on display in an adjoining room, each marked with the name of the donor. That's right — they're giving them *back*. Some I fear (the vases, crockery and the like) have become a bit dented as a result of those hearty marital arguments that led to the divorce.

That's about all I can think of for a divorce ceremony, but as the idea takes hold, each community no doubt will add its own enriching refinements.

"What's that, you say?" This essay should not have been written? Poor taste? How dare I poke fun at one of the most tragic of twentieth century manifestations?

But I am not poking fun at all, dear lady from Richmond Hill (who will be writing me tomorrow more in sorrow than in anger and signing her letter Disgusted). I have never been more serious, madam. The divorce ceremony is a step forward and ought to be made compulsory. Rather than go through with it thousands will be content to stay married.

The wedding ceremony has become so complicated that scores of young men and women would cheerfully remain in sober spinsterhood and bachelorhood were it not for the fact that there are simple alternatives. But there should be no alternative to the divorce ceremony. If you want to get a divorce that's the way it ought to be done — and no other way.

Is there anyone bold enough to say that it is more foolish than our present system?

When Joan Walker met that Canadian major in London she had no idea what she was letting herself in for. Already a successful author in England, she could hardly have forseen that she would find herself living as far away from civilization as Val d'Or, Quebec, or that she would win a Leacock Medal in 1954 with Pardon My Parka.

JOAN WALKER
from Pardon My Parka

My first Monday morning in Val d'Or dawned fine and bright. I talked myself out of getting up to breakfast with my office-bound husband quite easily. And in a perfectly logical manner. If anyone is looking for such an alibi for themselves they can have it for free. One bathroom — two people. Two into one won't go. This won't work out in the home, of course. One can potter around in a housecoat doing things to coffee percolators and toast while one's pride and joy shaves and showers, and take one's bath after he has left for work. But in a hotel room it works admirably.

Jim woke me up again when he left to tell me that he'd bring me up some coffee if I liked, or I could get breakfast in any of the umpteen cafés along the main drag when I finally got up. I said, "Ung," which he rightly interpreted as "Go away, darling, and don't bother me," and went back to sleep again.

Around ten I finally got up and bathed and dressed and hoisted myself onto a tall stool at the counter of a café a few doors up from the hotel, ordering orange juice, toast and coffee.

Faintly nourished by my breakfast, I went out into the street in search of my first project, a place to live. I called in a drug-store for a newspaper.

The man behind the counter wore a Stetson hat and an enormous cigar.

"The morning paper, please," I said, blinking slightly and wondering if a bad breakfast was giving me hallucinations.

"Which one?" the man asked as the cigar rolled and twitched.

I was delighted. I hadn't thought such a small town would have more than one.

"Which one carries the best apartment-vacant advertisements?"
I asked.

There was a horrible silence. The drug-store man rearranged a
package of cough drops with meticulous care. He removed his hat
and scratched a totally bald head. Then he said carefully, "The
Val d'Or Star isn't out until Friday. We're sold out of last week's
copy. I didn't know you meant a local paper. We have the Toronto and Montreal dailies. Only, of course, they're two days old."

I looked at him with horror. As a newspaperwoman I had
breakfasted for years behind at least four morning papers, scan-
ning the main items in each. I lunched behind the early editions
of the evening papers, and read the final editions as and when
they appeared.

"No daily paper," I said hollowly.

"No daily paper," he echoed. Then he added helpfully, "As a
matter of fact, no apartments either."

This, I thought, had better turn out to be a joke. Anyway, I was
used to people saying there were no apartments anywhere in the
world since the war, but somehow I had always managed to find
one. I said, "Where would I look for house agents, please? Are
they on the main street?"

The drug-store man sighed. I could see I was rapidly becoming
a bore.

"The house agent, singular," he told me, "is right across from
here. But he won't have any apartments for rent. There hasn't
been one vacant since 1941 when the apartment block was built
and the tenants moved in before it was finished."

"*The* apartment block?" I asked weakly.

"The apartment block," he said. "There are a few apartments
over the stores as well, but they are all owned and tenanted by the
store owners. I guess you're new to the North country?"

I nodded, thanked him and crossed the street, looking the
wrong way as usual and narrowly missing a truck. Having already
been snatched from death a thousand times by passing pedestrians, I wondered once again what demented Englishman decided that our traffic should keep to the left while the traffic of
the rest of the world kept to the right.

The house agent, who doubled as an insurance agent, stood an
imposing four foot ten in his stockinged feet. He hastily shuffled
his stockinged feet into a pair of slippers when I walked into his

office and bid me a cheerful *"Bon jour."*

I said, "Good morning," out of sheer laziness. I speak, or thought I spoke until I came to Quebec, passable French, but in company with every Englishwoman worthy of the name I prefer to speak my own tongue if I possibly can. We are, lingually speaking, the laziest race under the sun without a doubt.

"Ha!" he said. "Eengleesh."

I thought this showed remarkable acumen on his part. After all, I had only spoken two words, and I didn't think my accent was showing. Later I discovered that in Canada, English means anyone who isn't French-Canadian.

I told him about my little project. I wished to rent an apartment for preference, but if that was impossible, a small house would do. I would even, if the worst came to the worst, take a furnished place for the time being.

It was of a difficulty unsurpassed, he said, but as it happened he had one, just one furnished apartment on his books. I was the lucky one, was I not?

He wrote the address down on a grimy scrap of paper and told me how to reach it — two blocks down and turn to the right, very simple. I shot out of the office like a bat from hell, not even bothering to ask the rent, and broke all records for the quarter-mile to get there.

The apartment was one flight up and I rapped on the door.

It was opened by an enormous woman in a flowered housedress who entirely filled the hall. Only it wasn't the hall, it was the living-room. It was five feet wide by nine feet long and was furnished, apart from the proud owner, by a sofa and chair in a sort of nightmare Jacobean style with brightly varnished wood creeping in and out of red-and-green patterned plush, and about two thousand framed photographs of various people being married or taking first Communion.

The kitchen was roughly the size of Buckingham Palace and liberally sprinkled with rocking chairs, radios, washing machines, a dinette suite of chromium with bright-red leatherette trimming, and enough counter space to prepare a banquet for forty and still have room to lay out and embalm a few deceased relations if you were studying for a mortician's degree through the mail.

The bedroom consisted of a three-quarter double bed, a Habitant hooked rug and a statue of the Virgin Mary on a fretwood bracket. There might have been room for a very thin child to undress in it, but that is open to doubt.

The owner, apparently taking my shocked silence for bemused joy, led me swiftly out of the front door and across the passage to a minute room in which was squashed a very small bath, a basin large enough to wash one hand at a time and the inevitable john.

"We share the bathroom with the apartment across the hall," she explained.

We went back into the living-room and I made rapid calculations. I could slip-cover the horrific suite and remove the photographs; maybe I could screen off half the kitchen to make a dining-room. It was horrible, but it was a roof over our heads, and although a shared bathroom made my flesh creep, the rent couldn't be very much.

I enquired.

"One hundred and fifty dollars a month," she said happily. "And you may have it for three months while we are away. Naturally, you will also have to buy the fuel for the furnace."

When I regained consciousness, I explained that the rent seemed a little — how should I put it? — high, no?

"High?" she asked. "High?" She patted the plush sofa. "With such beautiful and valuable furniture?"

I tottered, literally, back to the house agent.

"Do you know what they are asking for that — that boot-box?" I said. "One hundred and fifty, plus heating."

The house agent raised his eyebrows.

"It is possible they accept one hundred and twenty-five," he suggested.

"Not from me, they don't," I told him. "Why, the only room in the whole apartment in which you can turn around is the kitchen. Let us not take leave of our senses."

He circled his thumb and forefinger in the air.

"Ah!" he said. "The kitchen. The room dear to a woman's heart. In which she spends all her time. Such a beautiful kitchen."

"Not me," I said, losing my grammar in the excitement of the moment, "I couldn't care less about the kitchen. But do you mean to tell me you think one hundred and fifty is reasonable for that rat-hole?"

"In Val d'Or, yes," he said. "This town is booming. People make their fortunes here."

"Not at my expense," I said brutally. "It can do its booming without me. Now what else have you got?"

He gave a Gallic shrug.

"Nothing," he said. "Nothing at all. That is the first apartment I have had for rent since I have been here, since 1937. People they come to Val d'Or, they buy a lot and they build. That is the way it goes. Now I have some nice lots for sale. Yes?"

"No."

"You have not been married long, yes?" He went on. "I am right, no?" I nodded absent-mindedly. "Then the life insurance your husband does not have? I call upon him."

"No," I said hastily. "No life insurance to-day, thank you." I backed out and went back to the hotel.

I sat on the edge of the bed, unmade, although it was a quarter to twelve, and stared at the sign on the door giving the price of the room as $3.00 single, $4.50 double. For this sum one had a bed with the aforementioned mattress stuffed with rocks, an uncarpeted floor, a dressing-chest with one leg missing, propped up on a Bible donated by the Gideon Society, a bare-topped, unstained table and two kitchen-type chairs and, the only joy, a private bathroom. Although the bath was so small that even I, height five foot three and a half, had to wear my knees under my chin when in it.

Suddenly the penny dropped and I multiplied $4.50 by the days in the month. Mathematics have never been my strong point, and after reaching totals of $1,350.00 and $13.50 respectively and discarding them hastily, the awful truth finally dawned upon me that to live here would cost us $135.00 per month, plus our food, which at Val d'Or prices, even eating at "greasy spoons" all the time, would total another six dollars a day at least for the two of us. Add on cigarettes, and we both smoke fairly heavily, the odd show and bottle of beer, and you have a grand total of four hundred bucks a month. Which wasn't even remotely funny. Especially as Jim didn't earn that much.

I lit a cigarette and thought how lucky it was I was a working woman. Next port of call was quite obviously the local weekly newspaper. In Fleet Street the lowest wage the journalists' union allowed for a cub reporter was £9. 9s. a week, and I was hardly a cub reporter. I should be worth a couple of hundred a month to booming Val d'Or and for that I was prepared to do everything;

report, re-write, make up the pages, proof-read, and even rustle up the occasional advertisement and write the copy for the advertiser, too.

When Jim came back for lunch I was still scribbling on the backs of envelopes.

"What you doing?" Jim asked.

"Facing the facts of life," I said. "Do you realise what it's costing us to live in this apology for an hotel?"

Jim picked up the envelope.

"Dear God!" he said. "What's this $1,350.00?"

"No, no," I told him. "That's a mistake.

"I hope!" he said quickly. "No luck with the apartment?"

I told him the whole sorry story.

"I thought as much," he said. "Matter of fact, I ran an advertisement in the local paper for a month before you came over, asking for an apartment. Not one single reply."

"It wouldn't be cheaper to take that horrible fox-hole at a hundred and twenty-five and eat at home, I suppose?"

Jim thought for a moment. He is the sort of genius who can do sums in his head, and what's more, sums that come out right. I am always lost in admiration.

"No," he said, "not with fuel on top, and electricity and telephone. Over a long period maybe, but not for three months. Besides, how do we know you can cook?"

He certainly had something there.

"Then a cheaper hotel?" I suggested, wincing slightly at the thought. This one seemed bad enough.

"Not unless you like bed bugs," Jim said.

"Well, what do people *do*?" I asked.

Jim shrugged.

"They run up a shack in their free time or live in a room in a private house. Most companies, C.I.L. and that sort, build houses for their managers and rent 'em cheaply."

"But not our company?"

"Not our company," Jim said. "Come on, let's eat."

After lunch — chicken noodle soup, purely a courtesy title; the nearest that soup ever got to a chicken may have been that someone dipped a bird in and out of lukewarm water and added aunty's knitting; an egg sandwich and cool coffee, price eighty-five cents — I toured the drug stores until I ran to earth a copy of the local weekly newspaper.

After all, I though it advisable to take a cursory glance at the thing first rather than to burst into the editor's office saying, "Lafayette, I am here!"

Not having the advantage of built-in over-stuffed cushions on my rear end, I decided that the foyer of the hotel, with its comfortable leather armchairs, would be more to my taste than the kitchen variety in my bedroom, so I settled myself down with cigarettes and the newspaper.

The lounge was on the dreary side. Brown armchairs, a potted rubber plant, a malignant and moth-eaten moose head on the wall and a series of brass objects on the floor that looked almost exactly like chamber pots. I puzzled over these for a few moments and then decided that, since they clearly could not be what they appeared to be, they must be ash trays, so I hooked the nearest towards me with my foot and flicked ash into it from time to time.

Minutes later I discovered my mistake when the man in the next chair leaned slightly to starboard and sent a stream of spittle expertly over my lap into the "ash tray." It landed with a startling clang. I was utterly entranced. As a child, when an occasion called for a spit I had always aimed for distance, never for any degree of accuracy, and I was seized with an almost overwhelming desire to try my luck. Only the thought of the possible disgrace and condemnation that would transpire should the wife of the manager of a finance corporation be found spitting in the public lounge of an hotel stopped me.

I brooded for a while on the deficiencies of my education. That one could reach years of discretion without recognizing a cuspidor seemed incredible. Happily, I didn't realise then to just what extent my education had been lacking in various other respects.

I thumbed my way through the *Val d'Or Star* and giggled to myself. The journalistic style had to be seen to be believed. All fires were conflagrations. Local ladies did not pour tea, they "presided at the urns." And the culminating glory was a report of a child who had died of pneumonia the week before, which started: "Death stretched out his icy hand and laid a finger upon a tiny tot in this community Tuesday. . . ."

It was too good to be true. I rolled my copy up and pasted

paper around it and mailed it forthwith to my ex-editor in London, where, I am told, it was received with loud cries of joy and pursued a more and more tattered course around the pubs and clubs of Fleet Street, gathering fame as it went, until it finally disintegrated.

At any rate, there was plenty of scope for my talents here. I just couldn't miss.

I hied me down the street to the newspaper office, and stopping off briefly in the advertisement section to insert a plea for an apartment or house — because you never can tell, can you? — asked to see the editor.

The owner-editor was very deaf, which didn't help matters any. I am cursed, or blessed, whichever way you happen to look at it, with a low-pitched voice which cannot or will not shout. But after half an hour of repetition and "I beg your pardon?" I managed to get some ideas across.

Yes, said the editor, they were very good ideas. He wondered he hadn't thought of them himself. Definitely. And thank you.

A further half-hour convinced him that I was not a Lady Bountiful presenting him with ideas for pepping up his circulation out of the kindness of my heart. I wished to put them into practice myself. For filthy lucre.

The editor looked at me with displeasure.

"Oh," he said. "Well, we'll see. You can come and work here for a few weeks on trial and then perhaps I could take you on the regular staff and pay you."

"And for the first few weeks?" I asked.

"I couldn't pay you for them," he said. "You'd have to prove yourself first, wouldn't you?"

"Look," I said patiently, "I was earning the equivalent of six thousand dollars a year up until the day I left England. I don't work for free." I showed him my Press pass and my wartime SHAEF card proving I had been an accredited war correspondent. He looked at them with all the interest of a bemused codfish.

"I couldn't pay you," he said; "not until I found out if you were any good. I tell you what, though," he brightened. "You say you are bi-lingual. You can report the Town Council meeting for me every week if you like; nobody here understands French. I can pay you ten cents per column inch. We could use a good five inches every week. Tuesday night the meeting is."

I put my Press pass and my SHAEF card back in my purse.

"Thank you too much," I said rudely, bowing from the hips like a German duellist. "You overwhelm me."

My cup of bitterness overflowed a few days later when I discovered through my bank manager that the newspaper had changed hands exactly two weeks before I reached Val d'Or for the ridiculous sum of two thousand-odd dollars.

And at that time I happened to have two thousand-odd dollars.

It is probably every journalist's dream to end up owning and editing a small-town newspaper. You don't trip over them for two thousand dollars every day of the week. I have never so nearly tripped over one before or since.

I returned to my hotel foyer and sat gloomily smoking cigarettes and watching the world go by.

Watching the world go by in Val d'Or, I found, was quite something.

A policeman strode through the lounge and into the bar at the back and returned with an armful of floozies, complaining bitterly in high-pitched voices. They had not been told, they argued, that there was to be a periodic round-up of the ladies of the town that week; it was unfair, unjust, deceitful. Later, a tough-looking type in knee boots, a mackinaw, and a hunting cap came in like a flash; said out of the corner of his mouth to the desk clerk, "Where's the game, bub?" and when the desk clerk twitched an eyebrow towards a door at the side of the foyer, vanished through it in the twinkling of an eye.

Presently all hell broke loose outside and I moved over to the windows, thus getting myself a ringside seat for a wonderful three-cornered street fight. No holds barred and plenty of blood and teeth on the sidewalk.

Jim came back at five o'clock to find me still in the foyer.

"Look, darling," he said with sweet reasonableness when we got to our room. "You really shouldn't sit around in the foyer like that. This isn't the Savoy, you know. There are some pretty tough characters drifting in and out, and before you know it you'll be picked up."

"And raped?" I asked. "Before your very eyes?"

Jim's lips twitched.

"Not if I know it," he said, "but seriously, Joan, you don't know this town. The mines get paid twice a month and on pay day the place is wide open. Then you have the bush workers coming in after a few months' logging with a thousand dollars or so to spend all at once. And the average French-Canadian logger is not a gentle creature when full of liquor and lust. Anyway, we shan't be here long. I've got good news, we're going to build a house."

"We're WHAT?" I asked.

Jim looked smug as only a potential house-owner can look smug.

"We're going to build a house. I have it all lined up. I've got a builder who can put it up in six weeks and there's a new subdivision opening up where we can get a Lot reasonably, and he tugged a booklet out of his pocket, "here are some National Housing plans to look through; we can buy blue-prints of any of them for a few bucks."

"And what, my love," I enquired, "are we going to use for money?"

Jim grinned.

"I can afford it," he said. "I can cash some bonds. We're not on our beam ends, you know."

"Aren't we?" I said, bedazzled by the thought that I had actually married a man with capital. In London I had known plenty of men who earned four times as much as Jim and more, but in Fleet Street it was easy come, easy go, none of them had a nickel to their name in the bank.

"Certainly we aren't," Jim said. "Hell, woman, I was overseas on a major's pay for six years, fighting damn hard most of the time. I didn't get a chance to spend it on anything but war bonds. Furthermore, I have my rehabilitation whoosit and credits."

I positively goggled at him and said, "?????"

"You are the most fantastic creature," Jim said. "Any other woman in the world would have found out my financial position months ago and gone through my bank book with a fine toothcomb. Don't you give a damn about security?"

I was forced to admit that I didn't, which made me sound a very feckless and non-profit-sharing type indeed. Not at all the sort of character who should find itself two thousand miles from home out on an unknown limb.

We spent an wonderful evening poring over the National Housing book and finally decided — very mutually, because our tastes

by some blessed arrangement of Providence are almost identical
— on a four-room bungalow, with alterations.

The alterations consisted of chopping off half the kitchen space
and adding it on to the living room, building a cater-corner brick
fireplace to break up the oblong look and arranging for built-in
bookshelves and an entrance hall instead of dashing madly
straight into the living-room, as is the fashion in Northwestern
Quebec, pursued by snowflakes and — maybe — wolves.

I argued with Jim about his six weeks. No man born of woman,
I stated rhetorically, could possibly build a house in six weeks, but
Jim howled me down, and after I had been in Val d'Or a very few
weeks I realised that he was right.

Building was going on everywhere and buildings went up so
fast it took your breath away. You would go to bed at night with a
clear view of bush before your windows, and in the morning you'd
draw the shades and there was the Empire State Building.

We went out to dinner happily arguing the respective merits of
clapboard versus stucco and red against blue for a roof. We could
hardly wait for daylight to start looking at Lots.

Somewhere during the course of the evening, tucked in among
the conversation about two-by-fours and insulation and
monolithic cement, Jim remembered that I had been job-hunting
that afternoon.

"How did it go?" he asked, "and when do you take over the
paper?"

My husband has a charming and touching faith in my writing
ability which is, unhappily, not always shared by the publishing
world. If only I, like Omar Khayyam, could "grasp this sorry
scheme of things entire" and then "remould it nearer to the
heart's desire," Jim would be an editor of great prominence and I,
ipso facto, a millionaire journalist.

"I don't," I said. "Let's not go into that now or I shall burst a
blood-vessel and end up in fumed oak with silver handles. After,
repeat *after*, working for them for a month or two or three for
nothing, I might be taken on the staff at, guess what — one
hundred dollars a month. Meanwhile I have a breathtaking offer
of freelancing. I can spend every Tuesday night at the City Hall
meetings for fifty cents a week.

Jim looked slightly shocked.

"Oh no! Oh NO!" he said, with husbandly tact.

"Oh yes," I said bitterly. Then I had a wonderful idea. "Hey! Why can't I work for you? You've done nothing but grumble that you can't find a bi-lingual stenographer. What's wrong with me? I know I use the hunt-and-peck typewriting method but I hunt and peck incredibly fast. And you wouldn't have to dictate letters to me. I can write a better business letter than you, my friend, any day. The only bookkeeping I've ever done was to forget to return my library books, but you could do that side of the business. How's about it?"

"It would," said Jim, "be ideal. There's nothing I'd like better, honestly. But it's no soap."

"What do you mean, it's no soap? It's wonderful. When do I start?"

Jim gulped.

"You don't," he said. "There's a company rule that husbands and wives do not run branch offices together."

"In case they run off with the petty cash?"

"In case they run off with the petty cash. Actually when the collections come in I do sometimes have an almost frightening amount of loose cash around," Jim said, "and it would be too easy for two of us working together to cook the books for months on end before anyone got suspicious."

"Well, it looks as if I don't earn any money," I said.

Jim shrugged.

"Doesn't matter much," he said. "After all, we can weather six weeks of this hotel without going in the red, and then we'll be in our own home."

Something he had said at lunch-time came back into my mind.

"Didn't you say something about people taking a room in a private house? Would that save money?"

"Sure," Jim said, "it'd save plenty. We ought to be able to get a bedroom for around ten bucks a week, *if* we can get one, if you see what I mean, because they're as scarce as hen's teeth."

"What does one do? Advertise?"

"One drives slowly around town peering at windows to see if there's a *'Chambre à louer'* notice. They go so fast nobody wastes the price of an advertisement."

I leapt up.

"Then what are we waiting for? It's only half-past nine."

So we got into the car and sneaked around the streets, and fate was kind, and right at the far end of town we saw our particular "Excelsior!"

It was a typical French-Canadian house, as clean and as bare as an unused packing-case. Papa and mamma sat in the kitchen surrounded by their offspring of all ages from one year to fifteen, and mamma swelled suspiciously once more under the apron. But she sprang to her feet and took us upstairs to show us the bedroom.

We knew it was a bedroom because it had a bed in it. But that was all it did have. Mamma had no English and I propped myself up in a corner while Jim got involved in a conversation about "*chaises*" and "*bureaux*" and "*chiffoniers*." Mamma said, "*Pas encore*" and "*Peut-être*" and made other encouraging noises.

It all boiled down to the fact that, as a rule, her roomers were miners, who didn't require such things as dressing-tables or chests of drawers or chairs. They came in to sleep and they slept. Perhaps in due course she might buy a chair or two, but after all, she could rent the room any time without it. And did we want it or did we want it? Twelve dollars a week, take it or leave it.

Jim was on the verge of saying no, but I did some fast thinking. After all, we had to buy furniture anyway; we might as well buy some fast and use it here.

"Let's take a look at the bathroom," I said.

Mama muttered something about "*le clef*" and rushed off downstairs, and I spoke fast and to the point to my husband. When she returned she explained that the bathroom was kept locked lest the children enter to disport themselves, which seemed an admirable arrangement to me, as it meant we had what amounted to a private bath. To this day I don't know where the family performed their toilet, but certainly we were the only people to ever use the extremely nice plumbing, and provided you didn't lose your head and go drawing enough water to reach above your ankles, our morning and evening baths almost always had the chill off.

We paid a week's rent in advance and arranged to move in the following morning.

Back in the car Jim said, "There's only one thing wrong with your ideas. Have you by any chance looked in the local furniture stores?"

I admitted that I hadn't.

"From what I remember of the Regency furniture in your apartment," Jim said, "I don't think you're the plush with gilt rococo decoration type. Exactly what furniture did you have in mind?"

I said vaguely, "Oh, a kidney-shaped dressing-table in chintz maybe and a small bedroom armchair in ice-blue satin with a buttoned sort of padded back — you know. Something that would fit into any decorating scheme we may have."

Jim said gloomily, "That's what I thought you had in mind. And to save you from apoplexy in a furniture store to-morrow I will tell you here and now that you won't find either. Or anything even remotely like a kidney-shaped dressing-table in chintz or an ice-blue satin armchair."

"Very well, then," I said, "I shall make them myself. I refuse to let this dam' town get me down. Or you either. I mean, let it get you down, not you get me down."

"Huh!" Jim said. "Pioneer type, eh? Do you by any chance know the first thing about making furniture?"

"Of course I don't," I said, "but I wrote a series of articles once for a woman's paper on how to furnish a flat with packing cases and they looked marvellous in the illustrations. If 'the average woman' can do it, I'm sure I can."

The next day I bought a perfectly plain knee-hole desk and nicely-shaped bedroom armchair upholstered in the most appalling cotton material I have ever seen, positively bursting with cabbage roses and butterflies and some rather obscene-looking objects that Jim assured me were merely leaves. For the time being the desk served as a chest of drawers, and provided one sat in the chair one didn't notice the upholstery. We piled our trunks one on top of the other and put a looking-glass on the wall behind for a dressing-chest.

To-day the knee-hole desk is covered with chintz and wears a plate-glass top. It isn't kidney-shaped, but it's the next best thing, and I nailed the chintz skirts on, using the heel of my shoe as a hammer, and they've stayed put with no trouble ever since. The chair got itself slip-covered in double-quick time, though not by me, because the only thing that comes of me trying to sew is knots. And the little seat I use in front of my dressing-table is made from a nail keg and very nice it looks, too, with its ballet skirts and padded top. And the only reason a nail keg lives in the bedroom is because Jim went yak-yak-yak about people who say they can make furniture from packing-cases and then buy knee-hole desks instead.

The editor must confess a sneaking preference for Norman Ward as his favourite Leacock Medal winner. A large part of this preference, of course, is because of the high quality of humour done by Ward. But it also seems so very appropriate that, like Stephen Leacock, Norman Ward is both professor of political science and humourist. Ward has been both gag writer and scholar but perhaps it is his long involvement with labour-management conciliation that has kept his sense of humour alive. His Mice in the Beer *won the award in 1961.*

NORMAN WARD

from Mice in the Beer

It was one of those bright winter mornings when it is so cold that even if you can get your car engine started you can still only run back and forth in a straight line until the grease in the steering loosens up. Uncle Bob and I had just listened to Mr. Upshott deliver himself of a well-rounded statement against deceit in all its devious forms, and Uncle Bob, warming to the thrum of the motor as we sat in his car, remarked that it must be a comfort to a man to be able to work off a head of steam at fixed intervals.

"You and I," he said, "have to await the opportunities afforded by chance encounters with uncouth tradesmen or civil servants, or the accumulated stupidities of our friends to release our pent-up disapproval of things in general. But old Upshott pulls the lanyard regularly every Sunday and blasts away to his heart's content."

This seemed to me to do less than justice to Mr. Upshott, and I said so. After all, I argued, going to church did something for Uncle Bob too. Whatever its effects were supposed to be, it invariably brought out the worst in him.

"I am no judge of these things," Uncle Bob agreed, "but I think if you were to observe me carefully you would find that I could behave in the same way at any other time of the week, depending on the provocation."

"Now that you mention that, I can believe it."

Uncle Bob studied the temperature gauge on the dashboard. "As a matter of fact, it was on a Wednesday that Upshott and I virtually single-handed — if the two of us could be said to work that way — not only deceived the entire population of this town, including the police, but also dealt a low blow at the temperance movement in this country."

"Surely Mr. Upshott did not voluntarily act with you in this venture?"

"Indeed he did. He played a leading role in starting it, and it took forbearance of the highest saintliness on his part to forgive me for finishing it."

"Tell me." Occasionally I liked to create the illusion that I could prevent Uncle Bob from recounting a tale if I wanted to. Besides, it was too cold to walk home.

"Thank you," said Uncle Bob. "It happened some years ago, when drunken driving was still in its infancy. The police had obtained a new gadget for measuring the spirit level of citizens arrested because of the eccentric behaviour of their automobiles, and they were anxious to try it out in a convincing public demonstration, particularly since the local magistrate was known to be suspicious of its accuracy. He was a gin drinker," he added, to prove his point.

"By some curious mischance," he went on, "the chief of police had a wife who was a demon worker in the cause of temperance, and in no time at all the cops and the temperance forces between them had laid on an elaborate exhibition of the effects of drinking on automobile driving. It was to take place in the arena, just before a hockey game between the local high school and its most offensive rival. It would thus be witnessed not only by the usual townsfolk who attended these affairs, but also plenty of young people, whose impressionable minds in those days were regarded as fair game."

"They still are."

"Yes, but nowadays the referees in charge of the game keep changing. The idea was," he proceeded, going firmly back on the track, "to have some driver negotiate a difficult obstacle course, driving between and around posts and other impediments, and give him a score to correspond with his performance. After each trip around the course he would be given a considerable charge of some beverage chosen by a committee of temperance workers, with the police acting in an advisory capacity. Then his physical condition would be attested to by resort to the police department's new gimmick for appraising the alcoholic content of taxpayers. After that he would tackle the obstacle course again, and carry on until the experiment was considered a success. That, presumably, would coincide either with the driver's reaching an intolerable state of cheerfulness, or the breakdown of the cops' machine."

"Or until the committee ran out of liquor."

"Not a chance. Since hot dogs were sold in the arena, the law required the committee in charge to take out a banquet licence to cover the drinking. And since the arena seated three thousand people, they could, at the legal half dozen beer and several ounces of spirits per customer, have got enough for a game of water polo."

"And did they?"

He grinned. "I'll tell you. As one of the leading characters in town, and an outspoken champion of interference of all kinds — as well as a man who would put up with no nonsense — Rev. Mr. Upshott was chosen to pour for the first hour. And I was chosen to drive the car."

"As one of the town's outspoken drinkers."

"Certainly not. The town's topers were not considered good clinical material for the experiment. Some of them had built up too strong a tolerance, and the experiment would have taken hours to complete. Others were not trusted to arrive in a sufficient state of dehydration to allow for accurate measurement of their intake by the cops' new toy. Several, of course, were disqualified because they had no driver's permit. In this kingdom the drinkless man was king."

"I'd still like to know how they chose you."

"Well, naturally there was a good deal of competition among the various interested organizations over the car's driver. Each of them was anxious to have a member of some other outfit selected, and I qualified as a non-joiner of anything. Besides, I'm afraid the notion of getting a few drinks at the expense of those fellows appealed to me, and I volunteered. Nobody else did, so I got the job."

"Did they let you pick your own brew for the show?"

"I was consulted about nothing, and things would have turned out a good deal better if I had been. As it was, when I arrived at the arena that night, I found a fierce obstacle course set up on the ice, with little posts and pylons set up for me to drive the car around. Old Upshott was sitting in the goal judge's seat at one end, flanked by representatives of the temperance strongarm squad, with a large bottle, suitably full, in his lap. The cops had their decontamination unit set up on a table, and a nice new sedan was waiting for me. All I had to do was say I'd drive the car to the best of my ability, and climb in. I got a big hand from the crowd when I started out on my first trip around the course."

His brow clouded. "It was terrible," he said. "I was a good driver even then, but the pylons were set too close together for the icy surface. The car skidded just enough on the sharper turns that I knocked over fifteen posts, nearly a third of the total. With that start, I figured I was going to end up smashing the arena."

"That might have pleased the committee."

"I believe it would. Upshott was delighted with my first trip, and said it would prove to the crowd that the obstacle course really was difficult, and not just a set-up. Then he poured me my first drink." He frowned disapprovingly. "It was cold tea."

"Tea!"

"Tea. I was going to stand on my right as a citizen and demand an audit of the books, but Upshott winked at me and whispered that he'd explain later. In the meantime, he said, he hoped I'd cooperate, as they were counting on me."

"I thought he knew you better than that."

Uncle Bob ignored me. "At first I was too annoyed to think much about it. I knocked back my tea like a little man, let the cops test me with their new erector set, and took another fling around the course. That time I pushed over the same pylons as before, and the crowd got restive. I don't know what they expected, but at least it was something different."

He paused and scrutinized the dashboard again. "The interesting thing about that second trip," he said as he straightened up, "was that I thought I saw what I was doing wrong. The car's steering was not familiar to me, and was responding more slowly than I expected. I took another slug from Upshott's jug, blew up a balloon for the cops, and went at the course again. By the time I'd gone over it four or five times, I'd got my pylon score down from fifteen to eleven, and was really getting the hang of it."

"But weren't you supposed to get worse instead of better?"

"So Upshott seemed to think. He told me that the tea had come up because his temperance yeomen, when they got right down to it, had been unable at the last moment to lend their patronage to so dubious an enterprise as pouring drinks into me. And so without saying anything to anybody they had substituted tea. He was against it, but they voted him down."

"But everybody at the arena thought it was *not* tea. Or did they?"

"Precisely the point I raised with Upshott between the fifth and sixth trips. But he said at least their consciences were clear. And of course they had taken for granted that I would fall in with their scheme, as an undrinking scholar and gentleman."

"I'm puzzled about the cops," I put in. "They must have got suspicious when their machine showed nothing. How did Upshott's crew expect to get around that?"

"I don't know, but I expect the wife of the chief of police would have an assignment in connection with that. At the time, by a curious coincidence, I had started from the beginning to suggest subtly to the police that they did not know how to run their machine, by the simple device of saying every few minutes that I thought they did not know how to run their machine. Cops were a lot more open to suggestion in those days than they are now, when they get a liberal education in everything from jiu-jitsu to child psychology. That day, they were soon wondering if I wasn't right."

"I expect you'll tell me, but were you?"

"As it turned out, no. But before we got around to that I had surrounded a pint or more of Upshott's special, and got my pylon score down from eleven to four. The crowd thought it was great, and gave me a tremendous cheer every time I went around with a new low score. It was my night, and poor old Upshott and his committee were nearly in tears."

"Did it ever occur to you to string along with them and knock over a few posts?"

"You're forgetting, the same as Upshott's committee did, that the program had required me to say that I would drive to the best of my ability, while they plied me with beverages of their own choice. I considered I had no honourable choice. Anyway, that obstacle course was tough and I wanted to lick it."

He chuckled appreciatively. "Finally on about the fifteenth or sixteenth trip around, when Upshott's bottle was practically empty, I got around without so much as scraping a post. The crowd went wild and poured out on to the ice. They pulled me from the car and carried me around on their shoulders, laughing and cheering like mad, and fighting just to get close enough to touch me. Many of them took out flasks and offered me a snort or two."

"And with your usual luck, I suppose you were too full of tea."

"Not a bit of it. I had several heart-warming nips, which I considered I richly deserved. Thanks to the cops' machine, which was applied to me in a last-minute effort to establish something after the crowd had quietened down, I can report that I accepted upwards of six ounces of mixed fluids in a relatively short time after the car-driving experiment ended. After that several hundred people paraded me home. But in the meantime the police were satisfied that their machine probably worked all right, provided they gave it enough time."

"This was no doubt a source of great satisfaction to you."

Uncle Bob nodded. "It was. Considering the trouble they all went to, it was nice that the boys had carried at least one point. On the other side, Upshott told me next day that he though I had set the temperance movement back at least thirty years."

"And what did you think?"

Uncle Bob tentatively slipped the car into gear. "I told Upshott," he said modestly, "that I could never have done it without his help. But he didn't seem to want any of the credit."

The car wasn't quite warmed up, and we lurched off like a bucking bronco. Somehow it seemed appropriate.

Doing his journeyman literary work in advertising, Robert Thomas Allen evidently learned values and people. His The Grass is Never Greener *will appeal to Canadians who have tried warmer, if not greener, fields only to return to the Northland. Allen has twice been honoured by the Canada Council and twice by the Stephen Leacock Associates. This selection is from his first Medal winner in 1957.*

ROBERT THOMAS ALLEN

from The Grass Is Never Greener

I learned a lot of things about selling a house which I'm willing to pass on to anyone who may be interested. The first thing to get into your head if you're going to sell your house is that the best prices for houses are being paid when you're trying to buy one. When you try to sell yours, nobody wants one, especially one with the down payment you have to get. This economic law apparently doesn't apply to your friends, who all sell houses just like yours for twice as much as they cost. Furthermore, they have so many customers the first night the ad runs that they almost have to call the cops to shoo leftover buyers off the lawn. I can't explain this. All I know is that if your experience is anything like mine, you'll get three customers.

One will be a middle-aged woman named Mrs. May, who glances around your house vaguely then sits in your favorite chair till suppertime, telling you a long story about her husband, who had a hernia two years ago and hasn't been any good since. At five minutes to six she'll look at her watch and say she must scoot.

Another will be a man named Morrison, who has thin black hair combed sideways and a brisk way of going through your house like a bus driver at the end of a run. Every time you apologize for anything, he laughs in a friendly way and says it doesn't matter, as he's going to knock the walls down anyway, move the fireplace over to the other end of the living room and put a breakfast nook where your bookcase is. You'll never see him again, unless someday you happen to be selling another house.

Around about the fifth week you'll have a visit from a sad,

plump little man with no eyebrows who walks around the outside of the house kicking the wall and whispering to a tall, thin friend he brings with him. The last time I saw him he got me out of a hot bath, where I'd been lying trying to figure out how to get my house out of the exclusive hands of a real estate man who had evidently moved to Europe. I came out clutching a bathrobe around me and followed him around peering at him through the steam on my glasses, like a river pilot in a fog. I stood around anxiously kicking everything he kicked. We all ended up in my bedroom gently kicking the baseboard. He walked out with thoughtfully lowered head, got into a truck and drove away.

Another thing, don't make the mistake at any point during the selling of your house of sitting back and saying, "Well, I've got the law on my side." Nobody ever has the law on his side but the lawyers. Any time I've ever said, "I have the law on my side," I've found myself fighting desperately to keep out of jail. One time during the rental mix-up after the war, before I owned a house, I checked with a man at the Rentals Administration of the Wartime Prices and Trade Board about whether I had to get out of my house by a certain date. He kept saying, "You're safe as a church." I ended up being threatened with charges of holding, resisting, stalling, contempt of court and everything but insanity, and finally had to move everything I owned, including a firmly bolted workbench weighing about half a ton, in twenty-four hours.

Signing an offer to purchase is the turning point in selling your house. It's a long legal form that is to a real estate man what an order blank is to a brush salesman. Everybody signs it, including you. The buyer makes out a check for a deposit of, say, five hundred dollars. This shows his good faith and is held, along with his good faith, pending the closing date, when you adjust all charges, like the gas bill. You turn over the key. You all smile and shake hands. You go ahead with your other arrangements — buying a new house or a ticket to Tahiti. You tell all your friends that you've sold your house. You've made a deal — unless the buyer decides he was only kidding.

I got an offer to purchase from a fat, chuckling man in an expensive-looking, pin-striped suit. My wife and I sat down and said, "Whew! Well, it's all over at last!" We went out that night and had lobster Newburg. A week later I was trying to get the fat man to stop hanging up on me when I phoned him. A rumor had reached me through the real estate man that he wasn't going to buy my house after all.

I couldn't just run out and cash his check, because he'd stopped payment on it, and, besides, I didn't have it. I think the real estate man had it as a token of somebody's good faith. Anyway I was concentrating on making the customer buy the whole house, not just five hundred dollars' worth of it. I said to my wife, "Well this is it! He asked for it. It's his problem. I'll take it easy if he has children."

I phoned the lawyer I'd intended to have handle the deal. I said, "When do we start dragging this man through every court in the land?"

"You sure you got the right number?" the lawyer said. "This is a lawyer's office."

"I *know* it's a lawyer's office. That's what I want. Look, this guy buys my house, signs an offer to purchase then just decides to change his mind about the whole thing. When do we slap him with everything in the book?"

"Mr. Allen," the lawyer said wearily, "I've given this my considered opinion."

"What's your plan?" I asked, baring my teeth at myself in the hall mirror.

"Drop it," he said.

"Drop it!" I yelped. "Whaddaya mean, *drop* it! We've got him on six carbon copies, three witnesses, the Small Loans Act, the short form, the long form and a check."

"Allen," the lawyer kept saying quietly, "drop it."

He was right, of course. It would have meant two years just to get the case *into* the courts, let alone get it out. It would have been fun only if I'd been a millionaire with a hobby of long legal chess games.

You can see how hopeless it is, anyway, trying to make somebody buy something. All he needs to say is that he doesn't want it. He can tell you that he hasn't any money and go to Bermuda, which is where you thought you'd be.

And, take it from me, the law won't have anything to do with anything hopeless when it comes to a showdown. The law will have very little to do with anything when it comes to a showdown. If there's anything a lawyer hates, it's getting tangled up with the law.

In the meantime, although the buyer was tentatively tied to my house, so was I. In other words, I couldn't sell it to someone else, because the fat man could still change his mind and start payment on the check, and I would suddenly be in the position of trying to sell my house to one person after I had a deposit and an offer to purchase from another.

Once I phoned the customer's lawyer about it. He said, "Look, Allen, my client hasn't been *entirely* unreasonable. After all, you misrepresented your mortgage, your down payment, interest, lot number, frontage and your wife's middle name." When I told my lawyer about it, he implied that if I would lie low he might be able to get me off.

It ended with my going to the buyer's lawyer and getting what is known as a release, or the customer's permission to sell my own house to somebody else. I thought for awhile he wasn't going to let me. If that's legal revenge, you can have it.

You're going to find yourself dealing with real estate men too. Maybe you'll strike a good one. But there's also a chance that you'll strike a few like one I got, a freckled little Irishman who advertised himself as Good Deal McGuire and who lived in the country and raised Holsteins as a hobby. He ran billboards all over town showing one of his prize Holsteins, with the caption, "Don't Be Bullheaded: Let McGuire Handle It." One of McGuire's men came up to the house, went around making notes and finally said, mysteriously, "Look, Mr. Allen, there's one little thing that I'd like to get straight right now. Do you mind *how* we sell your house?"

"Uh — how do you mean?" I said.

He winked. "Well, McGuire is an old-line circus man, and when he starts beating those publicity drums, well! — " he chuckled — "things move! It's just that his methods are a bit unorthodox. I like to get an okay from the client first."

I thought happily of blimps being moored to my chimney or maybe Miss Canada sitting on my doorstep trying on nylons. I lowered my voice and said conspiratorially, "After all, we *both* want to sell the house, don't we?"

Then McGuire moved behind the iron curtain. My wife and I sat waiting for the blimps. I'd read somewhere a few tips on selling a house. One was to leave all the lights on to make it cheery, and the other was to keep it neat and polished. By the end of the

month the only caller we'd had was Mrs. May. My head was sunburned from the glare of the lamps, and we'd rubbed the furniture till we almost had holes in the end tables. Finally I phoned
McGuire.

"This is Allen," I said.

"Who?"

"Allen."

"You want to buy a house or something?"

"Look, I'm selling a house."

"Sorry. Nobody wants them. You haven't got a second-hand
vacuum cleaner, have you?"

"For the — ! McGuire, *you're selling a house for me*. Allen, my
name is. Six-room bungalow with a corner window."

"Oh *that* Mr. Allen." He began to talk like a football announcer.
"We're doing all we can, Mr. Allen. We're pushing it. We're shov-
ing it. I'm advertising it extensively. I have six salesman banging
away at it. Been thinking up a little promotion scheme. Your cash
payment is a bit high, but I think we can move it."

It turned out that his wild promotion scheme was a sign that
he'd had his son letter placed in his window. It read, DON'T PASS UP
THIS JIM DANDY BARGAIN, but somebody had shoved a geranium in
front of it.

I took my house away from Good Deal McGuire and gave it to a
real estate man named Fairplay, a former used car salesman from
Vancouver, who got another offer to purchase for me. This house
of mine was right in the city, and I don't know how it became
connected with cows, but this customer was a technician in a government breeding station, a broody young man with brown
sideburns, gold-rimmed glasses and a built-in blush which gave
him a permanent expression of having been insulted. I found out
later that he was a friend of Fairplay.

Instead of kicking my furnace, he kept asking about my neighbors. My neighbor to the west was a middle-aged man with a
small face and a mustache. He always wore a black homburg and
stood motionlessly in his garden for hours, hands clasped behind
his back, smoking a cigar in the dead center of his mouth. I've
seen him stand that way beside a pile of burning leaves for most of
a week end. I had no idea what kind of man he was. As a result,
whenever my customer asked me about my neighbors, I bore
down on the one on the other side, a weather-beaten, soft-spoken

man with tragic brown eyes, a courtly manner, three noisy sons, a daughter who was studying drama, two rabbits and a mania for making pickles. The first words he ever spoke to me were, "Do you like pickles?" He told me with quiet confidence that he was going to make a pickle man out of me and that he'd made pickle men of lots of men who didn't like pickles. He chuckled as he cited cases of indigestion he had caused. He had pickles down in his cellar — pickled tomatoes, German pickles, dill pickles, sweet pickles, sour pickles and a laundry tub full of sauerkraut.

I told my customer he was one of the best neighbors I'd ever had, which was the truth. I was extremely fond of the whole family. I added that he was a fine Christian man who you wouldn't know was around the house, as he worked as a machinist on a Toronto Harbour ferry at night and slept all day. He would have been sleeping, too, if a load of coal he'd ordered hadn't arrived just as my customer was mooching around my back yard, sniffing nervously, winking one eye and asking if my neighbors were all right.

It was during the days of wartime shortages, and the coalman pointed out to my neighbor that there was a law that the coal was supposed to be delivered to the nearest cellar window.

I heard my neighbor say, "Well, I knew you fellas were getting pretty independent, but — " he cleared his throat gently — "surely to Christ you wouldn't dump a load of coal on top of a man's laundry tubs, would you?"

The coalman looked at him as if he were trying to sabotage the country. He said that rules were made for everybody and that he wasn't paid to worry about laundry tubs. It was the one and only time I saw my neighbor lose his temper. He swore for what seemed to me, and I suppose to my customer, about five minutes and ended up by kicking an empty garbage pail right out onto the street.

The next I heard of my customer was from his lawyer, who said his client had changed his mind. I went down to Fairplay's office. It was a couple of minutes before I realized that a man up a ladder painting the outside of the frame office building was Fairplay himself, who ignored me. All he'd say was, "I'm busy. See my lawyer."

If a man's up a ladder and won't come down, there's very little you can do about it, but this was sometimes hard to explain to lawyers during the following weeks.

"Why didn't you talk to the real estate man?" they'd say.

"Couldn't get him down off the ladder," I'd explain.

"I don't . . . quite . . . understand. Off a *ladder?* What has that to do with a real estate man?"

"I don't know *what* it has to do with a real estate man," I'd say. "I'm just telling you, he was up a ladder and wouldn't come down."

"Why didn't you get another ladder?" they'd say, humoring me.

A month later, in desperation, I knocked off a thousand dollars and, two weeks later, sold the house to a man from North Bay who looked at me sideways and said moodily that he guessed everybody had to get used to paying twice what everything was worth.

I secretly agreed with him and actually felt a bit sorry for the poor sucker for having to pay so much more for the house than I'd paid for it three years earlier, when all I'd done was to build a new veranda on it, paint the inside and the outside, wallpaper every room, move a radiator weighing about a ton to the back of the house and one at the back to the front, build a new fence around the whole property, sledge-hammer a trench in the cellar, lay tile in it to drain a low spot and cement it over again. But I afterward found out that a year later he painted the front steps and sold the house for four thousand dollars more than he paid me for it.

The winner of the first Leacock Medal for Humour was Harry Symons in 1947. Somewhat reminiscent of the earlier gentle British humour, Ojibway Melody *was a particularly apt choice because it was about the Ontario lake country that Stephen Leacock had loved.*

HARRY SYMONS
from Ojibway Melody

Why anyone, anywhere, should make a fuss or a bother about moving from the city to the summer scene is one of those incredible things you read about but never run into in real life. At least, you shouldn't.

After all, isn't it just a simple matter of each person throwing a bathing suit, one towel, one shirt and trousers, one pair of socks and pyjamas and shoes into a bag and marching off to the nearest station? There's the tooth brush, of course, and paste, if you will, as well as dollop of medicine, if you're inclined that way, plus your razor kit, and, if you're a girl, your lipstick, along with any other of those secret devices and weapons that turn mere men into swooning gorillas or faun-like replicas of their former masterful selves.

Food? Yes. If you must! But who ever heard of anyone starving to death at any well bred Canadian summer resort? There may have been some close calls, we will admit, amongst certain of the hotels and boarding houses, true. But we prefer to ignore these in our present discussion, because, although one loses weight at such places, it's just carelessness if one starves entirely to death.

But what we're driving at is simply this . . . why not buy your foodstuffs on arrival? At the nearest store or village? They may cost you a trifle more. But, after all, it's your holiday you know, and why quibble about a dollar here or there. And, besides, the local people have to live, and their season's a short thing at best. One has to be mature about such things, you know.

The nearest store is seven miles away? And you have no car, and only a rowboat? Hmmmm! Well, WELL, that IS a pretty fair row . . . fourteen miles! And you say the food costs you anything up to three times as much? Ho, hum! Very well then, as we've said all along, perhaps you'd better take just a few snacks along with you just while you're orienting, so to speak, in the beginning.

But with a LARGE family, say one of nine or ten, it's quite a different problem. Sixteen quarts of milk a day, yes sixteen, cost a lot more for the season at twenty cents than at twelve, say. Why not take cows? Now that's a pertinent question, to be sure. But how many? And who'd swim them out through eight miles of Painted Waters to our Island? And would they thrive on unripe blueberries and ground juniper and bulrushes? There's the crux of the thing, outside of the milking and all that sort of clerical work!

So, you see, with an early Victorian organization like ours, things shape up differently. Not only with milk, but with meat and vegetables, cereals and eggs, and all those sundries the good housewife knows about. The lists of them must be arranged, and the purchasing timed to a nicety. But THE job is the regimentation of them into quotas for each member of the party to transport. Send them by express, you say? But we're not there yet. The establishment isn't even opened in preparation for our descent upon it. And butter lying around on docks in the noon-day sun doesn't, to our knowledge, improve with age. Nor eggs either, for that matter. We knew a man who tried it once. His name was Cornelius. He's dead now, poor fellow. But he actually tried it, and when he arrived on the dock the next day his holiday butter had run down into the water and the eggs were beginning to hatch. The local people were pretty annoyed, too, because it spoiled their swimming for nearly a day. So they weren't sorry when old Corny broke down and returned to the city where he stayed ever after.

That just shows you what can happen if you're not mighty cautious.

With us, of course, it's all been worked out geometrically over a period of the last thirty years, so that now it's as simple as . . . well, simple anyway. And there's an Advance Party chosen to break the ground, so to speak. Everyone craves the job, but nobody really does want it. Because the Advance Party, in this case, anyway, really does go in advance. Not only that, but it's loaded to the guards with every conceivable thing it never will need, as well as a string of instructions that are quite impossible of carrying out.

At any cost each member of this party must have at least fifty pounds over the weight the railways may carry per person by law. In as many parcels as it is humanly possible to break them down into. Because the more there are the more confusing the whole thing becomes, and the sooner eyeryone in the Advance Party throws up their hands and says . . . "O well, I've forgotten it anyway. Mom'll never notice, anyhow. So just let's forget it, and get there, and have a swim, and if whatever it is doesn't turn up we'll double up on something else anyhow!" Theoretically this is all very elastic, but it has its possibilities as you can see.

Now, the basic duty of the Advance Party is simplicity itself. It is merely to get itself overloaded with everything unnecessary, then get aboard the train and disorganize it so successfully that the small matter of excess baggage is quite overlooked in the chaos. Then, on arrival at the disembarking point, which with us is Pointe-au-Baril, to get as much of its own baggage as seems feasible, coupled with as many of the most attractive looking packages belonging to other people that it can. So far as we can determine, this system works out admirably for all concerned in the long run. Most of your own best things disappear, and are replaced with such items as a carton of Skipper Playfair's Black Horse Ale, (he had three, anyway) which should help to fill in the time nicely one hot day; and a case of Mrs. Green's special oranges which she and her husband, whom every one calls Gerry, for some reason best known to themselves, which she and Gerry look forward to consuming with zest. However, they probably end up by getting our cabbages, and Skipper Playfair no doubt joyously discovers himself the unexpected owner of a box of beets and doesn't miss the fourth carton of beer until it's much too late, and then blames one of his helpers who tipples a little when no one is looking. So it all works out amicably, you see, and everyone feels well pleased and life rolls onward in one happy summer daze.

The next basic duty of the Advance Party is to proceed as best it can under its own steam to the seat of all the trouble, the Island and the cottage. This move sounds drab and uninteresting until you've tried it a few times. After years of experiment, however, our Advance Parties have gotten it down to quite a nice science. There are boats, parts of boats, skeletons of boats, and hulls of what once were boats up at the Island, of course. Because most everybody has a boat or boats. For where life, in a sense, becomes suddenly reversed, and you find all your streets are waterways and your habitat isolated miles from any store . . . well then you can see what we mean when we say most everybody has a boat or boats. But the boats aren't launched yet, you'll recollect. That's one of the Advance Party's basic duties, you know. To reach the Island by whatever devious method chance at the time affords, and then to sit disconsolately upon the dock and wish to blazes it'd never come. For now the fun really begins, as you may soon find out. The cottage to open. Everything to sort out. The boats to glue together for another season. The water system to hook up and wrestle over. The bedding to discover in its newest hiding-place, to de-mouse, to air, to sort out, shake up, patch and allocate so that when the main party arrives everyone will relax and be glad to know that they have someone else's blankets and nests of mice, and not their own.

But, as we say, after years of practice it's all resolved itself by this time into a simplicity that is effortless and charming. The Advance Party is now gathered exhausted on the main dock at Pointe-au-Baril amongst its assembled items of excess baggage. The day is just as perfect as those days more usually are. It is drizzling clammily and no one has come prepared for rain. This in itself is a ritual that is repeated unerringly year in and year out. Nobody remembers to connect the summer holidays with rain.

Everything will be quite all right, however. There's no doubt about that. You just wait. For the Advance Party, in its infinite wisdom, has long since written ahead to Albert Richardson (everybody writes to Albert, about everything) to see that a special boat is ready and prepared to transport the Party out through all that scenic beauty to the Island of Painted Waters. Of course the Advance Pary has quite forgotten that Albert hasn't run his private boat line for the past three years, but that doesn't much matter. They feel sure that Albert will somehow do the right thing by them. And of course Albert does. That's why everybody writes to him. Albert thinks it over carefully and then tells his crony, Smitty, that it's too bad but it looks as if that big city outfit was landing on them again, and could he help out. Smitty agrees, of course, because isn't his business boat hire and the like? To be sure it is! But once the tourist season starts it all gets pretty hectic for Smitty. Everybody wants him at once, and always to go in different directions. So Smitty, being sensible, just does the best he can, forgets as much as he can, smiles even in his sleep, and keeps going just in the one direction at the one time. This, you must agree, is highly commendable on his part, but can lead to heartache amongst his followers.

So there stands the Advance Party in all its faded glory on the main dock at Pointe-au-Baril, and it's still drizzling. Albert, being a gentleman, has not reminded it that he's been out of the boat-taxi business for these three years (he got tired of reminding it, and, besides, it should have known anyway) so it dazedly awaits the momentary arrival of Albert's fast launch which has not now arrived for some three solid years past. Waiting in the rain may have its attractions if you're nicely prepared for it. But when you're not prepared, as seems inevitable with the Advance Party, the time begins to drag for seemingly just no reason whatsoever.

To add to the glamour Smitty, as he is affectionately known by one and all, has run into one of those days. One of those days when half the world has taken it upon itself to arrive and to insist upon being driven in all directions at one and the same time. So Smitty smiles urbanely and rushes around like a wild thing and forgets all about the Advance Party and his undertaking with Albert.

After two hours of this sort of pleasantry, and Albert not having put in an appearance after only three years, it dawns with a rush on the Advance Party that some mischance must have come upon poor Albert. Probably his engine has dropped out. Or he's hit a reef and become marooned and may have starved to death. Such thoughts, unpleasant as they may sound, strike the Advance Party more and more forcibly as the rain dribbles further and further down toward the seat of its pants.

Thereupon a council of war is called and the whole situation is thoroughly combed. Who wrote Albert? When did he write? Was there an answer? What did it say?

The replies to these queries being all somewhat vague the Advance Party casts about for fresh tactics. There are other boat lines running out from the main dock at Pointe-au-Baril, of course. It'd forgotten about that, in the excitement. There was Mr. Reid's, which was always dependable, and Percy Woodward's, too. Their houses were right at the dock, one on one side and one on the other. So the Advance Party might try them. Particularly as it was nearly six o'clock and the day train which had deposited them had rolled in only one hour late, at about four-thirty.

You see, it was important for that Advance Party to arrive at the Island early. Otherwise it'd be in a mess trying to open things up in the dark. It would mean stumbling over familiar obstacles that somehow seemed to change location on just such occasions. Often as not it would mean falling into the water a few times, or swimming out after parcels that were heard to fall off the dock, and which were retrieved by the aid of spluttering match light, as the candles and lanterns would still be in the unopened cottage.

Mr. Reid's man, of course, would be very pleased to take the Advance Party out. But he'd have to have supper first. It was a hot supper that evening, and Mrs. Reid already had it on. And hot suppers and Mrs. Reid somehow stuck pretty close together through thick and thin. If Mr. Reid's man missed his hot supper he just missed it, and that was about all there was to it!

So, around seven o'clock, when the drizzle is settling down into a gentle and more successful shower, Mr. Reid's man emerges feeling cosy and well fed and all nicely wrapped up in a dry slicker and sou'wester.

"Settling in to a nasty night, boys," ventures Mr. Reid's man to the woebegone Party. "Barometer's dropping. Looks like we were in for a spell of weather, eh?"

In a case of this kind one is hard put to find an appropriate answer to such things. The only thing the Advance Party can readily think of is to nod grimly, and hold its silence rather than tear Mr. Reid's man (who is really a very pleasant gentleman) limb from limb; dump the mountainous pile of excess goods and chattels into Mr. Reid's boat and scramble drippingly aboard.

The drive to the Island through eight miles of heaven-sent beauty, toward which the Party had eagerly looked for one solid year, might better be imagined than described. In fact such episodes cannot be described adequately anyway. Suffice it to say that Mr. Reid's man drives splendidly and passes many a vivid remark that may not be countered happily. By chance, too, by the merest of chance, you understand, Mr. Reid's boat is well laden down with packages and parcels to be delivered to as many as a dozen points other than THE Island. And it is quite needless to say that ten out of twelve of these points are, yes, really not en route, but just a mere mile or so here or there, one way or another, of being so. In this way the fleeting time runs itself along to the discontentment of the Advance Party. There's a suspicious looking bundle for Freda Benson that smells stronger than it should. This is deposited safely on her dock while she waves cheerily from the cottage verandah. And a chemical toilet and tank, of all things, for that new establishment of the Max Haas. It takes some effort to unload, but with the Advance Party's help it's finally done. Then there's a crate for Hugh Aird with the handle of, well, you know, a commode sticking out of one side. Hugh comes down to claim it and laughingly invites the Party to lay over a spell. Laughing, but not with much heart in it, the reply is given in the negative. At Senator Peter Campbell's there's a pause while Mr. Reid's man delivers a special private message to Mrs. Campbell's cook. This takes only ten minutes and Mr. Reid's man returns wiping his lips on the back of his hand and smiling to himself. The Hobbs fall heir, apparently, to a new stove, while the Duggans, God bless the Duggans, pay no attention whatsoever to the boat's arrival, and receive in return a torn dunnage bag, an appropriate looking wheel chair, and a carton containing, amongst other things, a well known brand of toilet tissue.

By now, jovially enough, it's raining persistently. It's hard to pick out the channels and markers and spars and reefs in the settling gloom. However, Mr. Reid's old boat, the Island Cottager, knows her way well enough after all these years, and nuzzles along contentedly.

Now the Advance Party has actually arrived at its destination, the Island called Painted Waters. All it has to do now is to work. In two, three days the main vanguard of the family will appear, and before that time things must be whipped into liveable shape somehow.

Mr. Reid's man assists with the assortment of boxes, packages, dunnage bags, hampers and bundles. The rain has helped them immeasurably. They look even more than usually woebegone and drooping. Some of the paper parcels have suspicious looking coloured stains slowly but surely appearing upon them. One package bursts open in disgust and scatters potatoes and beets upon the dark water. That means there will be no potatoes and beets for a while. But hold on a moment. Perhaps that was . . . it might just possibly have been . . . well YOU know . . . one of those interchanged parcels. If that's so it may be that it's not the Advance

Party who'll be looking for beets and potatoes!

Mr. Reid's man waves goodbye through the rain and is well out of hearing when the Party discovers about the keys! Why must people always be discovering keys just at the wrong moment? Too soon, or too late, or too early! Why must keys be so endlessly lost? Why can't they stay put, and where they belong, and appear like clockwork just when they're wanted? Why must they be such a nerve wracking source of distress to so countless many people? Surely by this time the world should be old enough and trusting enough to do without keys of any kind. But, wait now. What's that you say? How about those potatoes, and how about those beets? Well, now, let's see, it was keys we were discussing, wasn't it? Not potatoes!

Of course the keys of the cottage are away up at Albert's place. Nearly two miles away. And it's dark and raining, and there are no boats, you remember. And the old Island Cottager is disappearing down the bay. Well, here's a new one for the Advance Party to ponder over. Really, there's never a dull instant in a day like this that you've planned out so carefully hour by hour, and item by item. You can count on it blissfully going wrong from the first moment, and continuing to go wronger and worser and madder until . . . well, until you begin all over again next day.

The Party finds the main cottage harder to break into with a pen knife and a nail file than it had expected. In fact the cottage resists stoutly all such cajoling and advances as may be made with either of these weapons. But it's surprising what a large wet rock bashed indiscriminately into the front door will do. In this instance the door collapses inward and falls in a shattered heap. It is found necessary to replace that door, but, regardless of all that, the Party now stands enthroned safely from the weather.

Groping around in a large dark room you have not been in for nearly a year is a form of sport you may not have indulged in since your childhood. If you're soaking wet and shivering it adds to the zest, if you need zest. Obstacles such as chairs and tables which your mind remembers as having been thus and so are no longer thus and so. Perhaps the northern winter tends to move them! All these things the Advance Party finds out to its sorrow, and at the cost of barked shins and bruised knees.

The vital problem of warmth and a fire is now an urgent one. With a fire all life will take on a new appeal. But where are last year's matches, if any? Are they on that mantel shelf where the iron candlesticks are, or would they be in the kitchen, perhaps?

While the Advance Party stumbles over itself, the rain patters drearily upon the roof overhead. A loud cry of joy announces success at long last. But no, it turns out only to be a candle stub badly chewed by the marauding mice. Spiritual gloom and chattering teeth return four-fold to the scene. It looks as if pneumonia would really win.

And then, unexpectedly, comes success. Matches in a soap dish. But who cares where, so long as they're matches, and they light. Even if there are only two of them!

Grimly the fireplace is prepared with old paper and dry wood from the wood basket. Heaven be praised for that wood basket!

Now for the moment of all moments. And with that, without even a fizzling protest, the first match swizzles out wretchedly. Desperation descends like a blanket upon the scene. The last match is struck. Cheerily it flares up. The dry old paper catches and crackles and whooshes. The birch twigs roar with glee. Brightness casts its spell across the high old rafters. Life is good. It seems a sweet thing again. Rapturous warmth steals outward with invisible fingers. The candle stump is safely lighted. And God's in His Heaven once again.

The Advance Party relaxes. Glowing warmth is stealing over it . . . until the smoke begins to come. Just slowly at first, you know, then in dense choking clouds. It spreads and seethes like some monstrous phantom. The Party chokes and gasps and rushes to the verandah. Perhaps the cottage is burning down. By this time nobody really cares much.

But it's only the cap on the chimney top after all. The flat stone, you know, that Pop carefully hoisted up bit by bit across the sloping roof and placed so precisely over the hole in the chimney last year when leaving, to keep out the snow and weather. Good old Pop. Bless his soul, he thinks of everything!

So the Advance Party drags out the life-saving fire bit by bit and flings it away onto the wet rocks at hand. Then it gets wearily out of its soggy clothes, seeks out two couches in the living room, pulls old rugs off the floor to shiveringly cover itself, and coughs itself, foodless, to sleep.

Good old Pop! That's only what some say.

But the next day is another day. The sun streams through the broken door, and the sleepers awaken to another world. Of wild bird song. Of pinewood smell. Of clean, crisp air and laughing waters. With a rush the Advance Party hurls itself off the old dock to besport itself in the velvet coolness.

And now for the grand opening, the first breakfast sizzling and steaming! Ah, what a difference that makes! Bacon, and eggs. Oranges (Mr. Green's) and heaped up cereal. Coffee and more coffee. And that first blessed cigarette!

The winter storm windows whirl off like magic. Pop's stone tumbles downward off the roof, aided by a jocose extra heave. The water system is hooked together and, as usual, coughingly refused to pump. The mattresses and blankets and bedding are hauled from the tin-lined storage cupboard and put on all the wrong beds. The chemical toilet is charily approached and "suitable arrangements" are completed. The boathouse is opened and the small boats dropped into shallow water, where they promptly fill and sink.

For two days pandemonium reigns between sleeping, eating and swimming. And at the end of it the weary-eyed Advance Party sits back on its hunkers and yawns. Nothing is left but only those things which really should have been done. Dishes are unwashed, and likewise the windows. The floors are really only partly filthy. The pump works under duress, spasmodically. The lamps don't operate. The chemical toilet has gone on a sit down strike. Most of the food has dissolved into thin air. The boats leak contentedly. And an air of tranquility pervades the happy scene.

For another epic year the Advance Party has demonstrated its efficiency. The Painted Waters stand waiting, resolute, and beautiful, for the weary city travellers.

Long may the Party flourish!

In 1956 Eric Nicol won his second Leacock Medal for Humour with Shall We Join the Ladies?

ERIC NICOL

from Shall We Join the Ladies?

Every spring I give cheerfully to the Red Cross, even though the Red Cross once almost killed me.

I never see the insignia of the Red Cross without remembering that grim night during the war, in that field of action so often neglected by the war's historians — the COTC camp near Nanaimo.

The Corps, in which I was a private, was being subjected to a fortnight of field conditions. This meant raw bacon and jam for breakfast, tents that permitted our paillasses to cruise about in a sea of mud, and a great deal of running around a golf course. If the officers lost a man in the rough they went back to the tee and drove another one.

A week of this had convinced me that even more than being an officer I wanted to be ineligible for enlistment. It was during morning roll call, while I was standing there trying to think of vital industries that could use me, that somebody beside me muttered:

"Route march tonight. Volunteer for guard duty."

When the sergeant called for volunteers for guard duty, I stepped forward. I knew that the all-night route march was to be led by student officers hot off the map-reading course, marching the Corps into the wilds of Vancouver Island where it could disappear forever. Guard duty meant staying up all night, but at least I'd know where I was in the morning. During break period I congratulated myself on a shrewd piece of military strategy.

Sure enough, as soon as everybody was in bed with his mud, the bugle blew, sergeants roared and in no time a long worm of cadets was vanishing into the gloom. I bedded down in the guardhouse, but was roused at midnight for duty at the main gate.

"Don't let anybody pass through that gate without proper identification," the corporal told me sternly. "Remember, the garrison has gone. The whole camp depends on you."

I nodded, causing my tin helmet to fall over my nose, straightened the helmet, shouldered my rifle and went out to find the main gate. I found it and backed into the sentry-box and waited, hoping that if anything came by it wouldn't notice me in there.

Nothing came. The deserted camp lay silent, the road curled empty in the moonlight. One o'clock came and went, two, and three, I began to feel more aggressive.

"Halt or I'll fire!" I said, under my breath, to avoid startling anybody who might be hiding in the bushes. Realizing I had no bullets for the rifle I revised this to "Halt, who goes there?" At that stage of the war ammunition was precious, too valuable to waste on officer cadets. A regular army corporal had shown us a bullet once, during a lecture, but he took it away with him.

In fact, we had drilled with lengths of wood until coming to camp. The old Ross rifles we were issued at camp had more parts to clean than the piece of wood, but were no more likely to go off. "Halt, who goes there, please?" I said to myself.

About four in the morning I suddenly noticed that the light outside the sentry box was getting brighter. I stepped out to greet the dawn. Instead of the dawn I found myself in the headlight beams of a truck barreling down the road towards my gate.

Waving my rifle I straddled the road, squeaked "Halt, who goes there," and jumped for my life. As the truck rushed past I saw the red cross insignia over the cab. The driver leaned out and called me something that blew the knot-holes out of the sentry box. Then the ambulance was gone, its tail-light twinkling towards the camp hospital.

It may not have been a Red Cross ambulance. It may have been an army ambulance. But it broke my spirit as officer material. I just picked at my duties till the camp broke up.

Still, as I say, I don't hold it against the Red Cross, come giving time. We got better grub in the Air Force anyhow.

After creating dozens of characters in more than a score of years in radio, Max Ferguson wrote And Now . . . Here's Max. *That Leacock Medal winner in 1968 revealed how his famous character "Rawhide" came about and lets the reader peek into the mischievous mind of Max Ferguson.*

MAX FERGUSON
from And Now . . . Here's Max

In preparation for my sojourn in this new, urbane, and polished land of gracious living that was CBC Toronto, I was careful to discard such bucolic accoutrements of my East Coast days as my cigarette roller that rolled five at once. The first person around the studios to whom I offered my new status symbol, a slickly packaged deck of readymades, was an executive of the Trans Canada Network. He declined with thanks, confiding that he really preferred the ones he turned out himself on a wonderful new machine he'd just discovered that could roll five at one time. The second person to whom I offered my ready-mades, with all the pride of E.P. Taylor opening his front door to guests, was Earl Cameron, voice of the CBC National News. It turned out that Earl not only disdained all ready-made cigarettes, but even scorned the effete practise of rolling cigarettes with the aid of mechanical devices. Earl rolled by hand. That first glimpse of him sitting in a little news studio wearing old denims held up by firemen's braces and spilling dry makings down the front of his rumpled woollen shirt came as a bit of a shock. For years, in my mind's eye, I had somehow pictured Earl in a long, flowing biblical robe reading the National News from a still-smouldering stone tablet. Nowadays, of course, when I watch young people sitting at Earl's feet and confessing their psychotic compulsion to divide into two groups before brushing their teeth, he seems to have approached, sartorially at least, much closer to that original father image I had of him.

An even greater disillusion than Earl Cameron's informal radio attire was waiting for me at the end of my second week round the

194

CBC Toronto studios. After being summoned to the office of the head of the Trans Canada Network, I learned that they had brought me to Toronto not so much as a successor to Lorne Greene, but as Rawhide. The decisionmakers had just finished reading all about the old fellow in the write-up that had just come out in the *Montreal Standard* and had decided to originate the Rawhide program from Toronto to the Eastern Network (Ontario and Quebec) as well as to the Maritime Network. They searched through the complicated network schedule to try to find a half-hour spot for the Rawhide program in the mornings and finally decided to remove a program called *Musical March Past* and insert Rawhide in its place. At the time it was an easy mistake to make and no one could have really foreseen the hornets' nest of protest that such a decision was soon to stir up.

Musical March Past had been on the air since the day the last little Havergal girl had scampered out of 354 Jarvis Street in her blue gym bloomers and the CBC, with its customary predilection for musty old buildings, had moved in. It was a half hour of martial music, interspersed with the voice of Peter Dawson singing either *In a Monastery Garden* or *They're Changing Guard At Buckingham Palace*. At the decision of the CBC, its millenium ended abruptly one Friday morning, and on the following Monday morning, February 14, the gravel voice of old Rawhide and those of all his demented cronies were sent out, like a grotesque CBC valentine, to assail the astounded ears of unsuspecting and unprepared listeners in Ontario and Quebec. It must have been quite a shock as the melange of madness passed through these two provinces for the first time on its way to an already conditioned East Coast audience. Fairly recently I unearthed and listened to an old recording of that first ill-fated Rawhide program, and in retrospect I can now understand and fully sympathize with the ululations and beating of breasts that errupted the following day.

On that second day, with my first broadcast to a new audience under my belt, I came down to the studios around 7:45 a.m. to get the second onslaught ready. I was met in the basement corridor of the old Jarvis Street building by De B. Holley, who was just turning into one of the studios to read the 8:00 o'clock news.

"I'm awfully sorry about all this, Max. I hate to have to read it over the air, but it's one of the lead stories this morning and I haven't any choice." These were the only words he tossed back at me over his shoulder before entering the studio and closing the door behind him.

Mystified, I wandered on down to the radio newsroom and asked what the trouble was. A gruff editor looked up from his typewriter long enough to grunt, "You!" and jerk his thumb in the direction of the closet-like room that housed all the teletype machines.

It was like reading my own epitaph as I watched dozens of unconcerned metal fingers dispassionately pounding out the words, "CBC announcer, Max Ferguson, who does a morning radio program in the guise of Old Rawhide, came in for a severe tongue-lashing yesterday on the floor of the House of Commons. Douglas Gooderham Ross, MP for the Toronto riding of St. Paul's, rose on the floor of the House to ask the speaker if he was aware of this program of meaningless ravings and tripe, disguised in the poorest possible English and an insult to the intelligence of thinking Canadians."

I was completely stunned — unable even to appreciate the wonderful irony of MPS being disturbed by poor English. I remember making my way in a daze upstairs to the announcers' lounge and slumping, limp and dejected, into a chair. I had been sitting alone brooding for possibly ten minutes when the phone rang and a huge, resonant voice asked for Max Ferguson. I identified myself suspiciously and asked who was speaking.

"This is Lorne Greene!" I fully expected a rundown on the day's news to follow, having heard that arresting opening line preceding the CBC news ever since I was in high school. I certainly wasn't prepared for what followed. "I've just read about you," the Golden Voice went on, "and your run-in with the House of Commons in the morning paper. My congratulations." I immediately took this as a piece of unsolicited sarcasm, and the hackles had just begun to rise on the back of my neck when the Voice went on, "Believe me, Max, you couldn't buy publicity like this for a million dollars. It won't do you a bit of harm. You're a lucky guy to get a break like this. All the best."

I mumbled my thanks and hung up the phone, which was still vibrating from the last vowel sound. Preposterous and all as his optimism appeared to be at the time, I was still amazed and gratified that he'd even bother to call a young neophyte in his blackest hour, and today every fist that Lorne gets in the mouth, every chair that's smashed over his head around the old Ponderosa, is like a lash across my own back.

Before the day was out, I was to learn that a St. Valentine's Day Massacre is just a word until you have one. Coupled with the MP's invective, a bucketful of hellfire and brimstone was also poured over my cowed head by a gentleman of the cloth in Ottawa, who volunteered in a press interview that my program was "a mixture of blasphemy and sacrilege that could only happen in Godless Soviet Russia." In the days that followed, the *Ottawa Citizen* devoted an entire page each day to its Letters to the Editor column to accomodate the overflow, pro and con, that resulted from the Rawhide controversy. There were, of course, small welcome shafts of sunlight that managed to filter down through the gathering storm clouds. One of these was a telegram sent to me from Ottawa by A. Davidson Dunton, then chairman of the CBC Board of Governors: "Having difficulty organizing support for campaign to make Rawhide mayor of Ottawa. Keep your fingers crossed and six-guns ready."

In Halifax, I was to learn later, students of Dalhousie University took over radio station CJCH for a "Defence of Rawhide" day. The Canadian Press carried on its wire service at the time an interview with Dr. Burns Martin, head of the English Department at Kings College in Halifax. He was a charmingly droll, white-haired old gentleman for whom I used to mark freshman English essays in my spare time during my Halifax days with the CBC. Asked to comment on the MP's indictment of Rawhide's English, he replied, "There was certainly no evidence of this shortcoming during the years he marked English essays at Kings College. If he has since required any bad habits in his use of the English language, they were undoubtedly picked up from some of the deplorable freshman English essays to which he was subjected."

Gradually, after two weeks of touch-and-go suspense, the tide began to turn in Rawhide's favour. Among the many letters that were still pouring in to both the CBC and the *Ottawa Citizen*, the "pros" began to outnumber the "cons". One of the last salvos fired by the retreating opposition was an absolute gem of a letter that appeared in the *Ottawa Citizen*, addressed to the editor. It was from an elderly retired army officer who couldn't have cared less what Rawhide said or how he said it. His complaint was of quite a different nature. Apparently for the past decade, his life had been

so well ordered that he shaved each morning with meticulous
military precision just as *Musical March Past* came on the air and
was in the habit of matching the strokes of his straight razor with
the lively martial theme that introduced the program. And so
when 8:30 a.m. arrived on that black morning of February 14, the
unfamiliar and erratic rhythm of *The Clarinet Polka* had completely fouled up his timing, and he was holding Rawhide and the
CBC responsible for a badly lacerated face.

There was a most unusual and, for me, memorable denoue-
ment to this whole House of Commons affair. It began with a
phone call late one evening at my home. On the other end of the
line was the corporate voice of the CBC asking me to catch a plane
to Ottawa first thing in the morning; the CBC thought it might be
fun if Rawhide were to attend the Press Gallery Dinner to be held
in Ottawa that evening. This annual dinner is quite an incredible
event, rarely witnessed by laymen, at which the members of the
press corps in Ottawa play host to the House of Commons and
invited guests from the various embassies. It is an evening of
lighthearted fun, during which the collective hair of all those
attending is let down with one great thud, the reverberations of
which fortunately never reach the newspapers, thanks to a
gentlemen's agreement among the Fourth Estate. Since I had just
survived two harrowing weeks which had left me with the dis-
quieting impression that the entire House of Commons would like
to see my dripping head nailed to the Peace Tower, I felt the CBC'S
insistence that I attend was an act of downright betrayal.
Nevertheless, I obeyed, and by six o'clock the following evening
Daniel was in the lions' den.

It was a large room somewhere in the Parliament Buildings,
and the moment I entered it I stopped dead in my tracks. On one
of the end walls hung a framed picture about five feet square. It
was a dramatic and very formal photographic study of the then
Prime Minister, the Hon. Louis St. Laurent. At least, the face was
his. The body on which the had had been cut out and mounted
was that of a convict wearing the traditional zebra suit. Under-
neath was the caption, "Louis the Lug". At the far end of the
room, on the opposite end wall, an equally distinguished head of
George Drew, leader of the opposition, gazed out impressively
from the shoulders of a musclebound wrestler. Here the caption
read simply, "Gorgeous George". In the ninety-foot area separat-

ing the two pictures, there were two hundred noisy, boisterous male guests milling about with glasses, enjoying a quick few before the dinner that was shortly due to commence. The only person who knew of my presence there was the president of the Ottawa Press Gallery who, after meeting me earlier in the day, had brought me to the dinner and was now leading me, openmouthed, across the room, where stood the only face familiar to me . . . A. Davidson Dunton.

After a handshake and a friendly greeting, Dunton turned and led me a few steps away to where a rather large figure was standing with his back to us. When Dunton politely tapped on the broad shoulders, the figure turned around with a big, amiable grin, and I was introduced to George Drew. We had just begun to shake hands when a man pushed in between us, fixed George Drew with a slightly belligerent look and said, "I understand you weren't too happy with that profile I did on you in *Time* last week." Throughout this line Drew had continued pumping my hand as if he were expecting water. When the man finished his sentence, however, Drew dropped my hand, folded his fingers from the gesture of friendship into quite a formidable fist and directed it into the side of the man's face. A couple of bystanders restrained Drew from landing a second haymaker, while Dunton, suave and imperturbable as always, decided to see how far he'd get with a second introduction.

This one turned out to be one of the best-known cabinet ministers of the day. He was already moving across the room in our direction and was about five feet from us when Dunton finished shouting the introductions over the din of voices. The figure extended his hand and his face broke into a big, affable grin as he continued to advance toward us. Considering the aura of prestige which always surrounded this man's name, I'd love to be able to tell my grandchildren that I once shook his hand, but that was not to be. Unfortunately, he chose the wrong me from the double image that was obviously registering on his semi-anaesthetized retina. Missing my extended hand by a good foot, he continued on gamely with the smile still frozen on his face and the hand still out, until his momentum was rudely arrested by a very solid wall, which some builder years ago had carelessly left lying around. By this time bodies had begun sagging to the floor in crumpled heaps all over the room as if some phantom sniper were taking random shots. Two commissionaires were kept busy hauling away the casualties. I can truly say it was the wildest social evening I've ever attended in my life. Through it all, A. Davidson Dunton, the greatest public relations weapon the CBC ever had, stood matching them drink for drink and with not so much as a slurred consonant warded off a continuous barrage of charges and allegations against the CBC with his charming diplomacy and his masterfully vague replies.

Sometime later that evening, as I understood it, we were all summoned to dinner in another large room just off the one in which the cocktail hour had dragged on to such a disastrous finale. I found myself seated between the Italian ambassador and the ambassador from Northern Ireland. I can remember telling the latter with a loud laugh that all my relatives came from the "bomb-throwing" south of Ireland and was just warming up to my diplomatic icebreaker when a hand tapped me on the shoulder. It was the president of the Press Gallery whispering into my foggy left ear that he'd like a word with me just outside the doorway.

Once we were outside he hastily outlined the scenario of a little leg-pulling jest which he felt would be fun to perpetrate on the assembled guests. My immediate role in the hoax was to conceal myself inside a type of collapsible cardboard wardrobe that had been set up just outside the doorway. I stepped in and the door closed behind me. The dark interior of my small cubicle was re-lieved by the light from one tiny crack, through which I could peer out and see about five feet of the head table. I noticed that a microphone had been placed inside with me. I could hear the steady buzz of dinner conversation and the rattle of plates and cutlery.

After standing in the semi-dark for what seemed like ages, I heard a burst of applause and then the voice of the Prime Minis-ter. I was appalled to hear his brief speech interspersed with rude and rowdy interjections from the audience. "Aw come on, Louie, you gave us that old line last year!" "Hey, Louie — you don't expect us to swallow that guff do ya?" I listened with bated breath for the sharp staccato of a Mountie's side-arm, but there was none. This was apparently par for the course at Press Gallery dinners.

Finally the president of the Press Gallery made his way to the microphone at the head table. In a believably serious voice he

explained the efforts that had been made all week to arrange for
Britain's illustrious Prime Minister, Winston Churchill, to be present at this function as guest of honour. (The old warrior was
indeed visiting in New York at that very moment.) Due to his
over-crowded itinerary, the speaker explained, such an appearance had proved to be out of the question; however, thanks to the
kind co-operation of both the CBC and the Columbia Broadcasting
System, the next best thing had been made possible. By direct line
from New York the assembled guests were now going to hear a
special message of greeting spoken by Mr. Churchill.

Inside my murky cubicle I recognized this as the cue for which I
had given up dinner. As the excited buzzing and restless stirring
died down, I leaned into my microphone and sent booming into
the room the best facsimile of Churchill's voice I could muster.
You could hear a pin drop as the vocal hoax rolled out. As Churchill I spoke of the great pleasure it afforded me to know that my
voice was reaching that distinguished gathering whose collective
hand rested on the helm of the Canadian ship of state. I larded
the speech with all the Churchillian expressions I could think of
and concluded by citing and paying tribute to one or two Canadian public figures whom Churchill wished to thank for the assistance they had provided him in his mastery of the English language. . . . "Men such as your own Prime Minister, Loo-is Saynat
Lor-ent, from whom I have learned much in the use of the Gallic
idiom . . . men such as your leader of the Canadian opposition,
George Drew, from whom I've learned the power of invective.
Yet, gentlemen, greater than any of these, as a teacher of that
magnificent tongue which Shakespeare spake, is the man who at
this moment stands by my side, the man whom I owe so much and
on whom I now wish to call."

At this point I made an abrupt change into old Rawhide's voice
and began to say, "Well, now, that's mighty nice of you to. . . ."
And that was as far as I got when the front of my hiding place
suddenly pulled away and I was left standing, naked in my guilt
before the entire multitude. There was an excruciating silence for
about five full seconds. My gaze was pulled like a magnet to the
steely look of Viscount Alexander, the then Governor-General,
sitting at the centre of the head table. Twenty years seemed to
drag by before he finally raised his hands and began to applaud.
Mind you, it was not a hearty handclap. With the fingers of one

hand he delicately patted the palm of the other as though he were packing an invisible pipe. It was, however, the official signal, the catalyst that drew from the entire room the most exciting ovation I've ever received.

While it was still ringing in my bewildered ears, three members of the press left their table and came running up to me. One of them shouted, "Tell Old Rawhide the only guy in the entire House of Commons we didn't invite here this evening was the one who lit into him on the floor of the House a couple of weeks ago!" Walking back to my room in the Chateau Laurier in the small and bitterly cold hours of that morning, I couldn't have wished for a more gratifying final chapter to the "House of Commons Affair". . . .

As the Rawhide program finished each morning at 9:00 o'clock Toronto time, my day as a CBC staff announcer would be just beginning. This, after all, was the job for which I was being paid by the CBC and the Rawhide program, for the eight years I was on CBC staff, was done without any remuneration simply because I enjoyed doing it and it provided a pleasant counterbalance to my more prosaic and less challenging announcer duties. Even before the Rawhide program came on the air at 8:30 each morning, I would often be assigned to the program *Morning Devotions* as the duty announcer. This meant that after introducing the guest minister and dozing lightly through the ensuing fifteen minutes, I would have to sign him off, deliver the CBC cue, and then be in my own studio one floor below, ready to begin as Rawhide. I had exactly twenty seconds in which to exit from the *Morning Devotions* studio, sprint down a hall, fly down two flights of stairs, execute a speedy fifty-yard dash to the Rawhide studio, and still have enough wind left to do the slow, relaxed drawl of old Rawhide.

One morning while the guest minister and I sat facing each other across the microphone, waiting for *Morning Devotions* to begin and making polite, general conversation, he suddenly asked me if I knew "this dreadful Rawhide character." I replied evasively that I had seen him around on occasion. He then began to fill the remaining few minutes to broadcast time with a spirited account of what he'd say to this wretch if he should ever run across him. What particularly bothered him was that one of his congregation, an English lady sent out to Canada by her doctor for reasons of health, was up every morning listening to Rawhide instead of getting extra sleep. I agreed that all this was a shocking state of affairs and that, really, something should be done about Rawhide.

With the arrival of airtime, he was forced to supplant his venomous views on Rawhide with fifteen minutes of sweetness and light directed to the listening audience. But immediately after I signed off the program and was preparing for my mad dash downstairs, he got back to the subject of Rawhide again. This time he asked me where the offensive program was perpetrated each morning. With precious seconds ticking by, I replied as vaguely as I could that it was done somewhere downstairs. Then, inventing the excuse that I had left my car in a no-parking zone on Jarvis Street, I gave him a warm Christian handshake and raced like the wind.

My Rawhide theme was already playing when I burst into the little studio downstairs, settled into my chair before the microphone, and began the usual facial contortions that always accompanied my slipping from Dr. Jekyll into Mr. (Raw) Hyde. When I heard the theme fading down, I began in Rawhide's voice, "Well howdy! This is old Rawhide bustin' out of CBC Toronto just in time to ruin that second cup of coffee for you which you shouldn't be drinking anyway if you're a decent, conscientious mother and have any intention of getting those poor little neglected kids off to school." At this point something extra-sensory made me look up, and there in the control room, peering through the glass at me over a stiff, clerical collar, was the very red and very bewildered face of my friend who, brief moments ago, had shared a common bond with me in our mutual loathing and hearty disapproval of Rawhide. I continued ad-libbing my opening remarks and followed him with a friendly smile as he slowly backed out of the control room . . . a visibly shaken man. . . .

Some of my more pleasant memories of the straight announcing duties I performed for the CBC in Toronto were those occasions on a Wednesday evening when I found myself assigned to James Bannerman's Introduction to CBC *Wednesday Night*. Long before I'd ever met Bannerman I had made him, through mimicry, a fairly frequent visitor to the Rawhide show. Considering the man's intellect, erudition, and prestigious position in CBC programming, he had every right to be furious at the outrageous nonsense I put into his mouth on such occasions. During one of

Marvin Mellobell's reports, for example, from a large Toronto department store one Christmas when he described the wide variety of toys available to shoppers, Bannerman turned up on the doll counter — a living, breathing Chatty Bannerman doll waiting to delight some tot on Christmas morning. When Marvin accepted the clerk's invitation to pull out the small ring in Bannerman's back, that distinctive voice, symbolic of all that's best in CBC radio, was heard with the plaintive appeal, "This is CBC *Wednesday Night* . . . please put me to bed."

For about four consecutive years in Marvin's ill-fated commentary on the gigantic parade which annually heralds Santa's arrival in Toronto, the CBC float was supposed to be the highlight of the parade. It was a huge, electronically activated effigy of James Bannerman. Under about a ton of paper-maché, the collective genius of CBC engineering minds had installed a complicated mass of electronic circuitry that was intended to make the figure both move and speak. Each year it was patiently entered in the hope of overshadowing old Santa himself and at the same time, getting in a dramatic plug for CBC *Wednesday Night*. Ideally the figure, which the CBC always stuck strategically in front of Santa's own float, would slowly turn its head from side to side, make waving gestures to the thousands of delighted children, and speak the characteristic line, "Good evening. This is James Bannerman!"

But it never quite happened that way. Invariably each year, as the float approached Marvin's broadcast position, his voice would mount hysterically with an effusion of CBC loyalty and pride as he prepared his audience for the CBC's finest hour. Then suddenly there would be a series of small backfirings and sputterings, and Marvin, in a voice chocked with horror and dismay, would be forced to describe the three CBC engineers armed with wrenches and screwdrivers who at that moment were running alongside the float, desperately attempting to correct their faulty wiring. All the while, the voice of the effigy would be heard in the background mouthing its garbled line, "Is . . . James . . . Bannerman . . . good . . . this . . . evening?" with a malicious inflection which obviously was inviting a negative reply.

Bannerman's reaction to these repeated and impudent affronts to his dignity was to either phone immediately or write me a letter expressing the most enthusiastic and jovial appreciation. It always amazes me when someone occasionally asks, "What's this Bannerman like . . . kind of stuffy?" I invariably answer by recounting what I know of the man's incredible background — a professional boxer, naval officer, race car driver, a guide cum gigolo available for hire by wealthy ladies who wished to see Europe, a man who can guess your weight to the pound, having learned the art while living and travelling with gypsies, and undoubtedly, a man who somewhere along the line has managed to amass a formidable knowledge of the world around him.

Bannerman, to my way of thinking, embodies the most fascinating blend of the scholarly academic and the earthy stevedore. His coherent and always stimulating speech is a remarkable mixture of Conrad and Rabelais. I well remember putting him on the air one evening out of the little cubicle called Studio J from which he originated his introductions to CBC *Wednesday Night*. The feature broadcast that evening was devoted to the work of a well-renowned contemporary English poet. Bannerman used his fifteen minutes of program time to discuss the man and his poetry. I remember sitting across the microphone from him, listening absolutely enthralled by his eloquently expressed and brilliantly researched material. When he finished the broadcast I signed him off and gave the Corporation cue. We both then headed for the studio door, and I couldn't refrain from complimenting him on a most scholarly performance. He thanked me with obvious embarrassment and then confided, "I'm afraid it was a bit long-winded but unfortunately, in CBC *Wednesday Night* language, it takes fifteen minutes of euphemism to say that the son of a bitch would have been a much better poet if his testicles had only descended." If I were to read volumes of biographic study on this "stuffy" personality, this is still the line by which I'll always remember James Bannerman.

Just as colourful and irrepressible as any of my imaginary Rawhide characters was a CBC staff employee who used to visit the program once each year in the flesh and not through the device of mimicry. Eddie Dunne, Ireland's wonderful gift to the CBC, came originally from Cork and looked like Victor MacLaglan compressed into about five feet, two inches. Eddie was a maintenance man around the studios, and I usually encountered him with a ladder under his arm on his way to replace a defective light bulb or a broken window. He had caches of beer hidden in strategic, secret locations all through the premises of 354 Jarvis Street. The hard liquor, however, was confined to one central hiding place — a glorified broom closet situated at the end of the long downstairs studio corridor. This was where Eddie held court in his spare time, divulging to an enrapt coterie of announcers, engineers, and junior producers top management program and policy secrets weeks before they were officially announced. His reputation as the Delphic oracle of the CBC was such that on one occasion, when a CBC executive had been missing on supposed CBC business in Europe for several weeks, a contingent of top management marched in one day to confront Eddie in the little broom-cluttered salon and ask him if he knew where the A.W.O.L. culprit was. Eddie led them to a wall on which he had thumbtacked quite an exotic collection of postcards sent to him from far-flung corners of Europe by the miscreant and each bearing the usual cliché about having a wonderful time. Judging from the semi-legible scrawl, such a piece of information seemed quite superfluous. Thanks to this telltale postal paper chase, the sleuths were able at least to discover that the last known whereabouts of their wandering boy was the Vatican.

Eddie's conversation was difficult to follow, as the thick Cork accent had to fight its way out through a nose that had been broken in several places, but it was magnificently larded with natural Irish wit. The tough little kids who shared the fashionable Jarvis Street neighbourhood with the CBC and whom Eddie often had to chase out of the building were always referred to by him as "brothel sprouts". He also had wonderful stories about the Irish wakes he'd been to right in the heart of Toronto. At one of these, he told us, the corpse had been removed from the casket in order to accommodate one of the mourners, who wanted to lie down for just a few minutes and ended up stretched out in the satin for three solid days.

It became a sort of tradition that Eddie would drop in as Rawhide's only live, flesh-and-blood guest every St. Patrick's Day morning. Since he always took what he called "a running start" at St. Patrick's Day, getting into the festive cup at about eight the previous evening, Eddie was always "delivered" to the studio each St. Patrick's Day morning by friends. After one or two Irish records, Rawhide would introduce Eddie and interview him about Ireland. No matter how assiduously Rawhide tried to introduce such topics as leprechauns, shamrock, and other innocuous bits of

Irish culture Eddie would always get onto the Black and Tans and would have to be washed out with a recording just as the profanity started.

One year, just after we had concluded the St. Patrick's Day edition of the Rawhide show, Eddie insisted we repair to the broom closet at the end of the hall and drink a toast to Ireland. Over a bottle of Bushmills' Irish Whiskey he asked me how I felt he had done on the air. I told him I thought he'd done very well, but there was something bothering him, and he wouldn't accept my assurance that it had been a good performance. He was upset that he had completely forgotten to tell the audience how shillelaghs are made. He told me that he'd been up all night riding the TTC all over Toronto and preparing a little treatise on the making of shillelaghs. Somehow, in the course of the broadcast, possibly due to nervous tension, the whole thing had gone out of his mind. He kept insisting that he'd let me down and also the audience. Eventually, he had me agreeing with him that it was a darn shame that he'd forgotten this little talk that would have been so interesting to the network audience. After fifteen minutes of mutual and maudlin lamenting over what Canadian radio had just missed, I innocently asked how shillelaghs *were* made and learned to my horror how close my career had come to ending. "Dey makes 'em," said Eddie in the most ingenuous voice, "out of a bull's penis."

In Children, Wives, and Other Wildlife, *Robert Thomas Allen seemed more secure than in his first book. This 1971 winner was close to Stephen Leacock's own perspective.*

ROBERT THOMAS ALLEN

from Children, Wives, and Other Wildlife

I wish people would stop telling me things in strict confidence. I've found myself lying to my own guests in order to keep someone else's secret, only to discover that everyone else in the room knew about it — but didn't know that I was such an accomplished liar.

I've had people tell me things I was to guard with my life, then suddenly move to another city, leaving me with a bunch of old left-over secrets that I couldn't figure out what to do with.

My ears bend forward at a bit of gossip the same as anyone else's, but when something is passed on in strict confidence, the facts are usually filtered through an intense state of emotions, and for that reason don't tell the whole truth.

A while ago I sat at a bar with a man I've known since I started work. He said he'd appreciate it if I never mentioned it to a living soul, but he was the victim of a tragic marriage. His wife, he said, was a cold, fatally popular, dazzlingly beautiful woman who treated him as a spineless worm. As he talked I began to picture her coming out of her bedroom after supper, dressed for the evening, making no effort to hide her scorn as she watched him fuss over babies' formulas and told him she was off to a night spot and wouldn't be home till dawn.

The next time I met him was at a picnic. I kept wondering who the nice little fat woman was who handed me wonderful sardine sandwiches, until I finally realized that it was his wife. They sat surrounded by milk bottles, blankets, a basket with a baby in it, little wads of cotton batting, toothpicks, their own firewood, an alarm clock, and an extra pair of dry socks. It all looked about as tragic as an ad for thermos bottles.

Every time I expected his wife to come out in her true character, she said something like, "Watch the sandwiches on brown bread, dear." Then she'd turn to me and say, "George has had trouble with his teeth ever since he bit into a walnut on our honeymoon."

What this man had told me had been the truth as he saw it. He obviously thought his wife beautiful and dazzling, and she'd got cold and brittle just the night before he told me the story of his life when they'd apparently had a fight about something. But the point is, it had nothing to do with their over-all relationship.

The trouble is that confidences rest on startling dramatic incidents, whereas the truth also rests on the long dull stretches in between. It's the uneasy realization that most confidences are overdramatized that makes some people, as soon as they've revealed some tragic aspect of their secret lives, begin to snub the person they confided in. One time I sat in a restaurant with a fried scallop halfway to my mouth while a salesman with an industrial insulation and plumbing company told me a tragic story that had begun a year ago when he had returned from a two-month business trip to Asbestos, Quebec. He had arrived home on Christmas Eve, loaded down with toys for his two children, a mink stole for his wife, two tickets for a vacation in Bermuda and the big news that he was being considered for vice-president of the industrial firebrick division.

"It was the happiest moment of my life," he said. "I'd reached the second from the top rung." He stopped and poked his bread roll whimsically, then looked up with a pathetic little smile. "Do you know what she said?"

I shook my head, still holding the scallop in mid-air.

"She said, 'Well you're just eight years too late. *Eight lonely years* while I waited for you to look at me, and you talked of nothing but number-three reducing elbows and left-handed threads. I've decided to leave you. Don't try to stop me.' "

He got up, creased his check carefully, looked up quickly and said, "I don't know why I told you all this. I've never told another soul."

Evidently he soon wished he hadn't told even me, because the next time I met him in the same restaurant he tried to hide behind a ketchup bottle. He's been trying to hide from me ever since, behind pillars, newspapers and distant looks.

I don't blame him. And I don't mean because of what he told me his wife said to him. Everybody's wife has at one time or another said she was leaving because of something like reducing elbows. I mean because he believed her. All marriages have to pass through these long, dark tunnels. We just have to sit still till we come out the other end. This man had just got claustrophobia so bad he'd cracked. He hadn't let me in on a secret, he'd let me in on a state of nerves, and he hasn't forgiven me yet for listening. The trouble with a confidence like this is that it's a compromise between a desire to be stoic and close-lipped, and to have someone appreciate how stoic and close-lipped we're being.

On one occasion a man my wife and I have known for years told me a gaudy story about an affair he was having with some girl at the office.

"I wouldn't have looked at her," he explained, "if Lois hadn't stopped speaking to me for a week. A man needs some respect and companionship, and, well I just sort of turned to this girl in Accounts Payable. I wish you could meet her. Not really beautiful, but smart. You should see her do algebra."

I tried to ease the grip of his moral dilemma with a few philosophical remarks, then left him to work it out himself, his secret safe with me. During the next couple of months, my wife accused me twice of not taking hold of practical matters the way Harry did. I wanted to tell her what old Harry had really taken hold of, but sat there keeping his secret and startling my wife with my expression, which was the same as if I'd just swallowed a mouthful of boiling tea.

After all this, I met Harry at a party. He got my wife and me in a corner, took a pull at a martini, gave me a rakish grin, and said, "Guess you've wondered how I made out with that little girl friend?"

He glanced at my wife to see how she was taking the news that all husbands weren't the domestic old bean pods her husband was. Then he said, "To tell you the truth, I haven't seen her for months. Got too busy on the new house in Orangeville." He looked at me and chuckled. "Always remember that advice you gave me, though, about marriages being as out-of-date as mustache cups, and that everybody should have a divorce who can afford one."

When we walked away, I tried pursing my lips and peering around the room briskly for people I knew. But I could feel my wife's gaze just beneath my ear. Finally I said, "Glad Harry got things straightened out, even if he did get everything I said wrong. Three months ago I thought he was going to get a divorce."

"You mean you've known about this for three months?"

"I had some inkling of it."

"Why didn't you tell me?"

"Because it was a secret. He told me not to tell anyone." My wife looked at me as if thinking if I'd keep one secret from her, I'd keep dozens, and probably about girls who were good at algebra. I was the villain of the piece.

Once, when I was employed by a textbook publisher, I worked with a quiet, stolid man with a large jaw who kept me in a state of suspense with secrets about things that never happened. He would come into my office, close the door carefully behind him, sit down, look out the window with a flushed face and say, "Well, I hear the lid's off. J.P. is being kicked upstairs, R.G. is out, and T.D. is slicing the department right down the middle. I understand there's something about a Russian mail-order firm taking us over. I'm just going to pretend I don't know anything about it. Don't breathe a word of this, will you?"

For the next week every time I got an interoffice memo my hackles would stand on end, until I realized they were just about things like using blue requisition slips in the future instead of the old pink ones.

It's surprising how far some people go with this desire to keep things confidential. I'll never forget a colleague of mine who always had a hectic manner, as if he'd just finished a tussle with someone. He was a self-conscious man, with an owlish expression. He'd come into my office quietly and say, "I've something to tell you that I wouldn't want to go any further. I — "

He'd stop and think, then say, "Oh, look — let's just forget about it."

By now I wouldn't be able to forget about it. I'd be sitting there looking reliable, ready to keep my lip buttoned up, and nearly bleeding at the ears with curiosity.

"Well, all right, I'll tell you," he'd say, with a sudden change of mind. He'd get up and close the door, first looking nervously up and down the aisle.

"Do you mind if I close that other door?" he'd say.

"No. Go ahead. Close the window too. Are you sure you want to tell me about this? I don't want to know if you don't want to tell me."

"No, I want to tell you," he'd say. "After all, what's friendship for? Well, to come right out with it, I'm going to start taking guitar lessons."

I'd sit looking at him, waiting for the secret. This would be it.

"I'd just as soon nobody knew about it till I know how to play. I mean, I don't want to be pestered with people asking me to play at parties and things."

I'd feel the way I did the night they postponed the first Louis-Walcott fight, when I stood in the middle of the living room, keyed up for fifteen bloody rounds and with nothing to do but make a scrambled-egg sandwich and some Ovaltine and go to bed.

But the thing is, this man's secret didn't have anything to do with guitars, really: his secret had to do with some weird idea of himself being pestered by fans, and probably forgetting how to play when faced by an audience.

Like a lot of things that are handled with the greatest discretion, it was a very romantic treatment of the facts. A confidence is essentially a romantic idea anyway. We create secrets around life's little problems the way an oyster creates a pearl around a piece of sand. Or we simply make a secret out of a wish, and project it on anyone who will swear never to divulge it, and I hope from now on it isn't me.

In The Salt Box *Jan Hilliard writes of one of those intriguingly looney families in which so many humourists seem to have been reared. And readers will find it easy to remember Old Tom from this 1952 medal winner about her rural life near a small town.*

JAN HILLIARD
from The Salt Box

Aunt Belle was not a particularly good cook. She could have been, if she had let herself go, but she always had one eye on the cost of whatever she was attempting. We possessed a well-thumbed copy of *The Boston Cooking-School Cook Book*, but the thumbing was mostly done by us children. Our favorite recipe was a wedding cake that took twelve eggs, one pound of butter and a cup of brandy, among other things. Aunt Belle made bread, a great many Washington pies and ginger snaps, and in summer we had a thing called blueberry fungee. For this, you stewed a pot of blueberries and just before dinner you dropped in dumplings and ate the business hot. We liked blueberry fungee, but in all probability we would have liked anything that filled our stomachs.

We had baked beans every Saturday night, porridge every morning, and an endless procession of rice puddings, with and without raisins. We detested those rice puddings, even when camouflaged with Devonshire cream, which we loved. Devonshire cream was made by placing a pan of sweet cream on the back of the stove in a spot that was warm but not hot, and letting it sit there (don't ask me how long) until a thick scum of cream formed on top. This top was taken off with a skimmer and ladled over strawberries, blackberries, applesauce or whatever fruit we were having. It was good, but of course we only had it once in a blue moon.

In those days, people had never heard of vitamins or calories. At least, we hadn't. We ate what was in season or what we could get, and our teeth and bones grew perfectly well without calcium and our blood pumped away without ever smelling iron.

215

We grew our own vegetables, and small fruits such as strawberries, currants and gooseberries. We put up preserves and pickles. We kept half a dozen hens and sometimes a cow. One spring Aunt Belle bought a little pig from Jeff Hibbs and talked all summer of the delicious ham and bacon we would enjoy the next winter. We called the pig Arthur. He lived in a small pen behind the barn. Uncle Harry complained that he couldn't read with all that snuffling and snorting going on, but he soon became accustomed to the disturbing sounds and by fall was quite fond of the pig.

Arthur was pink. I believe he had less hair than most pigs. At any rate, he was always getting sunburned. Aunt Belle rigged up a shelter spot in one corner of the pen where he could escape the sun's rays, but he wouldn't use it. By August he looked half cooked.

We never did eat the pig, simply because Uncle Harry made such a mess of things when killing time came. With his usual flair for the dramatic he hied himself to the back of the barn with the twenty-two rifle, opened the gate of the pigpen, and when curious Arthur followed him into the field Uncle Harry stalked him for a time to get himself into a hunting mood, then lay on his stomach, took aim, and shot him through the head.

He expected Arthur to drop dead in his tracks. Instead, the pig let out a horrible scream and began to run. He ran around the barn and into the yard. "What on earth have you done, Harry?" Aunt Belle tore from the kitchen. Arthur, blinded by the blood running from the hole in his head, charged into her and knocked her down. He bolted for the gate, and his screams were like a thousand people tortured beyond endurance.

"He got away!" Uncle Harry panted. "Damned pig. Shot him right through the head, too." Arthur reached the gate, bumped into it and headed back. "Right through the head," Uncle Harry repeated, bewildered. He jumped aside as Arthur charged his way and headed for the gate again. "He should be dead."

"Go after him," Aunt Belle wept. "Don't stand there like an idiot. Oh, the poor thing!"

"Damned pig!" Uncle Harry swore, starting obediently in pursuit. Far down the road we could hear Arthur's anguished cries, getting fainter.

An hour later Uncle Harry returned, very much out of sorts. He had been forced to borrow a horse and drag from Jeff Hibbs because Arthur was too heavy to carry. Aunt Belle looked at the fat pink blood-streaked carcass and paled. "I — I couldn't touch it," she said faintly. She turned suddenly and ran inside.

Uncle Harry nudged the dead pig with his foot. He glanced around helplessly, then drove the drag around to the back of the barn where he had laid out the big knife and the barrel for scalding. When he got there he discovered that he didn't know exactly what to do with a dead pig, and had to call on Hibbs and Captain Rogers for help. They managed to get Arthur's intestines removed and the rest of him cut into pieces. The next day, without saying anything to Aunt Belle, Uncle Harry took the pieces into town and sold them. "Little something I picked up," he said when he returned later, and handed her a roll of bills.

We had a rooster named Roscoe, a slim cocky White Leghorn with a high red comb, who bedevilled the daylights out of his hens. Aunt Belle disliked Roscoe. "The way he picks on those poor things," she said disparagingly.

"You underestimate the femininity of your hens," Emily said. "They love being pursued."

But Aunt Belle gave Roscoe away to Captain Rogers, anyway, because he embarrassed her. And immediately the hens, who had been laying eggs in great style all summer, became lethargic and refused to produce. A new rooster was introduced, but he was lazy and careless of his appearance. He slept half the day, reluctantly rousing himself on occasion to perform a duty. The hens disliked him.

"You see!" Emily said. "They're not happy unless they're — "

"Emily!" Aunt Belle objected.

It was Emily who got Roscoe back. She simply told Captain Rogers how unhappy the hens were, and he said he didn't care much for White Leghorns, anyway. So Emily carried Roscoe home in a bean bag and dumped him in the yard. The hens set up a great to do. They cackled and skittered about, trying to get in Roscoe's way while pretending to be headed in the opposite direction. By the next week they were shuttling out eggs again, sixty to the dozen, and when they weren't laying they were being chased. Uncle Harry was the only one who complained. He said he could never settle down for a nap behind the barn because the minute he closed his eyes some blasted hen would go frisking across his stomach, with Roscoe in pursuit.

The cow was an unpredictable yellow jersey with dark brown eyes and a wet nose. Aunt Belle had to milk her because Lance, who was supposed to do the job, made the cow nervous. She held back, and once or twice she became agitated and stepped in the pail. Another time she stepped on Lance. "I can't think what you do to her," Aunt Belle complained. "She never moves when I milk her."

"I guess she just doesn't like me," Lance said, cheerful because the odious job was being taken off his hands.

We also had a cat, a great gray tabby that slept all day and spent the nights with the O'Brien's cats next door, begetting numerous families.

Then, of course, we had Old Tom.

Nobody knew for certain what Old Tom's age really was. There was a good deal of controversy about it, which started when the *Herald*, being a bit short of news, printed a piece about the time he stopped the train (it was only an engine going up to the Y to turn). The *Herald* editor stated that Old Tom, who had been in our family about fourteen years at the time, was thirty-nine. Immediately he was deluged with letters from people all over the country, who were willing to testify that he was forty-two, or forty-five, even forty-seven. Old Doc Weir, the veterinarian, who was going on ninety and hadn't been out of bed for two years, drove down to the *Herald* office and swore under oath that Old Tom was forty-nine. He knew, because he had officiated at the birth and it was the same year his daughter Violet's Joe was born, and Joe would be forty-nine if he'd lived.

Doc Weir was a bit hazy about a lot of things. He thought Queen Victoria was still living and the Boer War still going on. He wrote numerous letters, in a shaky hand that could hardly be deciphered, to the *Herald* demanding to know why in thunder they didn't print the news and let folks know what was happening to the Queen's army. It was useless for his daughter to try to tell him that the Queen was dead and the Boer War over long ago. "Don't tell me," he would fume at her. "I know what's going on. I been reading the papers for ninety-five years." "You're only ninety, Papa," Violet would remind him. "I know how old I am," he would retort. He would ruffle through the *Herald* impatiently, peering at each headline, then wad the paper into a ball and throw it away in disgust. "All them fellers hitting out for the

Klondike, and not a word about it in the papers." "They're all back from the Klondike, Papa. Years ago," Violet would explain patiently. "Don't tell me," he would shout back. "I know what's going on." Nobody took Doc Weir's statement seriously, but there were plenty of people who were certain that Old Tom was forty-five, at least.

Old Tom didn't look old. He grew more eccentric and full of whims, his stomach rumbled louder and louder and he took cat-naps when nobody was looking, but when he was awake he stood proudly, his sorrel coat shining, his head lifted. He loved two things: to be looked at and to be fussed over. He would stand for hours while we combed his mane and polished his coat, and you could see he was thinking of the impression he would make. He would nibble at us affectionately if he thought we were doing a good job. He was a handsome horse, and he knew it, but he was so gentle and loving that we didn't mind his conceit.

We loved him. Even the humiliation we suffered when he took a turn couldn't alter that. And after fourteen years his turns became such routine affairs that they didn't bother us much, except when they happened on Main Street on a busy day, or on the way to church.

Old Tom's erratic behavior followed two patterns. He had spells and he took turns. When he had a spell he simply refused to allow himself to be hitched to the carriage. This generally happened at home, therefore was not embarrassing, but a spell might last for two or three days. When he took a turn, he would suddenly stop dead in his tracks and refuse to budge. People always gathered around, offering advice, prodding him with sticks or trying to stuff sod into his mouth. This last was supposed to be a sure cure, but it didn't affect Old Tom. He clenched his teeth together and no amount of prying could get his jaws apart. Nothing would move him. He stood with his feet braced wide, his head lifted, arrogantly surveying the crowd, and every once in a while he would glance around impatiently at Aunt Belle, or whoever was driving the carriage, as much as to say, "Well, you know what comes next. Let's get on with it." Then Aunt Belle would unhitch him and send a boy to the livery stable with a note, asking them to deliver the carriage and the harness. Then she would walk home, and Old Tom would follow her. He kept about ten paces behind, and if she stopped for a moment, he stopped too.

Once, completely exasperated, she decided to abandon him and ride home on the trolley. Old Tom stood stubbornly in the middle of Main Street for three hours, and Lance had to be sent down town as a last resort to walk home with him. . . .

Emily was the only one who really enjoyed it when Old Tom took a turn. It amused her, and the more people gathered around to watch, the better she liked it. "It makes them happy," she explained, "It gives them something to talk about."

The first automobile came to town before my time, when Old Tom was young. Then it was a common sight to see terrified horses rearing and plunging and upsetting carriages and generally making quite a fuss whenever they came within smelling distance of an automobile. Old Tom never carried on. He looked at them with mild disgust and went on about his business. If he happened to be cantering down the street, taking up more than his share of room, and an automobile hove in sight, no amount of pulling on the reins would make him move over. To hell with the thing, he seemed to say. If it wanted to get out of his way, let it ride on the sidewalk.

Callous people sometimes suggested that it might be a good idea to sell Old Tom (but who would buy him?) and get a horse we could rely on. Get rid of Old Tom? Why, we never dreamed of such a thing. He was one of the family.

Every once in a while a letter would come out from White's Bookstore in town, addressed to Uncle Harry, with a list of new books that had just arrived. Early the next morning he would drive into town, taking along anybody else who wanted to go. . . .

"You fetch Old Tom," Uncle Harry said to me, knowing he would make a bad job of it if he tried. He didn't have enough patience, and if Old Tom wasn't started off in the right frame of mind we'd never get to town that day. You had to use a special technique to catch him. You couldn't just go out and lead him in. You had to pretend you were taking a stroll in the pasture, not even noticing him. When he ambled up to you, seeking caresses, you ignored him. Having completed your walk around the pasture and returned to the gate, left conveniently open, you gave him an absent-minded pat and walked on up the pasture lane. Old Tom followed, puzzled by your casual attitude, anxious for more attention. You walked into the yard, Old Tom nibbling at your elbow, and there was Uncle Harry with the harness. Sometimes Old Tom allowed him to put it on, sometimes not.

As we set out for town, with Uncle Harry and Thad in the front seat and Eileen, Vicky and I in the back, Aunt Belle would remember an errand she wanted done. A spool of black thread or a yard of elastic. "Where's my list?" Uncle Harry would slap his pockets, searching. "Ask Emily what she's done with my list." Emily had the list in the hammock, marking off the books she wanted. Lance and Louise would look after us enviously, wishing now that they were going, too, though they were ashamed to be seen in the old double-seated buggy because the stuffing was coming out. "Mind you take care of the children, Harry," Aunt Belle called. "Don't let them out of your sight." She never allowed us to go all the way into town alone, because sometimes there were bearded sailors on shore leave, who got a little drunk. We often went to the shoemaker's shop or the hardware store, but they were on the edge of town.

"I won't," Uncle Harry turned, waving the buggy whip.

Arriving in town, Old Tom was put up at the livery stable behind the post office. We went to the bookstore first. Miss White always greeted Uncle Harry effusively, because he was a pretty good customer. "The *loveliest* lot of books today," she led him to the back of the store where the new volumes were being unpacked. "Now, I want you to browse to your heart's content. I'll be right here if you want me." She chucked Vicky under the chin and smiled coyly. "Such *lovely* children! What's *your* name, little girl . . .?"

"Oh, God!" Uncle Harry swore. He hated chatter when he was browsing. . . .

"Oh, for heaven's sake go out and look in windows, or something. You won't get lost. Here," he produced another nickel and handed it to Thad. "You look after them."

Thad was willing to oblige. He bought a nickel's worth of penny candy and divided it evenly among us. "You know what?" he suggested. "Let's go down to the docks."

"Well — " Eileen hesitated, remembering Aunt Belle's parting instructions.

"Come on," Thad made up her mind, and led us down the narrow street past the warehouses. He loved the bustling wharves, where dark foreign-looking sailors unloaded bales and barrels and laughed uproariously among themselves. A pungent smell hung over the water front, composed of decayed fish and oily water and tar and I don't know what else — rotting wood, maybe, and bilge water and sweat. We rather liked the smell. There was a whole row of wharves. The big one, where the Boston boat came in (that wasn't very interesting, it was too clean), gray wharves where the schooners came in front the Banks, dingy slips where small square-sterned coastal schooners nested by the dozen, and there were droves of pudgy little fishing boats in the shade of the slant-roofed fish houses, where Thad sat on a coil of rope and talked with old men who mended nets and smoked corncob pipes and spat.

Huge audacious gulls rested on the piles or strutted about, grabbing bits of fish and other refuse. "They clean up the harbor," Thad explained to us. He knew practically everything. . . .

We dawdled back to the bookstore, stopping to gaze longingly into the window of the bakeshop, where iced cakes and cookies and delicious-looking chocolate drops were displayed. "When I grow up I'm going to own a bakeshop," Eileen decided. The sight of food always moved her. "I'll eat a whole chocolate cake, with icing, every day." She still clutched the nickel Uncle Harry had given her, but of course one didn't spend so much money right away. One thought about it for a time.

Uncle Harry, having selected a dozen books, was anxious to get home and read them. No loitering about the sail loft today, or sunning ourselves on the courthouse steps. We bought Aunt Belle's elastic and went straight to the livery stable. "If that blasted horse acts up today — " Uncle Harry worried. It was usually on the way home that Old Tom took a turn.

We harnessed him, being careful to do nothing to displease him. Eileen fed him bits of apples, and even Uncle Harry gave him a few grudging pats. "Nice old boy," he said. "Nice old fellow." He added in a resentful aside, "Damned horse! I'll shoot him, one of these days. I swear I will."

We turned into Main Street and began the drive home, not speaking, holding our breaths. Uncle Harry held the reins gently, fearing that if he jerked them Old Tom would take offense. If nothing happened to ruffle Old Tom's temper, he carried us all the way home and Uncle Harry said, "Thank God!" when the hedge came into view, and switched the reins and put one foot on the dashboard. But sometimes things happened that displeased Old Tom (we never found out exactly what — a voice he didn't like? a piece of paper blowing? maybe a touch of indigestion) and then Uncle Harry's day was ruined indeed. Even the new books couldn't take his mind off his grievances.

A Good Place to Come From *won the Leacock Medal for Morley Torgov in 1975. A Toronto lawyer, Morley Torgov would rather define himself as a writer. This selection indicates he is entitled.*

MORLEY TORGOV

from A Good Place to Come From

In the summer of 1944 Thomas E. Dewey, New York's Republican governor, embarked upon the impossible task of replacing Franklin D. Roosevelt as president of the United States of America. It was an historic battle: Dewey, the sober young ex-district attorney attacking the gates of the White House demanding to be let in; Roosevelt, resolute despite his age, infirmity and war-weariness, insisting upon remaining in occupany for an unprecedented fourth term. One man desperately seeking the highest office in the land, the other just as desperately refusing to give it up.

In that same hot July of 1944 our Jewish community [of Sault Ste. Marie, Ontario] was engaged in the annual agony of hunting for a president. But in this case it may truly be said that the man did not seek the office, the office sought the man. Mind you, this was not a new state of affairs. Traditionally, a president was pressed into service in a manner very much resembling the recruitment of seamen into the British Navy in days of yore. In fact, the only difference lay in the technique of bludgeoning; where a potential sailor was persuaded with a wooden club, a potential president was persuaded with wild promises and even wilder threats. In either case, by the time the victim recovered consciousness, he was far out to sea and committed to a year of misery. Only in the rarest instances did a draftee for the presidency accept the call without putting up strong resistance. Such a man usually possessed a streak of vanity a yard wide. But by term's end vanity had changed to thorough disenchantment; consequently there was never a problem over an incumbent succeeding himself — the incumbent couldn't wait to abandon his gavel.

Putting aside all false notions of nobility, the truth is that leading a smalltown Jewish community was a thankless enterprise. A leader could rarely delegate authority simply because his peers were seldom — if ever — in a mood to take orders. If, however, the leader took matters into his own hands, he was forthwith accused of being autocratic and shunned anyway. The budget made generous allowances for nothing, and what little finances were available to support the rabbi-teacher-shoichet, the Sunday school, and the odd small capital purchase, depended upon the largess of two or three affluent members who had to be catered to as a rich old dowager is catered to in a hotel dining room. Decorum at meetings hung always in a precarious balance between anarchy on one hand and mass sleeping sickness on the other. A call to order at the beginning of a meeting was as futile a gesture as trying to halt a cattle stampede with a capgun. Motions to adjourn came with lightning surprise, entirely without invitation or welcome from the chair, and most òf the congregants were in their cars and halfway home by the time the motion was seconded by one of the president's less disloyal constituents.

With little hope of co-operation, no pay, and nothing to look forward to but an empty vote of gratitude when the term of office expired, was it any wonder that an intelligent man fled in terror when his fellows attempted to cast the presidential mantle upon his shoulders?

But now, in 1944, there was a fresh occupational hazard that made filling the post even more difficult. The war, the stories of Nazi oppression of Jews, and entry into the armed forces of a dozen local Jewish young men — all these events had made our congregation the object of considerable curiosity and sympathy. Thus it was that by 1944 the usual criteria for judging presidential material had to be expanded to include one new and important requirement: the incoming president would have to know how to handle himself among "the goyim."

Fully aware of this new turn of events, the "press gang," a quartet of self-appointed kingmakers in the Jewish community, gathered to pore over the list of potential chief executives. Their headquarters was the workroom at the rear of Wiseman's Bakery on Queen Street. Save that the room was filled with the aroma of freshly-baked bread rather than cigar smoke, it resembled any

back room where major political decisions are made. A swinging
door with a tiny peek-through window separated the workroom
from the public premises at the front. On the door was tacked a
handwritten sign: Private Keep Out!

In the days before the Gin Rummy Club rented luxurious quarters (one room about fifteen by twelve with adjoining toilet) over
Kleiman's Hardware, the closest thing in town to a Jewish men's
club was Wiseman's Bakery. To this place the men would escape
in the evenings, having assured their wives they would only be
gone long enough to buy a fresh loaf for tomorrow's breakfast.
Here too they discussed important questions of the day: how
come the town's most aggressive merchant managed to stage *three*
anniversary sales within a single year? Was there some brand new
element of time in the universe known only to him? And how
come the town's least lucky merchant was running another
going-out-of-business sale? How many times in a single year, in a
single store, could a man go out of business? Whose son was
sleeping regularly with a "Talyainichka" from the west end? And
was it any big surprise, considering the son's father had been
residing off and on with a "Polyachka" for years?

These musings were presided over by Wiseman himself. Bearing the physique of a grizzled old drayman, Wiseman flopped
about flat-footedly in his oversize flour-covered shoes, one minute
gruffly attending a customer out front, the next minute bearhugging a hundred-pound sack of flour and transporting it from
one end of the workroom to the other, moments later returning
to the long worktable laden with small mounds of dough waiting
obediently in neat rows to be shovelled into the hearth by their
master.

The men, seated at the worktable, were impatient. The July
heat and the heat from Wiseman's hearth were almost too much,
even when urgent affairs of state were on the agenda.

"Come on, Wiseman, put all this chazerai in the oven and let's
get down to business."

Having fed his ovens, Wiseman sat down on a high stool, his
broad wrestler's hands resting squarely on his baggy knees. The
House was now officially in session.

"So who's it going to be?" he began.

The first order of business — as it had been for years — was for
the members of the press gang to disqualify themselves from the

running. Of one mind when it came to the perils of electioneering, they agreed that they would be far more content to carry on as the powers behind the power. Not for them the big armchair, the head table, and the gavel. Better to sit in the shadowy background and watch "their man" perform, dosing him with flattery when his morale lagged, and lacerating him with scorn when he dared depart from their advice.

Once again they reviewed the list of desirable qualities. "It's got to be somebody who loves punishment . . . or somebody who's crazy for a little honour and publicity . . . or somebody who's a complete fool . . . or somebody who's got lots of time and nothing better to do. . . ."

"Plus" — Wiseman pointed an index finger skyward for emphasis — "plus he's got to be presentable when he goes among goyim."

The others agreed. That was the main requirement now. They needed a candidate who was reasonably fluent in English and who "looked good" too.

"Maybe we should hire Rockefeller if it's gotta be such a fancy duke," one man suggested.

"We don't need a Rockefeller," Wiseman replied. "You'll see, we'll go through the list, we'll find some damn fool who fills the bill." Wiseman beckoned imperiously to the committee secretary. "Read the list and we'll decide one by one."

The reading of the list began in alphabetical order.

"Altman."

"Altman's out. His health won't stand it."

"What do you mean his health won't stand it? We're not asking him to fight Joe Louis."

"He gets colds too easy. He wouldn't last past November eleventh. Don't you remember last year they invited the president to lay a wreath on Armistice Day at the cenotaph in front of the courthouse? The poor sonofabitch froze his tuchis off and was sick in bed for two weeks afterwards. No, Altman's condition isn't up to it, I tell you."

"Berger is next."

"Berger's out too. He's just too goddam smart, and you can't trust a smart guy. Besides, he uses a lot of fancy English words which he doesn't even know the meaning. A real show-off."

"Cramer?"

"Cramer you can forget about," one of the committee said. "He's got his hands full now, that's for sure." The men nodded sympathetically. Cramer did indeed have his hands full, having been charged with numerous violations of the law by an implacable inspector from the Wartime Prices Control Board.

Dorff was out of the question. He had his hands full with his wife and mother-in-law watching his every move. "They even follow him to the toilet," one of the committee said, "to see if he's hiding money there."

"Einhorn?"

Ineligible. Einhorn had served one term in the presidency several years ago and hadn't spoken to half the men in the congregation since.

So it went, on down the list, greatness still waiting to be thrust upon some one unsuspecting member of the Jewish community.

At last the committee came to R for Rosen.

"Rosen! Ah, here . . . here is a possibility," one of the men piped up. "Think about it. He's vain like a peacock . . . do you know he's the only storekeeper in town who parades around in the summer in white shoes?"

"And you know something else," another volunteered, "he's the only one that when he goes to Toronto on a buying trip he carries a briefcase around with him on Spadina Avenue."

"A briefcase! You're lying — "

"So help me God it's the truth may my children never have a good day if I'm lying. One of the coat manufacturers told me, and I believe him."

A briefcase: field marshals had their batons, bishops their mitres, lord mayors their chains of office. But a merchant carrying a briefcase as he made his rounds in Toronto's garment district — that had to be the last word in symbols of pomp and grandeur. Not for Rosen suitpockets stuffed with memos and invoices. Rosen had a briefcase, with his initials embossed in gold below the handle and cardboard files inside all arranged in order. Such vanity was unheard of.

"Didn't I tell you he's a peacock?" said the first critic.

"The man loves attention, no doubt about it," said the second.

"He must be a fool if he can't carry his business affairs in his head," said the third.

"A briefcase yet," said the fourth. "Have you ever heard of

anything so goyish?"

With this last remark, the presidential nail had been hit on the head. The committee realized they had their man.

The following night the press gang invited Rosen to Wiseman's Bakery ostensibly for an innocent game of poker. The approach was subtle — a couple of hours of card-playing, tea, spongecake, bits and pieces of local gossip. Eventually one of the players brought up the U.S. presidential race.

"That fella Dewey, he's gotta be some schvantz. Imagine taking on a giant of a man like Roosevelt. Only a hundred percent meshuganer would do such a thing!"

Wiseman, alert to this opening signal, immediately carried the play forward. "And for what? For a little power? A little honour? Who needs it. Life's too short."

"Oh, I don't know," Rosen said quietly, leaning back in his chair, his eyes fixed on some distant invisible horizon. He was deep in his own thoughts, no doubt speculating on how he would conduct his campaign if he were Thomas E. Dewey. "A man always has to reach longer than his arms. Otherwise nothing gets accomplished in this world," he said.

There was a quick exchange of glances among the members of the press gang. Rosen was clearly available. But one never pulls suddenly on the line when one has hooked a big fish. One has to "play" the line, now letting out a little, now pulling in a little; then, when all instincts are precisely right, there occurs a split second of unity when captor and captive fuse and become as one. That split second was at hand.

"I don't agree with you, Rosen," Wiseman said, making certain at the same time to refill Rosen's glass with hot tea. "A man's got to know his limits. Some of us are meant to be presidents, and some of us just aren't. That's all there is to it."

"Ach, that's old-country talk," Rosen said, plunking four pieces of lumpsugar into the steaming tea. "In Russia, in Poland, they always told you that you had to know your place. You were born a tailor? Then stay a tailor. Born a butcher? Stay a butcher. In America it's different. Why shouldn't Dewey be the president? Is Roosevelt God or something that he's always got to be Number One? Suppose they had told Abraham Lincoln he shouldn't bother running because he was born in such a lousy log cabin that

I wouldn't even park my car there, wouldn't that have been a tragedy?"

"But Lincoln," protested one of the committee, "was no ordinary man, you know. This man was pretty special. A really self-made man."

"We're all self-made men," Rosen interjected. "Tell me, did anybody hand you your business on a silver platter?" The men nodded thoughtfully; Rosen had a point.

"But Lincoln had a lot of talent," one of the men countered. "What gift of the gab. Did you ever read any of his speeches and his sayings? A golden tongue, that's what the man was blessed with."

Rosen was unimpressed. "Golden schmolden. You talk long enough in public you get used to being a big talker. All it takes is nerve and practice. A genius you don't have to be. Look at Mackenzie King. There was a time you wouldn't go from one end of this room to the other to hear the man talk. But today he's Prime Minister already a few years so everybody hangs on his words. Everybody says my goodness that man has a way of putting things. And look at the other King, the one in England. A stutterer, poor man. But when he's got to talk, he talks, and pretty good too. Did you hear him last Christmas? It's nerve, that's all."

"So how many of us have that kind of nerve?" Wiseman asked.

"We all have," Rosen replied. "Didn't we come to this country not knowing a single word of English. I went to a cheder in Poland; you think they taught me English there? No sir, I had nerve when I came here and today I can talk to people — to goyim — like I was born here, and they don't even know the difference. I was just saying to Reverend Ferguson's wife yesterday — "

"Reverend Ferguson's wife?" one of the men broke in. "She shops in your store?"

"Sure, what do you think, she shops only in goyishe stores? She comes in, I give her twenty off automatically. I'd like to see her get a discount at Eaton's. Bupkes Eaton's'll give her off."

"He comes in too?"

"The Reverend? Sure, lots of times. We even have some very interesting conversations. He's really a fine goy."

Unwittingly the fish had placed himself in the category of a catch. Wiseman prepared to net him.

"You know something, Rosen," the baker said, offering more

spongecake, "you're a lucky fella. In fact it's more than luck; you're a smart fella. Believe me, I'd like to have customers like the Fergusons they should buy from me."

Rosen, a little smug now, shook his head reprovingly. "People like the Fergusons don't buy rye bread and pumpernickel," he scoffed. "You have to know how to deal with their kind. They're not Polyacken or Talyainer, you know. With goyim like the Fergusons you talk first about the weather, about the news. You got to pretend you don't even give a damn if they buy or they don't buy because it's such a pleasure to have their company. Then, when they're good and ready, they tell you what they're looking for."

"You sure know how to deal with those people," Wiseman said.

"It's not just a matter of dealing any more," Rosen said, smugness having expanded into pride. "I've been Ferguson's guest already at the Rotary Club."

These were the magic words the committee had been waiting for. Of all the service clubs in town, the Rotary Club was the most prestigious. Eagerly the men questioned Rosen. Whom had he been seated with? Was his bank manager there? What did they serve for lunch and was he able to eat it? Who was the guest speaker? All these queries Rosen answered in great detail, relishing the special status he now occupied in his listeners' eyes. One of the men asked, "Did they say grace before they ate, like you see in the movies?"

Rosen beamed. "Did they say grace? You should hear the grace they said. It was such a grace, believe me every Jew in this town should only have such a grace before he sits down to eat. I only wish my wife and kids could have been there. They called naturally on the Reverend to say grace. Well, let me tell you, that man made a speech, there were tears in my eyes. He said they should thank God they not only had a good lunch coming but that — and listen to this — but that God was allowing them to share it with one of their distinguished — so help me God he said distinguished — Jewish neighbours. And you know what else — such a fine goy — he didn't use the name of Jesus once, not once! That's what I call a mensch."

Were there incongruities here? Subtleties not easily discerned? Lapses of logic? Unexplained differences and unbridgeable gaps? Perhaps, but it didn't matter. By all outward signs and superficial standards, Rosen was the perfect man for the job, a man whose time had come.

Looking Rosen directly in the eye with an earnestness he reserved for moments when he was being truly insincere, Wiseman, his voice quavering, spoke. "Rosen," he said, "you know it'll soon be time for us to elect a new president." There was a sense of history in the atmosphere. All eyes were on Rosen. "We've decided that the best man for the job . . . is you."

There was dead silence, so much so that the sound of the crusts browning in the hearth could be heard. Rosen looked at the men around him, one by one. "You're out of your goddam minds," he said at last. "You're crazy in the head if you think I would take on such a lousy job. Better I should commit suicide. Show me a man, show me one single man, who hasn't had anything but the greatest aggravation from being president. Look at Einhorn; to this day he doesn't talk to half the people in this congregation and it's already five six years since he was president."

Why argue? Rosen was absolutely right. So the press gang remained silent, permitting their catch to thrash about and convulse in the net. He would soon give one last heave, one last massive gasp, and lie still in total submission to the public will. Meanwhile they listened politely as Rosen reviewed the record of the past dozen presidencies. Each and every leader had left behind a trail of bitterness and discontent. "No thank you," Rosen concluded, "like I said before, suicide would be better."

One of the committee made as if to counter with a point, but Wiseman quickly raised a hand to command silence.

"You should see how the goyim run things at their clubs," Rosen went on. "You should just see the way they got everything organized with committees and reports and rules and regulations just like in Parliament. If I was president, believe me, things would be run the way *they* run them, not the way we run them."

"If I was president . . . " More magic words. Rosen was beginning to visualize himself in office. That was good. Without any urging, Rosen continued to spell out his reform program. "I would see that there was proper respect, and proper order. No more cross-talk and back-talk. No more jumping up in the middle of a meeting and saying to hell with it I move it's time to go home. And everybody on the executive would have to be called by their proper titles: Mr. President, Mr. Secretary, Mr. Treasurer."

The committee, including Wiseman, began to look just the slightest bit uneasy. Rosen, unaware of this reaction, warmed increasingly to his vision of the new order. "I would even have the rabbi give an opening benediction, like they do with their minister."

An opening benediction? The men looked at each other in disbelief. One asked hesitantly, "In what language?"

"In English, of course. You want dignity, don't you?"

No one responded. What, after all, did they want? Dignity? Decorum? Please Mr. Chairman, thank you Mr. Chairman, briefcases, filing systems? These were men who carried their own business affairs filed in the channels of their brains and on the backs of used envelopes. These were men who knew each other as Itzik and Yoshka and Yamkeh and more often by unflattering nicknames — The Weasel, Chooligan, Der Roiter, Grosser Verdiener. Were they now to be transformed into mock-Christians? And in the space of a single year under Rosen's administration? True, this was 1944, not 1934 or 1924; the younger generation, Canadian-born, English-oriented, would soon be moving in to take over community activities. The men couldn't go on forever doing things old-country style. Or could they?

The men of the press gang sat staring at nothing. Someone coughed, a chair scraped against the floor, a spoon rattled inside an empty tea glass.

Finally, Wiseman rose from his stool. "I better see how my bread is doing," he said wearily, shuffling to the ovens.

"Let's play another coupla hands," one of the men said, and he slammed the deck of cards decisively down at the centre of the table.

"Not me," Rosen said, leaving his chair and putting on his jacket. "I gotta go home. My wife'll kill me."

The other men watched Rosen depart. They said nothing until they heard the front door of the shop close behind him.

"You know," said one, "we had him right in the net, hooked and all."

"Sometimes," Wiseman said, "you think you've landed something good, and then you look at the end of the line and it's a lousy catfish. And who the hell eats catfish?"

The old baker turned to the man with the alphabetical list of prospects.

"What comes after R?"

Few writers have contributed more words or more quality to Canadian literature than Farley Mowat. Sometimes called the Peck's bad boy of Canadian literature, Mowat won the Leacock Medal for Humour in 1970 with The Boat Who Wouldn't Float. *This story of his love affair with a two-masted bummer is a splendid example of the man and his work.*

FARLEY MOWAT
from The Boat Who Wouldn't Float

One small difficulty still remained. We had no charts of the east coast of Newfoundland. The lack of charts, combined with a misleading compass and the dead certainty of running into fog, suggested we would do well to ship a pilot until we could make a port where charts could be bought and the compass adjusted.

The obvious choice for a pilot was Enos. Like most Newfoundland seamen he possessed, we presumed, special senses which are lost to modern man. He had sailed these waters all his life, often without a compass and usually without charts. When you asked him how he managed to find his way to some distant place he would look baffled and reply:

"Well, me son, I *knows* where it's at."

We needed somebody like that. However when we broached the matter to Enos he showed no enthusiasm. For a man who was usually as garrulous as an entire pack of politicians, his response was spectacularly succinct.

"No!" he grunted, and for emphasis spat a gob of tobacco juice on our newly painted cabin top.

There was no swaying him either. Persuasion (and Jack McClelland is a persuader *par excellence*) got us nowhere. He kept on saying "No" and spitting until the cabin top developed a slippery brown sheen over most of its surface and we were prepared to give up. I was, at any rate, but Jack was made of sterner stuff.

"If the old bustard won't come willingly," Jack told me after Enos left, "we'll shanghai him."

"The hell with him, Jack. Forget it. We'll manage on our own."

"Forget him nothing! If this goddamn boat sinks I'm at least going to have the satisfaction of seeing him sink with it!"

There was no arguing with Jack in a mood like that.

He arranged a small farewell party on board that night. It was one of the gloomiest parties I have ever attended. Six or seven of our fishermen friends squeezed into the cabin and ruminated at lugubrious length on the manifold perils of the sea. When they got tired of that, they began recalling the small schooners that had sailed out of Southern Shore ports and never been heard of again. The list went on and on until even Enos began to grow restive.

"Well, byes," he interjected, "them was mostly poor-built boats. Not fitten to go to sea. Not proper fer it, ye might say. Now you takes a boat like this 'un. Proper built and found. *She* won't be making any widows on the shore."

This was the opening Jack had been waiting for.

"You're so right, Enos. In a boat as good as this a fellow could sail to hell and back."

Enos eyed Jack with sudden suspicion. "Aye," he replied cautiously. "She be good fer it!"

"*You* certainly wouldn't be afraid to sail in her, now would you Enos?"

The trap was sprung.

"Well, now, me darlin' man, I don't say as I wouldn't, but a'course. . . ."

"Good enough!" Jack shouted. "Farley, hand me the log. Enos, we'll sign you on as sailing master for the maiden voyage of the finest ship you ever built."

Enos struggled mightily but to no avail. He was under the eyes of six of his peers and one of them, without realizing it, became our ally:

"Sign on, sign on, Enos, me son. We knows you'm not afeard!"

So Enos signed his mark.

Happy Adventure sailed an hour after dawn. It was a fine morning, clear and warm, with a good draft of wind out of the nor'west to help us on our way and to keep the fog off shore. We had intended to sail *at* dawn but Enos did not turn up and when we went to look for him his daughters said he had gone off to haul a herring net. We recognized this as a ruse, and so we searched for him in the most likely place. He was savagely disgruntled when we found him, complaining bitterly that a man couldn't even "do his nature" without being followed. Little by little we coaxed him down to the stage, got him aboard and down below, and before he could rally, we cast off the lines.

Happy Adventure made a brave sight as she rolled down the reach toward the waiting sea. With all sails set and drawing she lay over a little and snored sweetly through the water actually over-taking and passing two or three belated trap skiffs bound out to the fishing grounds. Their crews grinned cheerfully at us, which is as close to a farewell as a Newfoundland seaman will allow himself. There is a bad luck in farewells.

Before we cleared the headlands I celebrated a small ritual that I learned from my father. I poured four stiff glasses of rum. I gave one of these to Enos and one to Jack, and I kept one for myself. The fourth, I poured overboard. The Old Man of the Sea is a sailor and he likes his drop of grog. And it is a good thing to be on friendly terms with the Old Man when you venture out upon the grey waters that are his domain.

All that morning we sailed south on a long reach keeping a two- or three-mile offing from the grim sea cliffs. We came abeam of Cape Ballard and left it behind, then the wind began to fall light and fickle, ghosting for a change. The change came and the wind picked up from sou'east, a dead muzzler right on our bows, bring-ing the fog in toward us.

Enos began to grow agitated. We were approaching Cape Race, the southeast "corner" of Newfoundland and one of the most feared places in the Western Ocean. Its peculiar menace lies in the tidal currents that sweep past it. They are totally unpredictable. They can carry an unwary vessel, or one blinded by fog, miles off her true course and so to destruction on the brooding rocks ashore.

In our innocence Jack and I were not much worried and when Enos insisted that we down sail and start the engine we were inclined to mock him. He did not like this and withdrew into sullen taciturnity, made worse by the fact that I had closed off the rum rations while we were at sea. Finally, to please him, we started the bullgine, or rather Jack did, after a blasphemous half hour's struggle.

The joys of the day were now all behind us. Sombre clouds began closing off the sky; the air grew chill, presaging the coming of the fog; and the thunderous blatting of the unmuffled bullgine deafened us, while the slow strokes of the great piston shook the little boat as an otter shakes a trout.

By four o'clock we still had reasonably good visibility and were abeam of Cape Race — and there we stuck. The engine thundered and the water boiled under our counter but we got no farther on our way. Hour after hour the massive highlands behind the cape refused to slip astern. Jack and I finally began to comprehend something of the power of the currents. Although we were making five knots through the water a lee bow tide was running at almost the same speed against us.

The fog was slow in coming but the wall of grey slid inexorably nearer. At six-thirty Jack went below to rustle up some food. An instant later his head appeared in the companionway. The air of casual insouciance, which was as much a part of his seagoing gear as his jaunty yachting cap, had vanished.

"Christ!" he cried, and it was perhaps partly a prayer. "This bloody boat is sinking!"

I jumped to join him and found that he was undeniably right. Water was already sluicing across the floor boards in the main cabin. Spread-eagling the engine for better purchase, Jack began working the handle of the pump as if his life depended on it. It dawned on me his life *did* depend on it; and so did mine.

The next thing I knew Enos had shouldered me aside. Taking one horrified look at the private swimming pool inside *Happy Adventure*, he shrieked:

"Lard Jasus, byes, she's gone!"

It was hardly the remark we needed to restore our faith in him or in his boat. Still yelling, he went on to diagnose the trouble.

He told us the stuffing box had fallen off. This meant that the ocean was free to enter the boat through the large hole in the sternpost that housed the vessel's shaft. And since we could not reach it there was nothing we could do about it.

Enos now retreated into a mental room of his own, a dark hole filled with fatalistic thoughts. However, by giving him a bottle of rum to cherish, I managed to persuade him to take the tiller (the little boat had meanwhile been going in circles) and steer a course for Trepassey Bay, fifteen miles to the eastward, where I thought we might just manage to beach the vessel before she sank.

There was never any question of abandoning her. Our dory, so called, was a little plywood box barely capable of carrying one man. Life-preservers would have been useless, because we were in the Labrador Current where the waters are so cold that a man cannot survive immersion in them for more than a few minutes.

By dint of furious pumping, Jack and I found we could almost hold the water level where it was, although we could not gain upon the inflow. And so we pumped. The engine thundered on. We pumped. The minutes stretched into hours and we pumped. The fog held off, which was one minor blessing, and we pumped. The engine roared and the heat became so intense that we were sweating almost as much water back into the bilges as we were pumping out. We pumped. The tidal current slackened and turned and began to help us on our way. We pumped.

Occasionally one of us crawled on deck to breathe and to rest our agonized muscles for a moment. At eight o'clock I stuck my head out of the companionway and saw the massive headland of Mistaken Point a mile or so to leeward. I glanced at Enos. He was staring straight ahead, his eyes half shut and his mouth pursed into a dark pit of despair. He had taken out his dentures, a thing he always did in moments of stress. When I called out to tell him we were nearly holding the leak he gave no sign of hearing but continued staring over the bow as if he beheld some bleak and terrible vision from which he could not take his attention for a moment. Not at all cheered I ducked back into the engine room.

And then the main pump jammed.

That pump was a fool of a thing that had no right to be aboard a boat. Its innards were a complicated mass of springs and valves that could not possibly digest the bits of flotsam, jetsam, and cod-fish floating in the vessel's bilge. But, fool of a thing or not, it was our only hope.

It was dark by this time so Jack held a flashlight while I un-bolted the pump's face plate. The thing contained ten small coil springs and all of them leapt for freedom the instant the plate came off. They ricocheted off the cabin sides like a swarm of manic bees and fell, to sink below the surface of the water in the bilges.

It does not seem possible, but we found them all.It took twenty-five or thirty minutes of groping with numbed arms under oily, icy water, but we found them all, re-installed them, put back the face plate, and again began to pump.

Meanwhile the water had gained four inches. It was now over

the lower part of the flywheel and less than two inches below the top of the carburetor. The flywheel spun a niagara of spray onto the red-hot exhaust pipe, turning the dark and roaring engine-room into a sauna bath. We pumped.

Jack crawled on deck for a breather and immediately gave a frantic yell. For a second I hesitated. I did not think I had the fortitude to face a new calamity — but a second urgent summons brought me out on deck. Enos was frozen at the helm and by the last light of day I could see he was steering straight toward a wall of rock which loomed above us, no more than three hundred yards away.

I leapt for the tiller. Enos did not struggle but meekly moved aside. His expression had changed and had become almost beatific. It may have been the rum that did it — Enos was at peace with himself and with the Fates.

"We'd best run her onto the rocks," he explained mildly, "than be drowned in the cold, cold water."

Jack went back to the pump and I put the vessel on a course to skirt the threatening cliffs. We were not impossibly far from Tre-passey Bay, and there still seemed to be a chance we could reach the harbour and beach the vessel on a non-lethal shore.

At about eleven o'clock I saw a flashing light ahead and steered for it. When I prodded him Enos confirmed that it might be the buoy marking the entrance to Trepassey harbour. However be-fore we reached it the fog overtook us and the darkness became total. We felt our way past the lightbuoy and across the surround-ing shoals with only luck and the Old Man to guide us.

As we entered the black gut which we hoped was the harbour entrance, I did not need Jack's warning shout to tell me that our time had about run out. The bullgine had begun to cough and splutter. The water level had reached her carburetor and, tough as she was, she could not remain alive for long on a mixture of gasoline and salt sea water.

Within Trepassey harbour all was inky black. No lights could be seen on the invisible shore. I steered blindly ahead, knowing that sooner or later we must strike the land. Then the engine coughed, stopped, picked up again, coughed, and stopped for good. Sil-ently, in that black night, the little ship ghosted forward.

Jack came tumbling out on deck for there was no point in remaining below while the vessel foundered. He had, and I remember this with great clarity, a flashlight in his mouth and a bottle of rum in each hand. . . .

. . . At that moment *Happy Adventure's* forefoot hit something. She jarred a little, made a strange sucking sound, and the motion went out of her.

"I t'inks," said Enos as he nimbly relieved Jack of one of the bottles, "I t'inks we's run'd ashore!"

Jack believes *Happy Adventure* has a special kind of homing instinct. He may be right. Certainly she is never happier than when she is lying snuggled up against a working fish plant. Perhaps she identifies fish plants with the natal womb, which is not so strange when one remembers she was built in a fish-plant yard and that she spent the many months of her refit as a semi-permanent fixture in the fish-plant slip at Muddy Hole.

In any event when she limped into Trepassey she unerringly found her way straight to her spiritual home. Even before we began playing flashlights on our surroundings we knew this was so. The old familiar stench rose all around us like a dank miasma.

The flashlights revealed that we had run ashore on a gently shelving beach immediately alongside a massively constructed wharf. Further investigation had to be delayed because the tide was falling and the schooner was in danger of keeling over on her bilge. Jack made a jump and managed to scale the face of the wharf. He caught the lines I threw him and we rigged a spider web of ropes from our two masts to the wharf timbers to hold the vessel upright when all the water had drained away from under her.

When she seemed secure I joined Jack on the dock and cautiously we went exploring. The fog was so thick that our lights were nearly useless and we practically bumped into the first human being we encountered. He was the night watchman for Industrial Seafood Packers, a huge concern to whose dock we were moored. After we had convinced the watchman that we did not have a cargo of fish to unload, but were only mariners in distress, he came aboard.

He seemed genuinely incredulous to find we did not have a radar set. How, he asked, had we found our way into the harbour? How had we missed striking the several draggers anchored in the fairway? And how, in hell's own name (his words), had we found the plant and managed to come alongside the wharf without hitting the L-shaped end where the cod-oil factory stood in lonely grandeur?

Since we could not answer these questions we evaded them, leaving him with the suspicion, which spread rapidly around Trepassey, that we were possessed by an occult power. Witches and warlocks have not yet vanished from the outport scene in Newfoundland.

The watchman was a generous man and he told us we could stay at the wharf as long as we wished. He felt, however, that we might be happier if we moored a hundred feet farther to seaward.

" 'Tis the poipe, ye know; the poipe what carries off the gurry from the plant. Ye've moored hard alongside o' she."

Happy Adventure had come home with a vengeance and, for all I know, it may have *been* vengeance at that.

That was a singularly dreadful night.

We had to begin repairing the leak immediately, while the tide was low. We soon found that Eno's diagnosis had been correct. The outside stuffing box, or gland, had come adrift when both retaining lag screws parted, allowing the box to slip down the shaft until it rested against the propeller.

In order to repair it we had to borrow a big drill from the helpful watchman, drill out the remains of the old lag screws, fair off the dead wood where the shaft had chewed it up, and then screw the gland back into place. Perhaps this does not sound like much of a task, but let me try to paint the scene.

To reach the gland we had to wade knee-deep in black, stinking muck, a composite product consisting of aboriginal slime fortified over the decades by decaying contributions from the fish plant. We worked in darkness except for the light from two poor flashlights which could produce only a dim orange glow in the shroud of bitterly cold fog that enveloped us. We kept dropping things, and the recovery of a wrench or a bolt from the sucking slime brought to mind Hercules at his task in the Augean stables.

By three o'clock the job was done and just in time because the tide was rising. We waited impatiently for it to float the boat so we could haul her out along the wharf, away from the ominous presence of the "poipe." Half an hour before the plant began operations, the tide was full.

It was not full enough. *Happy Adventure* did not float.

We had run her ashore "on the last of springs," which is to say, on the highest tide of the month. Enos, who knew all about such things, pointed out to us it would be nearly twenty-eight days before the tide was as high again.

Enos also said he felt it was time for him to leave. He said he did not want to be a bother to us and, considering the cramped accommodation on our little vessel and the fact that we would be making a prolonged visit in Trepassey, he thought it would be better if he went away as soon as the fog thinned. He said he would sacrifice his own comfort and stay with friends ashore until he could find transportation back to Muddy Hole.

I did not attempt to dissuade him but Jack was displeased because, as an old Navy man, he took a dim view of people jumping ship. However after breakfast Jack found he was able to accept Enos's departure with equanimity.

I cooked that breakfast. It was a hearty one for we were all half-starved. I cut up and fried about three pounds of side bacon. It was fat bacon; it was tough bacon; and it had a rind on it a quarter of an inch thick.

Jack and Enos sat at the saloon table while I served them. What with the layers of muck that coated our clothing, and what with the stench from the fishy flats outside, the atmosphere was not salubrious. However for once Jack was too tired, too hungry, and too depressed to care about his mealtime surroundings. Grimly he went to work on his bacon while I turned back to the stove to cook my own rashers. Suddenly I heard Jack make a despairing, strangled sound. I spun around.

Jack sat rigid on the bench, his eyes staring glassily from a face that had lost its usual ruddy colour and had become grotesquely mottled. He was staring at Enos.

All unaware of the scrutiny Enos was busy eating his bacon. It had proved too tough for him to deal with while his badly fitting dentures remained in his mouth, so he had removed both plates. He now held them firmly in the angle between thumb and forefinger of his left hand, and he was making them snap open and shut with a dexterity that argued long practice. With his right hand he was passing a strip of bacon between the two sets of grinders. When this remarkable operation had macerated the strip of bacon sufficiently he threw back his head, poised the bacon over his mouth, and gummed it down.

Jack struggled to his feet, pushed his way past me, and vanished out the companion hatch. Before he returned, an hour or so later, Enos had packed his gear and gone ashore. I cannot in all conscience say that either of us was deeply pained to sign him off.

According to his own calculations, Richard Needham has written close to twelve million words since he started working as a newspaperman at the age of eighteen. Certainly some of the funniest of those words appear in the Leacock Medal for Humour winner of 1967, Needham's Inferno.

RICHARD NEEDHAM
from Needham's Inferno

Once upon a time, and in — of all places — Toronto, there was a girl named Fifi Fahrenheit. She had come here from Lunenburg, N.S., for precisely the same reason that other girls come here from Lindsay, Leamington, Lethbridge, London, and Luebeck — that is, to find an interesting, intelligent, polite, and (what is most important) unattached man.

She quickly obtained a job with the Irrational Trust Company, where she spent all day typing lengthy memoranda in Swahili addressed to junior executives who tore them up without reading them. She also made the acquaintance of the Bay Street belles, to whom she confided her real purpose in coming to Toronto. They laughed so loudly that they could be heard in the farthest Babbitt-warrens of Tormented Township.

'Foolish Fifi!" said one of them. 'You will shortly learn that there are no interesting, intelligent, polite, unattached men in Toronto. There are no interesting, intelligent, polite men in Toronto. There are no interesting, intelligent men in Toronto. There are no interesting men in Toronto. There are no men in Toronto. There are no men, and that is why I have taken up triple brandies as a way of life.'

Another one said, 'I was told you have to go out with creeps in order to meet real men, but all I have ever met by going out with creeps is or are more creeps. That is why I have taken up skiing, hat-making, and eating garlic sausage as a way of life.'

Another one said, 'Miracles do happen, and I deem it possible that you will find a man in Toronto who is interesting, intelligent, polite, and unattached. You will also find, however, that he has a severe drinking problem. Or else you will find that he is deeply attached to his mother, whom he calls Lover, Mumsy, or Sweetie-pie, and whom he telephones every half-hour when he is out with you. That is why I have taken up bowling, chain-smoking, and Kahlil Gibran as a way of life, if you can call it life, which I very much doubt.'

Like all Nova Scotia girls, Fifi was strong and brave. She refused to believe what the Bay Street belles told her, but insisted on finding things out for herself. As she did. For her first three months in Toronto, she didn't have a single date. Then she began meeting men and going out with them. But they certainly fell far below the standards she had set for herself when she boarded the MacKenzie bus at Lunenburg.

She went out with men who wore hats, men who wore rimless spectacles, and men who wore sharply pointed shoes with paper-thin soles. She went out with men who read Zane Grey, men who believed in British Israel, and men who were secretly in love with Juliette. She went out with men who carefully studied and added up the restaurant bill. She went out with men who furtively leafed through the photography magazines on the newstands.

She went out with men who didn't drink or smoke, but got their jollies by looking down the front of the waitress's dress. She went out with men who smoked cigars in automobiles. She went out with men who asked her humbly first, and thanked her profusely afterwards. She went out with men who tipped an exact 10 per cent, down to the last penny. She went out with men who took her to Fort-York, the Royal Ontario Museum, and H.M.C.S. *Haida*.

She went out with men who didn't call her the morning after. She went out with men who told her at length and with many tears that their wives didn't understand them, but they couldn't get a divorce on account of the kids. She went out with men who, on sitting down at the restaurant table, took the napkin and breathed upon and polished every piece of cutlery. She went out with men who combed their hair up over their bald spots. She went out with men who sucked Clorets just before they kissed her.

She went out with men who put unlit cigarettes behind their ears, and with men who held lighted cigarettes between their bent fingers with the glowing end toward the palm. She went out with men who got drunk and quarrelled with her; with men who got drunk and threw up; with men who got drunk and telephoned newspaper offices demanding to know who won the Kentucky Derby in 1897. She went out with men who put their correct names and addresses on LCBO purchase slips.

Fifi finally broke down. She started crying and drinking and wearing needle-heeled shoes and stockings with seams and sack dresses and dark fuchsia lipstick. She started reading newspaper editorials and voting in elections and listening to Johnnie Ray records. She stopped using eye make-up and joined the YWCA and enrolled for an evening course in conversational Australian.

In short, she was thoroughly mixed up and just about ready for a series of $75-an-hour sessions with Dr. Rorschach Blotz. As a desperate last measure, she sat down to her IBM electric, and wrote a single-word letter — 'Help!' — which she sent to Rudolph J. Needleberry, a venerable newspaper columnist who appeared to have some scant knowledge of the Toronto scene.

The kindly old philosopher naturally invited her to lunch at the Venetian Room of the Royal York. 'You can easily identify me,' he said, 'because I am eight feet tall, totally bald, and have a dark-green complexion. In view of our surroundings, I will of course be wearing my gondolier's outfit. I do not doubt that you and I will be the only mixed couple in the place, except for a husband and wife who after twenty-five years of marital bliss haven't a word to say to each other.'

After Fifi had finished her first manhattan, and he had downed his fourteenth, she described the nature of her problem to him. He beamed like a Cheshire cat and replied: 'My dear young lady, you are not alone. Hundreds and indeed thousands of Toronto women are in precisely the same situation. There are roughly 600,000 grown men in this vast metropolis; most of them are happily married and should therefore be written off, though I am led to believe that they are by no means averse to a nice furtive little week-end in some such handy place as Niagara Foibles or St. Calamity.'

He ordered a fifteenth manhattan, and continued: 'Now, as for the unattached men, you will find that a rather large number of them are madly gay, so they must be written off, too, at least so far as young ladies like you are concerned. The remainder are available, one might say, and some of them meet your specifications; but these are hard to find, and when you do find them are surrounded by a bevy of other women who got there first and defend their claim with razor-honed letter-openers. The rest are largely or totally unsuitable, and should not be allowed out with a female orang-utan, let alone a nice girl from Lunenburg, N.S.'

Lighting his eighty-seventh cigarette of the day, he concluded: 'The men of Toronto puzzle and amuse me. What they all have in common whether they are married or not, and perhaps especially if they are married, is that they don't really like women. To this situation I have devoted years of thought, oceans of Gilbey's gin, millions of Rothmans, and hundreds of dollars' worth of noisy heterosexual dinners at Hold Handgelo's, but have yet to come up with the reason for it, let alone the remedy. For my own part, I would say of women what Churchill said of brandy; they are God's greatest gift to suffering humanity; but I know only one other man who agrees with me, and he has been deported to Hamilton.'

Fifi started to cry, and he patted her hand. 'Dry your tears,' he said. 'There may be hope for you yet. I recently met a woman who in every sense is an absolute witch, and thus pleases me greatly. She is here in Toronto, being witchy hither and yon, and also witching at me through many a long and liquid lunch at The Hunters. I will ask her to perform a miracle of witchiness and produce, for you alone, what I like to describe as a first-class man.'

Fifi thanked Mr. Needleberry, but didn't really believe anything could come of it. 'He was just trying to cheer me up,' she thought that evening as she stumbled through a typical Toronto May blizzard to her apartment in the Village Grim. 'Poor old fellow, he means well, but it would take a whole battalion of witches to produce a truly first-class man in this creepy city.' It was then that she saw a man's feet sticking out of a snowbank, the rest of him being totally buried.

Fifi quickly cleared away the snow, pulled the unfortunate fellow to his feet, and gave him a nip from the bottle of Paul Masson brandy she kept in her purse. "Thank you very much,' he said, 'and permit me to introduce myself. My name is Yves Ladifférence, I recently arrived here from Montreal; and, being somewhat lonely, dipped too deeply into the Dewar's. It is true, as William Blake says, that you never know what is enough until you know what is more than enough. Had it not been for you, I would likely have perished, which means that the very least thing I owe you is dinner at La Scala with barrels of Bardolino and an immense bunch of flowers from Gallagher's.'

He saw her home, took her telephone number, kissed her lightly on the hand, advised her she was the most attractive woman he had ever met, and added, 'Mais vos yeux! Ma petite, que vous avez souffert!' As he departed, humming a pleasant allegro strain from Handel's *Water Music*, Fifi knew she had at last found a first-class man — one who weighed in, as sporting parlance might have it, with Marcello Mastroianni, Herbert von Karajan, and Peter O'Toole.

Yves was all the things a man ought to be with a woman, but rarely is. He took Fifi out to lunch every day; he was always on time with a bouquet of flowers under his arm; and, if she was late, insisted that the clock must be wrong. Every morning, she got a love letter from him at the office, and every evening she got two love letters from him at home. He wrote poems about her beauty and charm, and had them privately printed, and stuck them up all over downtown Toronto. He never criticized her in any way, for, as he pointed out to her (and especially in front of other women), there was nothing in her to criticize; she was perfection itself.

Fifi told him the story of her life, to which he listened attentively; and he told her quite a bit about his own. 'I must tell you, Fifi,' he said, 'that I have travelled in many parts of the world, and that there were other women before you — Dresden dolls, Worcester saucies, unorthodox Greeks, Tasmanian devils, Scotch friskies, Devonshire creamies, Icelandic volcanoes, Welsh minors, Chinese puzzles, Strasbourg geese, Persian lambs, Dover soulfuls, French undressings, San Francisco earthquakes, and a Bengal tigress named, as I recall, Jacqueline. But they were only the playthings of an idle moment; you are the first one whom I feel I can really love and trust.'

When the Bay Street belles saw the way in which Yves Ladifférence held doors open for Fifi, and helped her with her coat, and kissed her right in the middle of Simpson's and knelt down to put on and take off her high black suede boots — when they saw all this, their rage and jealousy knew no bounds. One would mutter, 'Only flits have manners like that.' Another would say, 'I wouldn't be surprised if he turned out to be a secret drinker,' and still another, 'You mark my words; the Montreal police will be along to pick him up for embezzlement, or for running dope, or for some awful offence involving small boys.'

But Fifi smiled; she knew what she knew — that he was absolutely first-class. They went happily along for many weeks until one day he showed up for lunch without any flowers. Fifi was a little bit upset, and asked rather coolly, 'Where are they? What's gone wrong?' He explained that a truckers' strike had prevented deliveries. She accepted his explanation, and their lunch was as pleasant — well, almost as pleasant — as the ones they had had before.

Then came the time when he was a bit low on funds; so instead of taking her to dinner at Le Provençal, he took her to Diana Sweets. Fifi made a little joke out of it, and said he must be spending his money on some other woman; but Yves didn't laugh, he just looked pensive and lit another cigarette. 'Tell me honestly now, Yves,' she said. 'How many packs a day do you smoke?' He said three, maybe four. 'That's an awful lot,' said Fifi. 'It seems to me you are asking for trouble. I think you should smoke a pipe instead and it just so happens that I have bought you one and have it with me.'

Yves smoked a pipe from there on. At Fifi's suggestion, he gave up rolling his shirtsleeves, and started keeping a budget, and wore striped shirts instead of white ones, and moved from his pad on Spadina Avenue to a much nicer one in Rosedale. One day, Fifi said to him: 'You frequently mention a woman in your past named Véronique, and I suspect you had quite a thing about her, and I want to know exactly who she is, and if she is in Toronto right now, and if you ever see her, and exactly what relationship you have with her. Am I the only woman in your life, or are there others whom you keep hidden away from me?'

He assured her she was the only one, and then she cried a bit, and said she didn't mind about there being other women, so long as she was the No. 1 girl. Some weeks later, she demanded: 'Who was the last woman you made love to before you met me, and what was it like, and how long was the interval between her and me?' The end came when, on reaching her office one morning, Fifi found Yves had written her only a three-page love letter instead of the usual five-pager. Telephoning him immediately, she said: 'I know now that you have deceived me, and are carrying on with one or more other women. Tonight, Yves, you and I are going to have a long and serious talk about us.'

At which point, Yves Ladifférence disappeared from Fifi's life and indeed from Toronto. Some people said he had fled to Madrid by CPA; and others that he had gone to Australia by BOAC; and still others that he had vanished into Finnair. Fifi is still here, of course. She is at present going out with a man who believes that the earth is flat, that poverty and war can be abolished, that the Senate plays a useful role in Canadian life, and that there really is such a person as Douglas Fisher.

With his fascinating look at the plains, and particularly the little red school house on the plains, Max Braithwaite won the Leacock Medal for Humour in 1972. Braithwaite has brought a high level of writing to his dramatic scripts for the air, having received the Ohio State University Award twelve times. The Night We Stole the Mountie's Car *is the kind of personal recollection that serves humour so well.*

MAX BRAITHWAITE

from The Night We Stole the Mountie's Car

I had learned to play auction bridge when I was in high school, but during the years I taught in rural schools there was little opportunity to play any kind of bridge. In Wannego I was introduced to the wonders and intricacies of contract bridge. It was not an altogether happy introduction.

Card-playing has always been important in Saskatchewan. As a kid I spent many long winter evenings by the flickering light of the coal-oil lamp playing rummy, old maid, or snap with my brothers and sisters. These were replaced, as we grew older with whist, euchre, five-hundred and, finally, auction bridge.

In Aileen's family they play a game which I'm sure Bob Treleaven must have invented, called "Blackout." It would be impossible for me to outline all the intricacies of this contest here, but a great deal of laughing and cursing are an integral part of it. Any number can play, each player being dealt one card on the first deal, two on the second, three on the third and on up while the cards last. You declare how many tricks you think you can take with a given hand and if you take more or less than that number you "blackout." It's a "gang-up" game, with everybody trying to make the highest player blackout and it can become very vicious. Those who make their bids squeal with glee while those who don't shout "Oh hell!"

The most ardent card player I ever knew, though, was Homer Willoughby who ran one of the elevators in Wannego. Since there was little wheat being hauled he had plenty of time on his hands. He spent it hanging around the restaurant or the hotel lobby and

255

in the inside pocket of his jacket he always had a long wooden cribbage board.

If you happened to stop near him he'd produce the board and a pack of cards, nudge you gently, lift his cheek in an exaggerated wink and say, "How about a little game?"

If you protested that you didn't have time, that you had to catch a bus or a store before it closed he'd say, "This won't take long," and begin dealing the cards. He was right, too. It never did take long. Before you knew it he'd fifteen-two'd you out of the game and your dime and was cutting the cards for another deal.

He would do this anywhere — in the post office, the general store, the bank, even on the street. If you paused for a second he had you. His greatest triumph, it was said, though I find it hard to believe, was when he engaged the preacher in a game on the way out of church one Sunday. The parson held out his hand to shake Homer's and got instead a cribbage hand. Some claim Homer won half the collection before the preacher could shake him.

In Wannego, besides the constant smear games in the hotel and the poker games in the livery barn, whist drives were organized by church groups to buy new choir gowns and euchre tournaments were common. But we sophisticates eschewed all of these mundane games and took up contract bridge.

As everyone knows by now, the game was developed from auction bridge in 1925 by Harold S. Vanderbilt when he and some friends were playing auction bridge on board ship. He subsequently introduced it to the New York clubs, where it was played almost exclusively until Ely Culbertson got hold of it and, by some of the slickest promotion in history, developed it into the world's leading card game.

Culbertson was everywhere in the Thirties. His long, lean face peered at you from newspapers and magazines. The *Reader's Digest* frequently ran articles about him. His syndicated columns reached millions and he even taught bridge playing by radio. I remember a movie short in which he demonstrated how, by stacking the deck, a grand slam could be made with a hand that held few of the high cards. It was very impressive, but I'm blessed if I can remember how it is done.

Contract Bridge came to Wannego in the mid-Thirties and soon became an obsession. Everybody wanted to get into the act. People with no more card sense than a rabbit drove other people crazy trying to play the game. This was particularly true of the bridge club we organized. We had all kinds, from Yvonne Beltier who had played duplicate bridge in the city to Edna Petrie who, I swear, during the four months the club lasted, had no notion whatsoever what card game we were playing, if indeed she knew that we were playing cards at all.

Besides the Petries, ourselves and the Beltiers there was Ernest Stoneman and his wife, Beulah. (The Kings much preferred playing smear. Harry was convinced, I'm sure, that there was something unmanly about bridge, perhaps un-British, too.) So, as they say in drama club circles, we had a well-orchestrated cast. There were bold players, timid players and those who said, constantly, "What the hell? It's only a game."

Larry Petrie was a sneaky player. As often as not he'd open the bidding with, "Let me see now . . . I think . . . I'll bid clubs — for now."

This had the advantage of being non-committal. He hadn't said how many clubs, and he'd indicated to his partner that he might be pretty strong in other suits. Sneaky.

Let's say his opponent bid one spade.

This would bring the bidding around to Edna Petrie who had been sitting there talking about the colour of her new kitchen curtains. When informed that it was her turn to bid, she would frown deeply at the interruption and look at her hand as though she had never seen it before, which indeed she hadn't, and begin to arrange the cards in some sort of order. Then she would say, "What did you people bid?"

On being advised that the opening bid was one club, she would begin to count the clubs in her hand by pointing to them one after the other with a long, bony finger and muttering under her breath, "I don't see how they can bid *spades*. What did you bid partner?"

"One club."

"One club! Well . . ." Now she would count the spades, also by pointing to them one at a time. "I don't really think . . . oh . . . clubs. That's supposed to mean something, isn't it?"

"Sometimes."

"But I can never remember what it means. Well, I guess I'll bid spades."

"That's what they bid."

"Oh . . . then I can't bid it again, can I? Well, I pass."

When she'd finally lay down her hand it would be full of diamonds.

"Why didn't you bid diamonds?" her husband would ask.

"Because they're not as high as spades, silly."

"You could have bid two."

"But I couldn't bid against you."

And there the argument would end. Something strange happened when Larry and Edna happened to be partners. An attitude developed that was completely foreign to this perfectly happy couple. Something that I didn't like.

For Larry Petrie had one bad vice. Normally a quiet, non-aggressive man, the bridge club revealed a hitherto suppressed passion for gambling.

I have seen this gambling obsession turn up in other odd places. When I was head schoolmaster at H.M.C.S. *York* in Toronto I had on my staff a quiet, unassuming, studious man who everybody thought had no vices at all. But he had one. All day he'd sit at his desk while the ratings worked away at arithmetic problems, or slept, or matched quarters in the back seats, and he'd make marks on a piece of paper. Everyone took it for granted that he was preparing lessons or marking papers, but actually he was doping the races for the weekend meet at Woodbine or Lansdowne park.

He was hooked on racehorse gambling as anyone has ever been hooked on dope. Whenever the horses were running he was there, trying out the system he'd so carefully worked out when he was supposed to be teaching. In the wardroom he'd explain this system to anyone who'd listen. It was always absolutely fool-proof. Couldn't miss. All that was necessary, he'd explain, was to stick to the system.

Invariably after the day he'd be asked by someone how the system had stood up.

"Great. Exactly as I worked it out."

"Then you made a lot of money?"

"No."

"How come?"

"Well, there was this long shot in the third that really should have won . . . but . . . it didn't. But the system was great."

It was always the same story. Instead of making the four hundred dollars he'd have made by following his system, he lost sixty-five. But it never cured him.

Larry Petrie was of the same genre. A gambling fiend lurking behind the benign facade of a contented schoolteacher. As soon as the members of the bridge club would assemble (we played alternately at each other's houses) and the tables were set up and the salted peanuts and sticky candy were in place, Larry would sit up, rub his hands together, breathe a little faster and say, "We should really play for a little money. You know . . . tenth of a cent a point or something like that . . . ha, ha."

Before any of us could comment on that, Edna, who knew his weakness, would disclaim, "I should say not. If you want to gamble go down to the livery barn and play poker."

"I was only kidding. You know that."

"Ha! When it comes to gambling you have no self-mastery."

Edna was great on self-mastery. She'd been raised by an aunt who was very strict and Edna remained true to her principles. She was strong against swearing, drinking, gambling, sex and all the other sins. On the rare occasion when somebody could afford a bottle we had to be careful that Edna didn't surreptitiously pick up half-empty glasses and pour the booze down the sink. A terrible thing to do at any time but in those hard days a dastardly crime.

The Beltiers were an interesting bridge couple. Yvonne played with the skill and precision of a true duplicate bridger while Danny showed a decidedly cavalier attitude towards the game. Because of his short-sightedness he never knew exactly what was in his hand and he had the titillating habit of bidding three no trump after everybody else had passed.

"Well, I guess it's time for three no trump," he'd announce happily just as everyone else was throwing in their hand. Yvonne never criticized him out loud for this. A fine-line frown would cross her forehead as she laid down her hand and looked for a magazine to read. The most annoying part of this performance was that, often as not, he'd make the damned bid.

But it was as a kibitzer that Danny really excelled. When he was dummy, which was often, he'd wander between the tables to check on the other players. A good kibitzer should be able to see the cards at least from a slightly bent position. Danny had to lean over the player's shoulder and get his eyes so close to the cards that all the player could see was the curly black hair on the back of Danny's head. By the time he'd got around the table and inspected all the hands — otherwise how could he gauge the play? — the game tended to be somewhat disrupted.

Beulah and Ernest Stoneman played the game strictly according to their natures. Beulah was quiet and contemplative; Ernest loud and disgusted. He hated the game and played it only because he hated reading or listening to the radio even more. He cursed his hand loudly if it were bad, banged on the table and filled his mouth with salted peanuts. If his hand were good, he'd tilt his chair away back — many a wooden chair collapsed under the strain — grin broadly and say, "Now, by gawd, this is more like it. What do you say there, partner? Let's go get 'em."

As often as not his partner would pass, and then he'd come forward with a roar, banging the chair legs down and bashing the table with his elbows. "How in the name of hell can you pass when I've got a hand like this?"

Aileen played the game shrewdly and well; I played it shrewdly and terrible. I caught on to the fundamentals of the game quickly enough and sometimes I could even apply them. My trouble consisted of mental blind spots and complete lack of interest which anyone who has ever lived with a writer will recognize. It's caused by constructing plots and devising dialogue when you should be concentrating on the matter in hand.

The bridge club lasted most of one winter and then, one cold, miserable night in March, it came to a terrible end.

March is the worst month of the year in Saskatchewan. It always seems that the long, cold winter should be ending by March and it never does. November isn't bad because winter begins then and there is always the fascination of the changing seasons. The first snow comes and it's clean and new and fresh. Kids chase each other through it and make fox and goose trails. Dogs frolic in it, and there is even some fun in the crunch it makes beneath your overshoes on wooden sidewalks.

December is saved by Christmas. January is bad, cold and windy and long. The relentless winds whine around the windows and blow in through the cracks. Pumps freeze up and snow piles high over the path to the backhouse. The brown stain of slops grows bigger and bigger at the back door and the coal in the bin shrinks at a great rate.

February is worse. That's when old horses in the fields give up and lie down in the lee of strawstacks and die. You can hear the coyotes tearing at their frozen carcasses at night. Old humans, too, often quit during February. The winter is just too long for them. Their tired old bones can't take it any more and, after the long, struggling years, they lie down peacefully and pass on to whatever reward awaits them.

And then comes the first thaw of March. The snow goes soft. Brown horse-turds show up in the deep rutted road; snow melts away from the side of the house, thus giving up its insulating quality; water drips from the eaves to form long spears of ice that reach the ground. And people say, "It's come at last. Spring is here. We've survived another winter."

But March is only playing one of her dirty little tricks. The cold winds come again and blow clear through the house where the banking has melted away and exposed it. The wind rises to gale force and shrieks and howls about the corners, tearing at the shingles, raising the crusted snow and dust into the air. Often new snow comes and joins the old so that the air is so full of swirling snow and dust that a man dare not venture the length of his own yard. Winter is taking its last savage bite. The March blizzards are the cruelest of the whole winter.

It was during one of these wretched evenings that we had the bridge club at our house. "I wonder if anyone will come out on a night like this," Aileen pondered as she waxed the linoleum floor.

"Oh they'll come," I said. "What else is there to do? I hope they all bring sweaters. I can't keep this house warm."

I was right. They came, each bringing with him his own hate against the weather and the hard times. Each with nerve ends rubbed raw with the promise of spring so cruelly snatched away.

And it was then that, when Larry Petrie suggested that we liven things up a bit by playing for small stakes, nobody, not even his wife, objected. We were all feeling mean enough to want to humiliate and deprive even our best friends. So we settled on a tenth of a cent a point and began the game.

People who can't afford to lose a little money shouldn't gamble, and not one of us could afford to lose a plugged nickel. Now the whole game took on an entirely different aspect. The peccadilloes and idiosyncracies of the players that had been highly amusing at best and slightly annoying at worst now became terrible.

Right off we established the rule that there would be no talking across the table, and that was like tying the hands of a deaf mute.

None of us but Yvonne knew anything of the neat little systems by which bridge players tell each other the nature of their hands. We could only sit, glum and suspicious, furtively peering at each other from the corner of our eyes, vainly trying to glean a straw of information.

It was a weird evening, as I remember it. The fierce west wind raging outside and the storms of avarice raging within. Gone was the easy banter and gay laughter that came when some fool play was made, replaced by grim, tight-lipped mutterings and fearful scowls. As luck in bridge often does, it all ran one way. Ernest Stoneman, the only man with a decent salary, got all the good luck, while Larry Petrie whose salary was less than mine got all the bad. And the worse his luck got the more desperate and intense he became.

"We've simply got to stop this," Aileen whispered to me in the kitchen. We had finished our rubber with the Beltiers and broken about even.

"How?" I asked.

"I could serve lunch."

"Try it."

So Aileen announced in a gay but firm tone that lunch would be served.

"Can't until we finish the rubber," Petrie snarled. He had just been set on a four spade bid, doubled, and dropped five hundred points. Which, added to the two dollars he'd already lost, would make a real hole in his budget.

So, there was nothing to do but watch the two couples fight it out. While the coffee perked away on the kitchen stove we watched them deal and bid and pass and their faces grow grey with the strain. Then it happened.

Out of the deck of cards came four of those crazy hands that can sometimes turn up in this crazy game. I can see them yet. The men had all the good cards, the women nothing. Larry had no less than ten spades from the king down to the deuce with only the ten and five missing. Edna had the ace and the five. Yvonne had no spades at all and Ernest, who was on Larry's right, had the lone ten.

Ernest had the other three aces and a long string of hearts including the top honour cards. It was clearly a fight between Larry and Ernest. And that's exactly what it was — a fight. For now all their natural antipathy for each other came boiling to the surface. Each disliked the other's type immensely. Ernest called men like Larry egghead milksops, while to Larry, Ernest was an insensitive bully. And there, in our tiny house, with the March winds fussing outside, the battle was joined.

The rest of us stood around uncertain and unhappy. There was no way to stop it. Larry saw his chance to win back the money he'd lost. It was more like a poker game than a bridge game. Up and up went the bidding — four, five, six — and then Ernest banged the table with a big fist and declared, "Grand slam in hearts. God damn it beat that!"

Larry was shaking like the fender of a Model-T. He wiped his face, carefully laid his cards on the table and said, "Grand slam in spades. God damn it beat *that*."

It was the first time any of us had heard him swear, but not the last.

Ernest couldn't take that — not from a milksop. I think for a moment he thought he was playing poker and could bluff his way out. Anyway, to the surprise of the kibitzers and the horror of his wife, he banged the table even harder and bellowed, "Grand slam in no trump."

"Double!"

"Redouble!"

Then, as the realization of what he'd done came upon him, his face became very red, his jaw muscles jumped and for a split second it looked as though he would hit somebody. Instead he glanced at his wife and that quieted him. Something there told him all would be well.

Slowly and deliberately Larry led the nine of spades and held his breath. Where was that ace? Yvonne laid down her hand. It wasn't there. Ernest blanched. He was done for. From the dummy he played a small club.

Now it was Edna's play and she was terrified. She was seeing a new Larry and what she saw dismayed her. All through the bidding it was this and not the disposition of cards that had absorbed her mind. Now she began to think, and that was a mistake.

From the fragments of bridge lore that had filtered into her mind in the past months she tried to pick one that would fit the occasion. There was something about third player playing high — or was it low. Oh dear. And aces, they always confused her. In one of the rare occasions when she'd paid some attention to the game she'd seen Yvonne hold back an ace and everyone had commented on what an astute play it had been. Oh dear. She wished people would say something and not stare so. "She who hesitates is lost," she mumbled sickly, and played the five.

Ernest took the trick with the ten and all the other tricks after it. That is, he would have taken all the tricks, but he never got the chance. Larry Petrie flew screaming into the air when the ten was played and upset the bridge table, spilling candy and cards all over the floor. In a few brief but concise sentences he went over his married life with Edna and it was plain that inherent in their relationship had been a certain amount of frustration. He referred to her family and the wedding and even to the matter of their having no children. Then, without pausing he threw a five-dollar bill onto the coffee table, grabbed his coat and tore out into the storm.

We persuaded Edna, who by now was bawling like a baby, that she should stay with us for the night and sleep on our couch. In silence we ate our salmon sandwiches and drank our coffee. Then the Stoneman's left, saying that under no circumstances would they take Larry's money. It had all been in fun.

The next day Edna was subdued and pensive. At breakfast she ignored her food and sat thinking. She had learned something about her husband that she'd never suspected. He actually could get mad. Maybe he'd hated her all along and only his mild nature had kept him from blowing up long before this. For the first time in her life she was unsure of this seemingly mild, inoffensive, non-aggressive man.

Larry dropped in on his way to school. He was bewildered and mumblingly apologetic. I guess he'd learned something about himself, too, that he'd never suspected. Behind the apologies and bustle of getting ready to go, we noticed them looking at each other speculatively. Never again would they be completely sure of each other. I suspect their marriage improved immensely.

Spring came shortly after that. Crows cawed from the poplar trees and horned larks carolled on the wing. The sun shone, the snow melted, the frogs sang in the sloughs. Winter had finally let go. The time for long evenings had come with gardening and tennis and walks on the rutted roads. There was no more time for bridge and our little club never met again.

Harry J. Boyle's second medal winner was a novel, The Luck of the Irish, *in 1976. Among many other things it is about a pilgrimage "Wee Tom" and his sister Carrie make to Fort Ste. Marie after their barn burns down.*

HARRY J. BOYLE

from The Luck of the Irish

The barn went up in flames and smoke the next Friday morning. It was at the beginning of July, when everything was held in the sun's fists of heat, without a breath of air stirring. Tom and Carrie were at St. Patrick's making their First Friday devotions; as the less devout observed, they were long on faith and short on luck.

The Brophys heard a whoofing sound and spied the smoke and flame whipping out the door of the mow. But fire in the country was always something that people were helpless to do much about. By the time the Brophys got there, all they could do was pull a pair of calves out of the stable. When the Macraes arrived, half the people of the township were standing staring as the barn's fiery remains collapsed into the stone walls of the stable.

Charlie Wilson, as usual, made his sly nudge of the tongue, this time about the fervor of the Marcraes.

"They'd've been better off pumping water than praying."

Mulligan was defensive.

"Ah, there's little you can do when you get the spontaneous combustion."

"I suppose" said Charlie, "them tongues of fire of the Holy Ghost came down in the wrong place."

Some of the women gasped when Charlie said it, but the men were silent. Men in the country are always quiet after a barn fire, especially when livestock is involved. It's their way. They went around picking up things and putting them in other places. Others picked the same things up and moved them again, in the dazed, dance-like way of men faced with something they can do nothing about.

"Big Tom was a so-so farmer anyhow," suggested Mulligan the drover, "and I don't suppose he could have taught the boy much. That hay must have gone in green. I've told him where he can pick up another sow at a decent price."

In spite of being a man never known to give an inch in a deal, the drover had a soft spot for Tom. The Brophys said his car was often in the Macrae laneway when there wasn't a blessed thing he could buy. Once when he stopped at the O'Briens' store to buy Stag tobacco, the soft black plug he chewed, Dan McCabe twitted him a bit.

"Is it Carrie you're thinkin' of takin' off the wee lad's hands?"

Mulligan, the slightly bulging eyes turning bluer, stroked his moustache, left and right, and answered without amusement.

"I do feel a bit for those that never have the luck at all, and stick at it without giving up. There's plenty that have the luck who squander it."

Mulligan, when he had a mind to it, could give as well as anyone. O'Brien chuckled at Dan McCabe's discomfiture, because Dan was a great one for sitting around the store when he should have been minding his farm. But Dan was a caustic one: "Ah, if there was such a thing as luck, Mulligan, you'd be buying it up and selling it in Toronto to the packing house along with all them dying bulls you get them for making the baloney."

The drover smiled. But when O'Brien was outside with him, cranking up the red gas pump with the overhead gas tank, Mulligan spoke what was on his mind.

"Will, that pair sure enough get the bad of it. I picked out a sow over at St. Clement's and got Tom a good deal and got old Francis Dee Costello to lend the money. Told Tom to be careful this time when she farrowed, and Friday night some dogs chased her in the lot behind the bar while that pair were at devotions, and he's had to butcher her."

"The truth is, Father Gibbons," explained Will O'Brien, relating it later as a kind of appeal, "somebody has to do something to save them. You can't tell Carrie anything, and the small man hasn't a notion about how to really farm. Putting green hay in the barn before it was dry was like setting a match to the whole thing. Mind you, they pay for what they get with the eggs and the cream, but they've cut their buying short, and you notice they walk to mass now. It's six weeks since they bought gas, and only two gallons at that!"

Father Gibbons nodded solemnly in the way of men who haven't the faintest idea of how to solve the problem in hand. Will O'Brien knew it, but he felt better for passing on the problem. Of course, it came right back to him, because the priest sent Nellie McGuigan over to talk to Mrs. O'Brien.

The two women came up with the idea of having a lawn social.

"Good God, woman," exploded the priest when the housekeeper suggested it. "And what about the new roof for the church we must get from a garden party?"

It upset her so much that for a week she gave him boiled eggs for breakfast, which she knew he didn't like. There were ideas about a dance, but Father Gibbons was cool. The last one he agreed to had ended up with a deficit and a fight. Constable Walsh took the two Cormac boys and the Finlon twins to jail for the ruckus. The priest had a hard time explaining to the bishop the headline in the *Handrich Signal* about the fighting and possession of bootleg whiskey. The part that really hurt was the first paragraph which began, "A wild donnybrook at St. Patrick's Church. . . . " Several Catholics threatened to cancel their subscriptions to the *Signal* because of the strong language. It was a fuss, they were agreed, but to call it a donnybrook was too strong. But since they were all in arrears on their subscriptions, anyhow, they dropped the matter.

After the fire the Cormacs, the Brophys, and the Redmonds helped make a kind of barn out of the Macrae driving shed. But the stone foundation of the barn was still there in the early fall, as a standing reproach to the whole congregation. There was a lot of talk and no action amongst the Irish, until the Methodists stirred and collected grain and several loads of hay for Tom.

"God help us, men," exclaimed Will O'Brien to the half-dozen of them sitting on the front stoop of the store on an early September evening. "Is there nothing to be done for them? Here we are sitting around like crows in January, and the Protestants showing the only Christian charity in the community."

So the Catholics raised some more hay and grain for the Macraes. Ned Fitzpatrick gave them a heavey horse; it was felt that he wanted to get rid of the poor thing, and didn't have the heart to shoot it. Then a delegation went to see Father Gibbons. They waited in his study until he took off his vestments and came from the vestry.

"What'll we say to him?" demanded Sean Casey.

"Well, maybe he can think of some way to sort of . . . "

"Gentlemen, is this the Holy Name Society meeting . . ? "

They were silent while he sat down by his roll-top desk, selected a cigar and lit it, puffing carefully before uttering another word.

"Now, will you be having a Communion Breakfast this fall? I might get Father Foley to come over from Queensbridge and make a speech."

The laughter was shaky. Foley was a great, fat one with a drum voice who loved to raise hell about fornication and drinking. Father Gibbons asked him whenever he detected some backsliding, and couldn't bring himself to give the hellfire and brimstone bit. It was Father Foley who had preached a sudden Forty Hours, two weeks after the bulging Flannery twins married the town lads who had taken them to the Dominion Day celebrations in Handrich, some six months before.

"We've been thinking about Carrie and Wee Tom."

The priest groaned.

"Ah, who hasn't. Who hasn't indeed?"

It was a go-around conversation. The smoky, little study was gloomy with old drapes, class pictures from seminary, the portrait of a sad pope, and a rather unartistic drawing of the Blessed Virgin awkwardly holding a half-grown Infant Jesus, with a baby's face stuck on the body.

"My sister painted that," was the way the pastor explained its presence when a visitor stared at it in horror or simple curiosity.

The Macrae matter concerned, when they managed to get anywhere near the nub of it, money. There had been rain the night of the lawn social and so the proceeds were not enough to buy more than a third of the shingles needed for the church roof. The man running the wheel of fortune was a misfortune, since he gave out more than he took in. It was agreed that whatever was made at the fowl supper (originally intended to repair the paint damaged by the leaking roof), would have to go for the shingles. The streaks on the walls and the Stations of the Cross that the leaky roof had washed out, including Christ Consoling The Women of Jerusalem, would remain as they were.

The question of how much good a new barn at Macraes was really going to be remained unspoken when the meeting broke up. Truth is, the women got tired of waiting. The younger children were restless, and the older ones were getting out of control. A few toots of one car horn set off a full cacophony. Normally a man could ignore such a display, but this time they were relieved by the excuse to break up the confab. The priest released them.

"Now men, I'll take it under advisement, say some prayers, sleep on it and we'll see what comes up. The Lord has a way of providing answers to problems like this."

That seemed adequate. It at least gave them a sense of some accomplishment. They left and, of course, huddled on the rectory steps for a while, to make it clear that they weren't leaving in submissive response to the horns. Then a week passed and nothing happened. Father Gibbons did a lot of pacing on the walk between the church and the rectory with his breviary in his hand. O'Brien noticed that he was staring more than reading. Cars in the evening drove slowly by the Macrae place to look at the blackened stones of the stable foundation. There was a lot of talk at night in O'Brien's store but, as Joe Cormac said, the gab chased itself like a snake after its own tail.

"Wee Tom might buy the barn on the Redmond grass farm."

"Billy would never sell it."

"Ah, look at it another way. What would Tom have then except another old barn? He should buy a new steel one."

"With what? That place has been mortgaged since the day Old Tom bought it."

Which, as Will O'Brien observed after listening to the men who sat around his store each night, brought it all back to where it started. On Friday, tired of the talk, Josie McGuire, Ned Flanigan's wife Rose Mary, and Adeline Brophy called on Carrie Macrae. They were the executive of the Young Ladies of Mary and they had a notion a quilting bee might help the Macraes.

Carrie met them on the back stoop. All of them had been together at St. Patrick's Separate School, but that didn't ease the tension. Carrie made no move to ask them in. There was some niff-nawing back and forth about the weather, until finally Carrie took the wind from the sails completely.

"Josie, Addy, Rose Mary, if you won't say what it is you're about, I suppose I'll have to say it for you. I can't give you much for the Young Ladies of Mary Mission fund, with our trouble and all, but here."

With that, she dug into the pocket of the grey sweater and sorted two twenty-five cent bills from the chaff. The Young Ladies of Mary mouthed air until Josie accepted the money. They were quiet for a mile down the fourth concession.

"Lord love a duck," explained Adeline, "they must really be having it hard. Carrie's mother used to save those little shin plasters."

"How do you know that?"

"She told my mother, and that was years ago."

The story heated up the talk, and the dependence on Father Gibbons to come up with a solution grew. When they told him, he acted uncomfortable because he knew how Moira Macrae had been a saver. She had to be, with a Kearney background, and her husband's ways; Josie's mother recalled how she had put odd bits and pieces of change away in a cracked tea pot "unbeknownst to her husband, for rainy days." It was natural to assume that Carrie was down to scratching bits left from her mother's saving.

Now there was a cold cast to the wind and although it was only September, it made everyone think of fall. Fall meant stabling the stock. There was Tom Macrae with his few cows, four yearlings that needed winter feeding before market, some calves, and a team of horses, as well as the heavey one, and only the poor shed that leaned to one side as if it was too tired to face another winter as a stable.

There were questions but no answers, and the news about Father Gibbons was disheartening. At confessions on Saturday night he had been abrupt, slamming the shutters on both sides of the confessional and handing out penance as if his mind wasn't on the sin he was hearing at all.

"My gracious alive," exclaimed the widow Rose Kennedy in O'Brien's after confession on Saturday night, "He's giving out the three Our Fathers and three Hail Marys like a machine. You could give him a murder this night and you'd get the same thing as you would for — for — "

"Go on," nudged Charlie Wilson, "as for what?"

Rose blushed, picked up her tea and sugar and swept out of the store.

There was a touchiness in everyone on Sunday at the ten o'clock mass. The fact is Mrs. Joe Walsh, who always confessed on Sunday mornings, didn't get a chance because Father Gibbons didn't even set foot in the confessional that morning. In church there was much less foot-scraping and coughing than usual. The McGuire youngest, who always got his father to take him out by sniggering, got a cuff on the ear that surprised him into a sullen silence. Tom and Carrie were in their usual seat, second from the front on the epistle side. The O'Donnell sisters, after sweeping majestically up the centre aisle, genuflecting and then making their little head-dips to the statue of St. Thérèse of Lisieux on the gospel-side alter as if she were a close friend, sat in the front pew.

Father Gibbons read the Gospel standing behind the commun-ion railing, took what seemed a long time with the announce-ments, and then, pulling a a handkerchief from his sleeve, he mopped his brow. He stuffed it back carefully and blessed himself in a fortifying way.

"This world is a place of trouble and mystery — that's the Lord's way of doing it. We may be leading what we consider to be good — holy lives and yet the troubles do come on us. Job . . . now there was one case where the trouble piled in. . . . "

He lapsed into silence. He apparently had difficulty keeping his train of thought about Job. After another swabbing of his face and a further disposal of the handkerchief, he went on, "I have been reminded recently that many of us do our duties . . . quite well in attending mass, devotions . . . some even making the First Fridays. But perhaps we could just stir ourselves a little extra and . . . ."

Father Gibbons paused. He was a man of simple homilies. As he said himself, he had made it through the seminary by the skin of his teeth, faith, and by his mother's prayers.

"At this time when we have had a good harvest — and some troubles — we might consider, for instance, that the Lord re-warded our prayers with rain when the dry spell looked so bad in early June. And now maybe we should do a little extra. . . . "

By this time the general speculation was whether he was going to suggest two fowl suppers or a box social, and most people felt let down. The problem was that Carrie was the kind who would never accept what she felt was charity. But the sweating man in the vestments surprised them.

"Here in Canada, we are very fortunate. In France there is the great shrine of Lourdes — a marvellous place where our Lady herself has responded to pilgrims since the child — now the Bles-sed Bernadette — saw the vision. And there are even here some who know the generosity of the — well."

He had strayed into a subject of controversy. It was known that Murphy, the lawyer in Handrich, had made the trip to France because of a hernia, but it wasn't a clear case of cure because there were rumours that he still wore a truss. Then again, there were people who said he kept on wearing it because he simply used it as an excuse to avoid work. The priest abandoned subtlety.

"I've been reading this week about the martyrs, Brébeuf, Jacques, Lallemand, and others at a place north of Toronto, where there is a shrine. Of course, it is run by the Jesuits. . . . "

He hesitated. Father Gibbons had stopped asking Jesuits to conduct Forty Hours devotions after one had rejected a nightcap and devoted his fierce sermons from then on to the evil of drink.

"For all that, Fort Ste. Marie, near Midland, is a grand place and there are reports of some tremendous help for people who go to it with — ah — their intentions. Now there may be some great problems in your life and you don't quite know what to do. Wouldn't it be a grand thing in this time of year if you found the way to make a pilgrimage?" He was hitting his stride now. He went on, quickly. "Make a good confession, go to communion and ask them blessed souls who braved a new world to bring the world of Christ and the Church to the Indians and were awarded with martyrdom by scalping and hot coals."

Letting that sink in, he half turned to the alter and then added, "They perished in the flames. It was a purifying and sanctifying flame that some day will elevate them to the highest rank in heaven as saints. How could our own Canadian martyrs refuse our requests — especially those of need — genuine need?"

Tom and Carrie walked home. As usual, they weren't using the car. When they were gone, the congregation of grown-ups crowded into O'Brien's store. There was some confusion. Some thought it was stretching a point to call French priests Canadians, but the main fuss was about determining where the Shrine was located.

Mulligan, the most travelled one present, settled it.

"The best way is go down through Guelph, take the road north of Toronto and then go north. You go up through Barrie and then to Midland. It's next to Penetanguishene where they speak French, but you don't have to go in there. A grand place it is. It's not French so people say, they mostly talk English."

Robertson Davies is perhaps the most truly literary winner of the Leacock Medal for Humour. Presently serving as master of Massey College of the University of Toronto, Davies has already been editor of Saturday Night *and editor and publisher of the Peterborough* Examiner. *With great success, he has written both plays and novels. Like Leacock, he has won both the Lorne Pierce Medal and the Governor General's award. The selection here is from the beginning of his 1955 medal-winning* Leaven of Malice *and can only whet the reader's appetite to read the whole novel.*

ROBERTSON DAVIES

from Leaven of Malice

It was on the 31st of October that the following announcement appeared under 'Engagements', in the Salterton *Evening Bellman:*

> Professor and Mrs Walter Vambrace are pleased to announce the engagement of their daughter, Pearl Veronica, to Solomon Bridgetower, Esq., son of Mrs Bridgetower and the late Professor Solomon Bridgetower of this city. Marriage to take place in St Nicholas' Cathedral at eleven o'clock a.m., November 31st.

Few of the newspaper's readers found anything extra-ordinary about this intimation, or attached any significance to the fact that it was made on Hallowe'en.

When fortune decides to afflict a good man and rob him of his peace, she often chooses a fine day to begin.

The 1st of November was a beautiful day, and the sun shone with a noble autumn glory as Gloster Ridley, editor of *The Bellman*, walked through the park to his morning's work. The leaves rustled about his feet and he kicked them with pleasure. It was like tramping through some flaky breakfast food, he thought, and smiled at the unromantic fancy. That was not in the least what his colleague Mr Shillito would think about autumn leaves. He recalled what Mr Shillito had written yesterday on the subject of Hallowe'en — which Mr Shillito had managed five times to call All Hallows' Eve and twice 'this unhallowed Eve' — and his face darkened; the Old Mess had been at his most flowery and most drivelling. But Ridley quickly banished Mr Shillito from his mind; that was a problem to be dealt with later in the day. Meanwhile, his walk to his office was his own, for his own agreeable musings. His day had begun well; Constant Reader had prepared an excellent breakfast for him, and the hateful Blubadub, though faintly audible in the kitchen, had kept out of his sight. He sniffed the delightfully cool and smoky autumn air. The day stretched before him, full of promise.

In less than a week he would be fifty. Middle-aged, unquestionably, but how much better he felt than ever in his youth! From his seventeenth year until quite recently, Anxiety had ridden him with whip and spur, and only when well past forty had he gained any hope of unseating her. But today . . . ! His bosom's lord, he told himself, sat lightly in his throne. Who said that? Romeo. Pooh, Romeo knew nothing about the quiet, well-controlled self-satisfaction of a man who might well, before he was fifty-one, be a Doctor of Civil Law.

To be Doctor Ridley! He would not, of course, insist upon the title, but it would be his, and if he should ever chance to be introduced to a new acquaintance as Mister, there would almost certainly be someone at hand to say, probably with a pleasant laugh, 'I think it should be Doctor Ridley, shouldn't it?' Not that he attached undue importance to such distinctions; he knew precisely how matters stood. After what he had done for Waverley University they must reward him with a substantial fee or give him an honorary doctorate. Waverley, like all Canadian universities, was perpetually short of money, whereas its store of doctorates was inexhaustible. They would not even have to give him a gown, for that glorious adornment would be returnable immediately after the degree ceremony. It would be a doctorate, certainly, and he would value it. It was a symbol of security and success, and it would be another weapon with which to set his old enemy, Anxiety, at bay. He would feel himself well rewarded when he was Doctor Ridley.

He had fairly earned it. When it had occurred to some of the Governors of the University two years ago ago that Waverley ought to establish a course in journalism, it had been to him that they turned for advice. When the division was taken to make plans for such a course, he had been the only person not directly associated with the University to sit upon the committee; tactfully and unobtrusively, he had guided it. He had listened, without visible emotion, to the opinions of professors upon the Press and upon the duty which some of them believed they owed to society to reform the Press. He had discussed without mirth or irony their notions of the training which would produce a good news-paperman. He had counselled against foolish spending, and he had fought tirelessly for spending which he believed to be neces-sary. Little by little his academic colleagues on the committee had recognized that he knew what he was talking about. He had triumphed in persuading them that their course should occupy three years instead of two. His had been the principal voice in planning the course, and his would certainly be the principal voice in hiring the staff. Next autumn the course would be included in the Waverley syllabus, and now his work was almost done.

One task still lay before him, and it was a pleasant one. He was to deliver the first of the Wadsworth Lectures for the current academic year. These public lectures, founded twenty years be-fore to inform the university opinion on matters of public impor-tance, were to be devoted this year to 'The Press and The People'. A Cabinet Minister would speak, and the United Kingdom High Commissioner; a celebrated philosopher and an almost equally celebrated psychologist were also to give their views. But the first of the five lectures would be given by himself, Gloster Ridley, editor of the Salterton *Evening Bellman*, and he was determined that it should be the best of the lot. For, after all, he knew at first hand what a newspaper was, and the other lecturers did not. And it was widely admitted that under his guidance *The Bellman* was a very good paper.

Yes, he thought, he had a shrewd idea what the Press was. Not a cheap Press, nor yet the pipedream Press that the university re-formers had talked about at those early meetings. And he knew about the People, too, for he was one of them. He had had no university education. That was one of the reasons why it would fall so sweetly upon his ear to be spoken of as Doctor Ridley.

Oh, yes, he would tell them about the Press and the People. The Press, he would explain, belonged to the People — to all of the People, whether their tastes and needs were common or uncom-mon. He would speak amusingly, but there would be plenty in his lecture for them to chew on. He would begin with a quotation from Shakespeare, from *All's Well that Ends Well*; a majority of his listeners, even in a university audience, would not have read the play, but he would remind them that people outside university halls could be well-read. Of a newspaper he would quote, 'It is like a barber's chair that fits all buttocks; the pin-buttock, the quatch-buttock, the brawn buttock, or any buttock'. And then he would develop his theme, which was that in any issue of a good daily paper every reader, gentle or simple, liberally educated or barely able to read, should find not only the news of the day but something which was, in a broad sense, of special concern to himself.

It would be a good lecture. Possibly his publisher would have it reprinted in pamphlet form, and distribute it widely to other papers. Without vulgar hinting, he thought he could insinuate that idea into his publisher's mind.

Musing pleasantly on these things, he reached the newspaper building.

He climbed the stairs to his second-floor office somewhat furtively, for he did not want to meet Mr Shillito and exchange greetings with him. He was determined to do nothing which might appear two-faced, and Mr Shillito's greetings were of so courtly and old-world a nature that he was often enticed into a geniality of which he was afterward ashamed. He must not feed the Old Mess sugar from his hand, while concealing the sword behind his back. But his path was clear, and he slipped into his office unseen by anyone but Miss Green, his secretary. She followed him through the door.

'No personal mail this morning, Mr Ridley. Just the usual. And the switchboard says somebody called you before nine, but wouldn't leave their name.'

The usual was neatly marshalled on his desk. Miss Green had been solicitous about the morning's item since the day, more than three years ago, when somebody had sent him a dead rat, wrapped as a gift, with a card explaining that this was a comment upon *The Bellman's* stand on a matter of public controversy. She had failed, since then, to intercept an envelope filled with used toilet paper (a political innuendo) but in general her monitorship was good. There were ten Letters to the Editor, and he took them up without curiosity, and with a thick black pencil ready in his hand.

Two, from 'Fair Play' and 'Indignant', took the Salterton City

Council to task, the former for failing to re-surface the street on which he lived, and the latter for proposing to pave a street on which he owned property, thereby raising the rates. Both writers had allowed anonymity to go to their heads, and both had added personal notes requesting that their true names be withheld, as they feared reprisals of an unspecified nature. From 'Fair Play's' letter Ridley deleted several sentences, and changed the word 'shabby' to 'ill-advised'. 'Indignant' required more time, as the writer had not used enought verbs to make his meaning clear, and had apparently punctuated his letter after writing it, on some generous but poorly conceived principle of his own.

The third letter was so badly written that even his accustomed eye could make very little of it, but it appeared to be from an aggrieved citizen whose neighbour spitefully threw garbage into his back yard. Other iniquities of the neighbour were rehearsed, but Ridley marked the letter for Miss Green's attention; she would return it with the usual note declining to publish libellous material.

The next three letters were legible, grammatical and reasonable, and dealt with a scheme to create a traffic circle at a principal intersection of the city. They were quickly given headings and marked for the printer.

The seventh letter urged that a hockey coach who had trained some little boys the winter before be prevented, by force if necessary, from training them in the winter to come. He was, it appeared, a monster and a heretic whose influence would prove the ruin of hockey tactics and the downfall of that sport in Canada. It was signed with a bold signature and a street address, but the editor's eye was not deceived. He consulted the Salterton *City Directory* and found, as he had suspected, that there was no such number as 183 Maple Street, and no such person as Arthur C. Brown. With a sigh for the duplicity of mankind, he threw the letter into the wastepaper basket. He was a little pleased, also, that the intuition which suggested to him that a signature was a fake was in good working order.

The eighth letter was from a farmer who charged the Salterton Exhibition Committee with great unfairness and some measure of dishonesty in the matter of awarding prizes in the Pullet subsection of the Poultry Division of the Livestock Competition at the fall fair. He was aware, he said, that the fair had taken place seven weeks ago, but it had taken him a little time to get around to writing his letter. It went into the waste basket.

The ninth letter caused Ridley both surprise and annoyance. It read:

Sir:

Warm congratulations on the editorial headed 'Whither The Toothpick' which appeared in your edition of 28/x. It is such delightful bits of whimsy as this which raise the tone of *The Bellman* above that of any other paper which comes to my notice and give it a literary grace which is doubly distinguished, in a world where style is rapidly becoming a thing of the past. This little gem joins many another in my scrapbook. Happy the city which can boast a *Bellman!* Happy the *Bellman* which boasts a writer who can produce the felicitous 'Toothpick'.

Yours, etc.
ELDON BUMFORD

No error about that signature; old Bumford, at eighty-four, was reversing the usual tendency of old men to damn everything, and was loud in his praise of virtually everything. No reason not to publish it. Dead certainty that if it did not appear within a day or two old Bumford would be on the telephone, or worse still, in the chair opposite his desk, asking why. And yet it was out of the question that the thing should be published. Ridley laid it aside for later consideration.

The tenth letter was in a well-known hand, in green ink. Letters in that hand, and in that ink, appeared on Ridley's desk every two weeks, and thier message was always the same: the world had forgotten God. Sometimes it showed this forgetfulness by permitting children to read the comic strips; sometimes drink — invariably referred to as 'beverage alcohol' — was the villain; sometimes it was the decline in church attendance which especially afflicted the writer; in winter the iniquity of ski-trains, which travelled during church hours and bore young people beyond the sound of church bells, was complained of; in summer it was the whoredom of two-piece bathing suits, and shorts which revealed girls' legs, which was consuming society. The writer was able to support all her arguments by copious quotations from Holy Writ, and she did so; now and then she related a modern enormity to one of the monsters in Revelation. The letter at hand urged that the Prime Minister be advised to declare November 11th a National Day of Prayer, in which, by an act of mass repentance, Canada might be cleansed of her wrong-doings, and at the end of which her iniquity might be pardoned. The letter was marked 'Urgent — Print this At Once'. Wearily, Ridley laid it aside. This was, perhaps, the voice of the people, and the voice of the people, no editor is ever permitted to forget, is the voice of God. It was a pity, he reflected, that God's utterances needed such a lot of editorial revision.

Disposing of the remainder of the morning's mail was easy. . . .

He threw the whole lot into the waste basket, filling it almost to the brim. . . .

Sighing, Ridley turned to his next task, which was a consideration of the editorial pages of thirty-eight contemporaries of *The Bellman*, which had been cut out and stacked ready to hand. He would have liked to take ten minutes to think about Mr Swithin Shillito and the problem which he presented, but he had not ten minutes to spare. People who form their opinions of what goes on in a daily newspaper office upon what they see at the movies imagine that the life of a journalist is one of exciting and unforseen events; but as Ridley intended to say in his Wadsworth lecture, it was rooted deep in a stern routine; let the heavens fall and the earth consume in flames, the presses must not be late; if the reading public was to enjoy the riotous excess of the world's news, the newspaperman must bend that excess to the demands of a mechanical routine and a staff of union workers. Before one o'clock he must read all that lay on his desk, talk to the news editor, plan and write at least one leading article, and see any visitors who could win past Miss Green. He could spare no ten minutes for pondering about Mr Shillito. He must read, read, dig, dig, and plan, plan as the Old Mess himself advised.

Upon the right-hand drawboard of his desk was his typewriter; he slipped a piece of paper under the roller and typed a heading: *Notes and Comment*. It was an ancient custom of the paper to end the editorial columns with a few paragraphs of brief observation, pithy and, if possible, amusing, and Ridley wrote most of them. It was not that he fancied himself as a wit, but the job must be done by somebody, and better his wit than Shillito's; the Old Mess had a turn for puns and what he called 'witty *aperçus*'. He picked up the first of the editorial pages, and ran his eye quickly over it: a leader complaining of high taxation, and two subsidiary editorials, one sharply rebuking a South American republic for some wickedness connected with coffee and another explaining that the great cause of traffic accidents was not drunkenness or mechanical defects in cars, but elementary bad manners on the part of drivers. There were no paragraphs which he might steal, or use as priming for the pump of his own wit. . . .

Ridley hurried on. The next page which came to hand carried a sharp warning to the Government that continued high taxation would beget a dreadful vengeance at the next general election, and a lesser piece which said that modern children would be less prone to delinquency if they read fewer comic books devoted to the doings of criminals and fixed their admiration upon some notable hero of the past, such as Robin Hood. This paper also carried an editorial which took issue with some opinions *The Bellman* had expressed a few days before, on prison reform; the editor of *The Bellman*, it was implied, lacked a kind and understanding heart. Ridley made a note to write a counterblast, pointing out that Robin Hood was a criminal and a practical communist, and that no one but a numbskull would hold him up as a hero to children.

Thus he worked through the pile of contemporary opinion. He paused to read what a medical columnist in one paper had to say about gallstones. They could, it appeared, 'sleep' for years, causing little or no distress beyond an occasional sense of uneasiness. Ridley wondered if he had sleeping gallstones; he certainly had a sense of uneasiness, though it was nothing to what it had been a few years ago. To sit in an editor's chair, even reading epidemic jokes and groping for witty *aperçus*, was a good life; better, certainly, than his days as a reporter and, later, as a news editor. He read on, plunging deep into the pool of Canadian editorial opinion: the wickedness of the Government, the wickedness of the nation in spending several times as much on liquor as it gave to charity, the wickedness of the U.S.A. in not sufficiently recognizing Canada's greatness, the wickedness of Britain in not spending more money in Canada: he scanned these familiar topics without emotion, thinking only that the newspapers, like the churches, would be in a poor way if there were no wickedness in the world. Indeed, a good many editors seemed to think of themselves, primarily, as preachers, crying aloud to a godless world to repent of its manifold sins. Some who did not regard themselves as preachers, appeared to think of themselves as simple, shrewd old farmers; they wrote nostalgically of a bygone, Arcadian era, when everybody was near enough to the farm to have a little manure on his boots, and they appeared to think that farmers were, as a class, more honest and less given to gaudy vice than city folk. Ridley, who had lived in a rural community for a few years when a child, had never been able to find out where this opinion had its root. Other editors, who were disguised neither as preachers nor farmers, donned newsprint togas and appeared as modern Catos, ready to shed the last drop of their ink in defence of those virtues which they believed to be the exclusive property of the party not in power; these were also exceedingly hard upon the rising generation, whom they lumped together under the name of 'teenagers'. To be an editor was to be a geyser of opinion; every day, without fail, Old Faithful must shoot up his jet of comment, neither so provocative as to drive subscribers from his paper, nor yet so inane as to be utterly contemptible. The editor must not affront the intelligence of the better sort among his readers, and yet he must try to say something acceptable to those who really took the papers for the comics and the daily astrology feature. Truly, a barber's chair, that fits all buttocks.

While musing, Ridley had drawn moustaches and spectacles on pictures of four statesmen which appeared in a paper under his hand. He sketched a wig of curly hair on a bald man. With two deft dots of his pencil, he crossed the eyes of a huge-breasted girl under whose picture appeared the caption: 'Miss Sweater Girl for this month is lovely Dinah Ball, acclaimed by outstanding artists for her outstanding physique'. If a new Sweater Girl every month, why not an Udders Day, for the suitable honouring of all mammals? Could a witty *aperçu* be made of that? Probably not for a family journal.

But this was idleness. He must work. The editor of an evening daily has no time for profitless musing until after three o'clock. He tore up the defaced pictures, so that Miss Green should not find them, and turned once again to his task.

When another twenty minutes had passed he had perused the editorial outpourings of his thirty-eight contemporaries and had produced four more paragraphs of *Notes and Comment*. It was possible, he knew, to buy syndicated material of this sort, but he rather liked writing his own; the technique had its special fascination. It was possible, when desperate for material, to make an editorial note about virtually anything, or out of nothing at all. Consider, for instance, his startling success of the previous June a mosquito in his office had annoyed him, and when he mentioned it to Miss Green she borrowed an atomizer filled with some sort of spray from the janitor, sought out the monster, and stifled it. 'There's a spray for every kind of bug now. Mr Ridley,' she had said. 'Except the humbug, Miss Green,' he had replied, thinking of Mr Shillito. And there had been a Note, ready to hand. He had typed it at once:

> An eminent scientist asserts that there is now a spray for the control of every form of bug. Excluding, of course, the humbug.

One always attributed any foolish remark upon which one intended to pun either to an eminent scientist, a prominent physician, or a political commentator; it gave authenticity and flourish to the witty *aperçu* which followed. This gem so quickly conceived and executed, had been copied by eighteen other newspapers, with appropriate credit to *The Bellman*, stolen by several more, and had appeared a month afterward in the magazine section of the New York *Times*, attributed to the late Will Rogers.

It was now time for him to settle down to work on the leader for the day, his editorial on the St Lawrence seaway. This was a nervous moment, for he hated to make a beginning at any piece of writing. As the Old Mess had told him it was already written in his head, but what is written in the head is always so much more cogent and firmly expressed than what at last appears upon the page. He longed for a discretion, something that would postpone beginning for a few more minutes. His wish was gratified; Miss Green came in, carrying three books.

'Shall I put these with the other review books, Mr. Ridley?'

'No, let's have a look at them, Miss Green.'

Books for review always gave him a moment of excitement. There was the chance, faint, but still possible, that among them there would be something which he himself would like to read. But not this time. The first was a volume of pious reflections by a well-known Canadian divine; just the thing for Shillito. Next was a slim volume of verse by a Canadian poetess. Why are such volumes always 'slim', he wondered; why not 'scrawny', which would be so much nearer the truth? Miss Green could polish off the poetess. Next — ah, yes, the choice of an American book club, a volume somewhat larger and heavier than a brick, with a startling jacket printed upon paper so slick as to be somewhat sticky to the touch. *Plonk* was its title, and the inside flap of the jacket declared that 'it lays bare the soul of a man and woman caught up in the maelstrom of modern metropolitan life. Rusty Maloney fights his way from Boston's Irishtown to success as an advertising executive, only to fall under the spell of Siva McNulty, lovely, alluring but already addicted to Plonk, the insidious mixture of stout, brandy and coarse-ground poppyheads which brings surcease to screaming nerves and abraded passions. An Odyssey of the spirit on a scale rarely attempted, this novel is redolent of . . . ' No use giving that to Shillito; his usual reviewer of novels which were redolent of something was in hospital, having a baby, and he did not want the Old Mess being offensively moral through four inches in the review column. Who, then? Ah, Rumball!

He rang the bell and asked Miss Green to find Mr Rumball and send him in. Meanwhile he made a bet with himself that the first sex scene in *Plonk* would be found between pages 15 and 30. He won his bet. It was by no means a certainty. Sometimes this important scene came between pages 1 and 15.

Henry Rumball was a tall, untidy young man on the reportorial staff; his daily round included visits to the docks, the university and the undertakers. He presented himself wordlessly before the editor's desk.

'I thought you might like to review *Plonk*,' said Ridley 'I know you take an interest in the modern novel. This is rather special, I believe. Stark stuff. Say what you think but don't frighten any old ladies.'

'Thanks, Mr.Ridley. Gosh, *Plonk*,' said Rumball, seizing the volume and seeming to caress it.

'You know something about it?'

'I've seen the American reviews. They say it moves the novel on to an entirely different plateau of achievement. The *Saturday Review* man said when he'd finished it he felt exactly as if he had been drinking plonk all night himself. It's kind of tactile, I guess.'

'Well, say so in your piece. Tactile is a handy word; tends to make a sentence quotable.'

Rumball rocked his weight from foot to foot, breathed heavily, and then said, 'I don't know that I really ought to do it.'

'Why not? I thought you liked that kind of thing?'

'Yes, Mr Ridley, but I'm trying to keep my head clear you see. I'm avoiding outside influences, to keep my stream unpolluted, if you know what I mean.'

'I don't know in the least what you mean. What stream are you talking about?'

'My stream of inspiration. For *The Plain*. My book, you know.'

'Are you writing a book?'

'Yes. Don't you remember? I told you all about it nearly a year ago.'

'I can't recall anything about it. When did you tell me?'

'Well, I came in to ask you about a raise — '

'Oh yes, I remember that. I told you to talk to Mr Weir. I never interfere with his staff.'

'Yes, well, I told you then I was writing a novel. And now I'm working on my first draft. And I'm not reading anything, for fear it may influence me. That's the big danger, you know. Influences. Above all, you have to be yourself.'

'Aha, well if you don't want *Plonk* I'll find someone else. Will you ask Mr Weir to see me when he has a free moment?' . . .

'Certainly, sir. But there's just one thing I'd like your advice about. Names. Names are so important in a book. Now the big force in my book is the prairie itself, and I just call it the Prairie. But my people who are struggling against it are two families; one is English, from the North, and thought of calling them the Chimneyholes, only they pronounce it Chumnel. The other is Scandinavian and I was to call them the Ruokatavarakauppas. I'm worried that the vowel sounds in the two names may not be sufficiently differentiated. Because, you see, I want to get a big poetic sweep into the writing, and if the main words in the novel aren't right, the whole thing may bog down, do you see?'

'I want to see Mr Weir at once,' said Ridley, in a low compelling voice.

'I'll tell him right away,' said Rumball, moving toward the door, 'but if you should happen to thing of a name that has the same rhythm as Ruokatavarakauppas but has slightly darker vowel shading I'd be grateful if you would tell me. It's really going to be a king of big saga, and I want people to read it aloud as much as possible, and the names are terribly important.'

Reluctantly, he left the office, and shortly afterward Edward Weir, the managing editor, came in and sat in the chair from which Rumball had been driven with such difficulty.

'Anything out of the ordinary last night?' asked Ridley.

'Just the usual Hallowe'en stuff, except for one story we can't track down. Some sort of trouble at the Cathedral. The Dean won't say anything, but he didn't deny that something had happened. Archie was going home a little after midnight and he met Miss Pottinger coming from the West Door of the Cathedral. He asked her if anything was wrong and she said, "You'll get nothing out of me," and hurried off across the street. But she had no stockings on and bedroom slippers; he spotted them under her coat. Now what was she doing in the Cathedral at midnight on Hallowe'en with no stockings on?'

'At her age lack of stockings suggests great perturbation of mind, but nothing really interesting. Did Archie try to get into the church?'

'Yes, but the door was locked. He could see light through the keyhole, but there was nothing to be heard.'

'Probably nothing at all happening, really.'

'I don't know. When I called Knapp this morning he was very short, and when I asked him if it was true that someone had tried to rob the Cathedral last night he said, "Where did you hear about that?" and then tried to tell me he meant nothing by it.'

'Why don't you try the organist? You know, that fellow — what's his name? — Cobbler. He never stops talking.'

'Called him. He said, "My lips are sealed." You know what a jackass he is.'

'We'd better keep after it. Tell me, is that fellow Rumball any good?'

'Fair. He was better when he first came on the staff. He moons a good deal now. Maybe he's in love.'

'Perhaps Mr Shillito could give him one of his talks on the virtue of digging in the Newspaper Game.'

'God forbid. Are you going to do anything about that matter?'

'I'm moving as fast as I can. It's very difficult. You have no heart, Ned. How would you like to be thrown out of your job at seventy-eight?'

"If I had a pension, and a house all paid for, and a nice little private income, and probably a good chunk of savings, like Old Shillito, I would like nothing better.'

'Has he all that?'

'You know it as well as I do. He just likes to prowl around this office and waste everybody's time.'

'He says he prays to whatever gods there be that he may drop in harness. He's not a conventionally religious man, but that is his prayer.'

'The old faker! When he caught on to this Cathedral story this morning he was in my office like a shot out of a gun. "Ned, my boy," he said, "take an old newspaperman's advice and let this thing drop; I've been a staunch church man all my life, and there's nothing I would not do to shield the church against a breath of slander." Of course I tried to find out if he knew anything, but he shut up like a clam. Gloster, why don't you give him the axe? He's just a pest.'

'I inherited him. And he was editor himself for a few months before I was appointed. I don't want anybody to be able to say that I was unfair to him.'

'It's your funeral. But he's a devil of a nuisance. Always in the news room, keeping somebody from work. The boys are sick of him. They aren't even civil to him any more, but he doesn't notice.'

'I'm going to do something very soon. I just want to be able to do it the right way. If we could ease him out gloriously, somehow it would be best. I had a notion involving an illuminated address which might work. But leave it with me for a few days more. Nothing else out of the way?'

But the day's news was barren of anything else which the managing editor thought Mr Ridley should know, and he went back to his own office leaving the editor once more with the task of writing his leader. To postpone the dreary moment a little longer he picked up the few typewritten sheets which Mr Shillito called 'his stint'. . . .

Ridley sighed and then, slowly and painfully, was possessed by rage. His weakness in failing to get rid of the Old Mess condemned him to publish this sort of hogwash in the paper of which he was known to be the editor. The mantle of the eighteenth century essayist — old, frowsy, tattered, greasy and patched with

Addison's gout-rags and the seat of the gentle Elia's pants — had fallen upon Swithin Shillito, and he strutted and postured in it, every day, in the columns of *The Bellman*. And why? Because he, Gloster Ridley, lacked the guts to tell the Old Mess that he was fired. He hated himself. He despised his weakness. And yet — a pious regard for old age and a sincere desire to be just and to use his power wisely restrained him from acting as he would have done if the offender had been, for instance, Henry Rumball. And, who could say, might not many readers of *The Bellman* — even a majority of them — share the opinion of Eldon Bumford, who revelled in Mr Shillito's essay on the fate of the toothpick and exulted in his discussions of the importation of snuff and bird-seed? To what extent was he, Gloster Ridley, justified in imposing his taste upon the newspaper's subscribers? Still, was it not for doing so that he drew his excellent salary and his annual bonus reckoned upon the profits? What about the barber's chair; might there not be a few buttocks for Shillito? But he could go on in this Hamlet-like strain all day. There was only one thing for it. He rang for Miss Green.

'Please call Mr Warboys and ask if I may see him for half an hour this afternoon,' said he.

'Yes, Mr Ridley. And Professor Vambrace called again and said he couldn't come at eleven and insists on seeing you at two.'

'Very well, Miss Green. But what is all this about Professor Vambrace? What does he want to see me about?'

'I don't know sir, because he wouldn't give me any hint on the phone. But he was very crusty. He kept repeating "Two, sharp," in a way I didn't like.'

'He did, did he? Well, whenever he comes, keep him waiting five minutes. And I don't want to be disturbed until lunch.'

'Yes, sir. Here are a few letters which came with the second mail.'

These were quickly dealt with. A temperance league called for 'renewal efforts', and Moral Re-Armament asserted in three paragraphs that if everybody would try to be decent to every-body else, all problems between management and labour would disappear. A young Nigerian wrote 'I am African boy but always wear American shoes,' and wanted a Canadian pen-friend, pref-erably a girl between 14 and 16. Another, deeply critical of *The Bellman*, was so eccentric in grammar and spelling that it took five minutes of Ridley's time to prepare it for the printer; there is nothing that makes an editor feel more like St Francis — a loving brother to the ass — than this sort of remedial work on a letter which accuses him of unfairness or stupidity. At last Ridley was ready to write his leader.

After all his fussing it came out quite smoothly, and by mid-day he had everything prepared for the printers and was ready to think about his luncheon. . . .

He liked his lunch-time, because it gave him an opportunity to think. On this first of November he moved the little hot-plate out of his cupboard as usual, took two eggs and other necessaries from his brief case, and made himself an excellent omelette. He sat down at a small table near his window and ate it, looking down at the Salterton market which was one of the last of the open-air markets in that part of Canada, and a very pretty sight.

He was thinking, of course, about Mr Shillito. When he saw his publisher that afternoon, he would explain that Mr Shillito must go, and he would ask Mr Warboys to help him to ease the blow. Execrable as Mr Shillito might be as a writer, and detestable as he might be about the office, he was an old man with somewhat more than his fair share of self-esteem, and Ridley could not bring himself to wound him. But there must be no half-measures. Shillito must have an illuminated address, presented if possible by Mr Warboy himself. The whole staff must be assembled, and Mr Shillito must be allowed to make a speech. Perhaps the Mayor could be bamboozled into coming. And a picture of the affair must appear in *The Bellman*, with a caption which would make it clear that Mr Shillito was retiring of his own volition. It would all be done in the finest style. Why, if Mr Warboys were in a good mood, he might even suggest a little dinner for Mr Shillito, instead of a staff meeting. Ridley found that his eyes had moistened as he contemplated the golden light in which Mr Shillito would depart from *The Bellman*. . . .

Thus, rocking between anger against Mr Shillito and pity for him, Ridley ate his biscuits and cheese, drank his excellent coffee, put his dishes on Miss Green's desk to be washed, and composed himself for his invariable twenty-minute after-lunch sleep in his armchair.

Miss Green coughed discreetly. 'Professor Vambrace is waiting,' she said.

Ridley leaped from his chair. He hated being caught thus; he had an uneasy conviction that he was unsightly when asleep. And he had overslept by ten minutes. 'Keep him till I ring,' he said.

When Miss Green had gone he combed his hair and rinsed his removable bridge in his tiny washroom. Sitting at his desk, he fussed with some papers, but he could not calm himself. He was disproportionately ashamed of having been found asleep. His nap, like his lunch, was no guilty secret but he hated to be caught unprepared. How long had Miss Green watched him, perhaps listened to his snores, considered the dry and iridescent matter, like the sheen on a butterfly's wing, which formed on his lower lip when he slept? To escape this uncomfortable train of thought he rang his bell, and Professor Vambrace stalked from the door to the space before his desk, and glared down upon him.

'Well,' he said, and his deep voice vibrated with anger, 'have you decided what you are going to do?'

'As I have no idea what you are talking about, Professor,' said Ridley, 'I can't say that I have. Won't you sit down?'

The Professor sat, majestically. 'I do not believe you, but I'll soon tell you what I'm talking about,' said he, 'and I'll tell you what you're going to do, as well.'

Walter Vambrace was a tall, gaunt man who looked like a tragedian of the old school; his large, dark eyes glowed balefully under his demonic eyebrows. From an inner pocket he produced a wallet, and drew a clipping from it with great care. Ridley, to whom the faces of newspapers were as familiar as the faces of his friends, saw at once that the clipping was from *The Bellman*, and prepared himself for trouble.

'In the next three issues of your paper you will publish this, and the retraction and apology which I shall also give you, in large type at the top of your front page,' said Professor Vambrace.

'Aha,' said Ridley, in a noncommital tone. 'May I see the clipping, please?'

'Do you mean to tell me that you are not aware of its contents?' said the Professor, working his eyebrows menacingly.

'I have no idea what you are talking about.'

'Good God, don't you read your own newspaper?'

'Of course I do, but I still don't know what has offended you.'

'Refresh your recollection, then,' said the Professor, with a rich assumption of irony, and handed Ridley the scrap of newsprint upon which was printed the engagement notice with which the reader has already been made familiar.

The editor read it carefully. 'This seems quite in order,' said he.

'In order! There is not one word of truth in it from beginning to end. It is a vile calumny!'

'You mean that your daughter is not engaged to Mr Bridgetower?'

'Is not, and never will be, and this damnable libel exposes me and my wife and my daughter to the ridicule of the entire community.'

Ridley's heart sank within him. Physicians say that this cannot happen, but editors know a sensation which may not be described in any other phrase.

'That is most regrettable. I shall do everything possible to find out how this notice came to appear in print. But I can assure you now that we have a system which provides every possible safeguard against this sort of thing, and I cannot understand how it could have failed.'

Professor Vambrace's expression, which had been one of anger, now deepened to a horrible grimace in which rage and scorn were mingled. 'You have a system!' he roared. 'Read it again, you fool, and then tell me, if you dare, that you have a system, or anything except the mischievous incompetence of your disgusting trade to explain the insult!'

Ridley was thoroughly angry himself, now, but caution was ingrained in his nature, and he turned his eyes once again to the clipping.

'To take place November 31st,' hissed the Professor. 'And when, you jackanapes, is November 31st? Is that date provided for in your system? Hey?' he was shouting, now.

All Ridley's anger was drained out of him, and a great but not unfamiliar weariness took its place. He was a good editor, and when praise came to *The Bellman* he took it on behalf of the staff; when blame came to it, he took that alone. He was, in law and in his own philosophy of journalism, personally responsible for every word which appeared in every issue of his paper. He looked into the eyes of his visitor and spoke the speech which was obligatory on him on such occasions.

'I cannot tell you how much I regret this,' he said; 'however, it has happened, and although this is my first knowledge of it, I accept the full blame. Someone has played a tasteless joke on the paper, and, of course, upon you and your family as well. I am deeply sorry that it has happened and I will join you in doing everything that can be done to find the joker.'

'Pah!' said Professor Vambrace, with such violence that quite a lot of spittle shot across Ridley's desk and settled upon the papers there. 'What kind of newspaper do you call this, where nobody knows how many days there are in November? That alone should have been enough to warn any intelligent person, even a newspaper editor, that the thing was a vile hoax. Quite apart from the ludicrous implication in the notice itself; whatever made you think that my daughter would marry that nincompoop?'

'As I have explained, I have not seen this notice until this moment. And how should I know whom your daughter might or might not marry?'

'Don't you see what goes in your own paper?'

'I see very little of it, and certainly not the engagement notices. These matters are left in the hands of our staff.'

'A fine staff it must be! The thing is preposterous on the face of it. Do you know this Bridgetower?'

'I have met him two or three times.'

'Well? An idiot, nothing better. What would my daughter be doing with such a fellow?'

'I do not know your daughter.'

'Do you imply that she would take up with any simpleton who came along?'

'Professor Vambrace, this is beside the point.'

'It is not beside the point. It is the whole point. You have linked my daughter with this fellow Bridgetower. You have coupled them in the public mouth.'

'I have done nothing of the sort. *The Bellman* has been the victim of a practical joke; so have you. We must do what we can to set matters right.'

'Exactly. Therefore you will publish this notice on your front page, along with the apology which I have here, for the next three days, beginning today.'

'We shall publish a correction. . . .'

'Not a correction, an apology.'

'A correction, but not on the front page, and not for three days.'

'For three days, beginning today.'

'Impossible. The paper has gone to press.'

'The front page.'

'The page on which these announcements appear. For you must understand that our correction will appear for one day only, in the same place that the erroneous notice appeared.'

'That is what you will publish.' The Professor pushed a piece of paper at Ridley. It began rather in the rhythm of a Papal Encyclical: *With the uttermost apology and regret we make unqualified retraction*; Ridley read no more.

'Look here, Professor,' said he, 'we've both been made to look like fools, and we don't want to make matters worse. Leave this matter in my hands, and I'll deal with it in a way that will make an adequate correction and attract no unnecessary attention.'

'This will be settled in my way, or I'll take it to court,' said Professor Vambrace.

'All right, then, take it to court and be damned,' said Ridley.

The Professor glared horribly, but it was the glare of a man who was wondering what to say next. Ridley saw that he had the advantage for the moment and followed up his lead.

'And spare me your histrionics,' said he; 'I am not intimidated by them.'

This was a shrewd thrust, but tactically it was a mistake. The Professor was a keen amateur actor, and fancied himself as the 'heavy' of the Salterton Little Theatre; Ridley's remark disconcerted him, but deepened his anger. However, the editor had at last secured the upper hand, and he continued.

'You must understand that I have had more experience in these matters than you have.'

'That is a confession of incompetence rather than a reassurance,' said Vambrace.

'Kindly allow me to say what I have to say. *The Bellman* will not apologize, because it has acted in good faith, and is just as much a victim of this hoax as yourself. But we will correct the notice, printing the correction in the same place and in the same size of type as the original; we shall do this once only, for the notice appeared only once. If you will think about the matter calmly, you will see that this is best; you do not want an undignified fuss, and you do not want people to hear about this false engagement notice who have not heard of it already. Comparatively few people will have seen it — '

'My family is not utterly obscure,' said the Professor dryly, 'and the Personal Notices are one of the few parts of your paper which are widely read. Scores of people have been asking me about this already — '

'Scores, Professor Vambrace? Did I understand you to say scores?"

'Yes, sir, scores was the word I used.'

'Now, now, precisely how many people have spoken to you about it?'

'Don't take that one with me, if you please.'

'My experience has been that when angry men talk about scores of people they mean perhaps half-a-dozen.'

'Do you doubt my word?'

'I think that your annoyance has led you to exaggerate.'

'A man in your trade is hardly in a position to accuse anyone of exaggeration.'

'Now let us be reasonable. Of course we shall do everything in our power to find out who perpetrated this joke — '

'I don't call it a joke.'

'Nor do I. This outrage, then.'

'That is a better word. And what do you propose to do?'

It was here that Mr Ridley lost the advantage he had gained. He had no idea what he proposed to do. Therefore he looked as wise as he could, and said, 'That will take careful consideration. I shall have to have a talk with some of the other men on the paper.'

'Let us do so at once, then.'

'I shall talk to them later this afternoon.'

'Let me make this plain to you that at this moment my daughter and my whole family rest under a vile imputation of which this newspaper is the source. Anything that is to be done must be done at once. So get your men in here now, and I will talk to them just long enough to find out whether you really mean to do anything or whether you are stalling me off. And unless you have an immediate plan of action I shall go straight from this office to my lawyer.'

The Professor had the upper hand again, and this time he did not mean to lose it. Ridley rang for Miss Green. 'Will you find Mr Marryat and ask him if he will join us here,' said he; 'it is urgent.'

When the secretary had gone he and the Professor sat in painful silence for perhaps three minutes until the door opened again, and the general manager of *The Bellman* appeared.

Mr. A. J. Marryat's principal interest was in advertising, and he had the advertising man's optimism and self-assurance. He came in smiling and greeted the Professor warmly. He told him that he was looking well. 'And how is Mrs Vambrace?' said he.

'My wife is in bed, under strong sedatives, because of what you have done here,' replied Vambrace, and breathed noticeably and audibly through his nostrils.

Ridley took the general manager by the arm, guided him to a chair, and explained the trouble as briefly as he could.

Mr Marryat's rule was never to display perturbation. He continued to smile. 'That's bad,' he said, 'but we'll find out who did it, and then we'll show him a joke or two.' He laughed comfortably at the prospect; but under cover of his bonhomie he was taking stock of the situation. Ridley, obviously, was in a tight spot or he would not be discussing a matter of this kind with himself in front of the injured party. Well, A.J. Marryat knew all there was to know about tight spots, and one of his most valuable pieces of knowledge was that the sharpest anger can be blunted by good humour, courtesy and a relaxed manner, all of which could be combined with a refusal to do anything you did not want to do. He turned to Ridley, 'Let's hear the details,' said he.

When he heard the details concerning November 31st Mr. Marryat was disturbed, but his outer appearance of calm was maintained without a ruffle.

'That was inexcusable stupidity,' he said, 'but I'm sure you know, Professor, how hard it is to get people to pay attention to things of that kind.'

'It is your work to do so, not mine,' said the Professor. 'I am only concerned with the fact that your paper has involved my family in a scandal. My professional dignity and my family honour make it imperative that this announcement be denied, and a full apology made, with the least possible waste of time. I want that done in today's paper.'

'That's a mechanical impossibility,' said Mr Marryat. 'The presses will begin rolling in about fifteen minutes.'

'Presses can be stopped, can they not?'

'They can be stopped at very great expense.'

'Probably less than it will cost you if I take this matter to court.'

'Now just a minute, Professor. Let's not be fantastic. Who's talking about court?'

'Your associate, Mr Ridley, told me to take my case to court and be damned.'

'I apologize,' said Ridley, 'but you were very provocative. You called me a fool and a jackanapes, you know.'

'I did, and I see no reason to retract either term.'

'Oh, come now, Professor,' said Mr Marryat, with his genial and ready laugh; 'let's not lose our perspective on this thing.'

'Mr Marryat,' said the Professor, rising, 'I have not come here to be cajoled or lectured. I came to tell you what you must do, and it is plain to me that you will twist and squirm all day to avoid doing it. I have no time to waste and this atmosphere is repugnant to me. You will shortly hear from my lawyers.' The Professor walked rapidly out of the room.

'Well, how do you like that?' said Mr Marryat.

Mr Ridley moaned, and wiped his brow.

'The gall of that guy,' said Mr Marryat. 'Professional dignity! Family honour! You'd think we did it on purpose. And what's all this scandal he talks about? Do you know this fellow Bridgetower?"

'Yes. He's a junior professor.'

'Well? Has he got two heads, or a common-law wife, or something?'

'So far as I know there's nothing against him except that he is the son of old Mrs Bridgetower.'

'That's plenty, mind you. And Vambrace's daughter, what about her?'

'I haven't seen her for two or three years. I think she's in the Waverley Library, somewhere, but I never meet her there. So far as I know she's just a girl.'

'Probably she's engaged to somebody else. That notice was somebody's half-baked joke. Well, I'll trace it. I'll get busy on it right now, and if we hear anything from Vambrace's lawyers, we can explain to them. They'll soon put a stop to that talk about scandal.'

'I'd be grateful if you'd let me know anything you find out as soon as possible, A.J.,' said Ridley. . . .

It was half-past three, and Mr Ridley was to see his publisher at half-past four. At four o'clock he received a call from the legal firm of Snelgrove, Martin and Fitzalan, asking that he see Mr Snelgrove at ten o'clock the following morning on a matter of urgent importance.

Clerebold Warboys was not primarily interested in the publication of the Salterton *Evening Bellman*; he had been born wealthy, and in the process of becoming much wealthier he had acquired several properties, of which *The Bellman* was one. It had come upon the market as an ancient and almost bankrupt newspaper, and he had bought it because he did not want to see an institution which was so much a part of his native city disappear from that city's life; he also thought that the application of business acumen to the newspaper might improve its fortunes. He was right, as he usually was about such matters, and Mr Marryat and Mr Ridley had made *The Bellman* not only a very much better paper than it had been before, but a profitable business, as well.

Mr Warboys never interfered with the paper, and this was a source of disagreement between himself and his daughter-in-law, Mrs Roger Warboys, who lived with him and was his housekeeper and hostess. Mrs Roger Warboys, who had been widowed before she was forty, had a great store of energy which was not fully absorbed by her stewardship for Mr Warboys and the many women's causes into which she threw herself. Her dearest dream was to 'take over' *The Bellman* and to give it a policy more in line with her own opinions. She had a passion for crusading, and she felt that with a newspaper at her command she could do tremendous things to defeat juvenile delinquency, the drug traffic, comic books, immodest bathing suits and other evils which were gnawing at the foundations of society; she would also be able to do much to improve the status of women which, in her view, was unsatisfactory. But her father-in-law, who had passed the greater part of his life in public affairs and had acquired a considerable store of worldly wisdom, refused to pay any attention to her wishes. He was wont to say; 'Nesta, you have what most of the world wants: leisure and the money to enjoy it; why don't you relax?' But for Mrs Roger Warboys there could be no happiness which was not also turmoil and the imposition of her will upon other people. Perhaps twice a year she renewed her attack upon her obdurate father-in-law, and the rest of the time she seized what opportunities she could to call his attention to what she believed were fatal weaknesses in the editorship of Gloster Ridley.

It was with no quickening of the spirit, therefore, that Ridley found Mrs Roger Warboys in the publisher's study, pouring tea.

'Ridley,' said his employer, 'I've got the title for my book, at last.'

'Splendid!' said Ridley, with false enthusiasm.

'Yes. *Politics: The Great Game*. What do you think of that?'

'Absolutely first-rate!'

'Really? Don't give a snap decision. Do you really think it's what I want?'

'It's very original,' said Ridley.

'It sounds well. But of course most people won't hear it. They'll read it. How do you think it would look? Nesta, give me that dummy.'

His daughter-in-law handed him a book from the desk. Upon it Mr Warboys had put a piece of white paper, to resemble a dust jacket, and had crudely lettered *Politics: The Great Game*, by CLEREBOLD WARBOYS, across it.

'Very fine,' said Ridley: 'it has a kind of ring about it, even in print.'

Conversation as they drank their tea was all about Mr Warboy's book. This work had been *in utero*, so to speak, for eight years, but even at the age of seventy he could not find time to write it. Instead, he made copious notes for it, which he revised whenever a political contemporary died; when they were all dead, and the decks cleared, he might actually write it. Meanwhile he sustained the enthusiasm of an author at a remarkably high level, year in and year out, and Ridley rarely visited him without being asked for advice on some point relative to the great work. But at last the moment came when Ridley was able to raise the question of Mr Shillito.

'It is by no means easy,' he explained, 'because Mr Shillito is in a sense a legacy from the former management. He is a link with the past of the paper. But the sort of thing he writes no longer has a place in *The Bellman*, and I feel that it is not in the best interest of the paper to postpone his retirement.'

'There's no doubt about it that he's a bloody old nuisance and not worth his keep,' said Mr Warboys, who was only eight years

younger than Mr Shillito and felt no need to beat about the bush.
'Well; we've got a pension scheme. What's it for? We'll bounce him
with all honours, as you suggest.'

'Mr Shillito never subscribed to the pension scheme,' said Mrs
Roger Warboys, unexpectedly.

'How do you know?' asked her father-in-law.

'He asked me to tea on Sunday last. The poor old man is getting
very frail, Father, and he has some nice things he wants to see in
good hands before he dies. He was really very touching about it.
He gave me the loveliest little bronze bowl — Chinese, and very
good; I have it in my sitting-room. He hasn't much in the way of
money, he says, but he has a few treasures, and he doesn't want
them to go to just anybody when he dies. He told me that he had
never felt able to contribute to the pension scheme.'

'I don't know how that could be,' said Ridley. 'Miss Ellis has
always been very good about arranging payment plans for anybody who needed special help.'

'Perhaps you don't understand Mr Shillito's way of looking at
things, Mr Ridley,' said Mrs Roger Warboys, quietly censorious.
'He's one of those proud old Englishmen who would rather die
than ask anybody for help.'

'Then why didn't he take advantage of the pension scheme?'
asked Mr Warboys.

'Because he didn't think he would ever live to enjoy it,' said his
daughter-in-law. 'He told me that he worked himself so hard in
the last few years before you took over *The Bellman* that he never
expected to reach his present age. He has always expected that he
would drop in harness.'

'Well, let him have the good sense to get out of harness,' said Mr
Warboys, 'and he needn't drop so soon.'

'I know I have no right to interfere,' said Mrs Roger Warboys,
in the tone she always used when she meant to do so. 'I think Mr
Shillito should have every consideration. His judgment alone
should be worth something. Even if he simply stays at *The Bellman*
to keep an eye on things in general, he would be valuable. His
knowledge of the city and its people is surely the most extensive of
anyone now on the staff. For instance, I'm sure he would never
have passed that ridiculous engagement notice about Pearl Vambrace and young Bridgetower.'

'That matter is in hand,' said Ridley, turning white.

'That's just as well,' said Mrs Roger Warboys, smiling unpleas-antly. 'For Professor Vambrace phoned me about it this after-noon, just to make it clear that if he has to take it to law, there is nothing personal intended toward myself. I have worked very closely with him for years,' she explained, 'on the Board of the University Alumni.'

It was then necessary for Mr Ridley to explain to Mr Warboys what the dispute was between *The Bellman* and Professor Vam-brace. Mr. Warboys was not inclined to pay too much attention to it. 'These things soon blow over,' said he.

'Nevertheless, I think my point about Mr Shillito is well taken,' said Mrs Roger Warboys. 'The Professor was hardly off the phone before Mr Shillito called about it. He said that the minute he saw it he knew there had been some dreadful blunder, for the feud between the Vambraces and the Bridgetowers dates from when Professor Bridgetower was alive. He just wanted me to know that he would never have permitted such a thing to appear in print, but of course his power on the paper is very limited — at present.' These last words were directed with a special smile to Ridley.

'The damned old double-crosser,' said Mr Warboys, who un-derstood these matters very well.

Ridley could think of no comment save lewd and blasphemous variations on that of his publisher, so he held his peace, and soon returned to his office.

It was after six o'clock when he reached it. He stopped in Miss Green's office, and after some rummaging, he drew a sheet of paper from a file and took it to his desk. It was an obituary, prepared some years before and kept up to date, for use when it should be needed. It read:

VAMBRACE, WALTER BENEDICT, b. Cork, Eire, March 5, 1899 only son Rev. Benedict V. and Cynthia Grattan V., a second cousin to the Marquis of Mourne and Derry; Educ. at home and Trinity Coll. Dublin. (M.A.) Emigrated to Canada 1922 joined classics dept. Waverley as minor professor. Married Elizabeth Anne Fitza-lan dr. Wolfe Tone Fitzalan, June 18, 1925, one daughter Pearl Veronica b. 1933. Full professor 1935; head classics dept. 1938. Supported for Dean of Arts 1939 but defeated by one vote by the late Dean Solomon Bridgetower. Did not stand again after Dean Btwr's death in 1940. Author: *Contra Celsum with Notes and*

ROBERTSON DAVIES

Commentary 1924; *Enneads of Plotinus Newly Considered* 1929 (*Times Litt. Supp.* says 'valuable though controversial' in review which might have been by Dean Inge) *Student's Book of Latin Verse* 1938 (sold 150,000).

> Professor Vambrace was no austere scholar, but a man who gave richly of himself to a variety of worthy causes. Always accessible to his students, he opened to them the stores of scholarship which he brought from famed Trinity College, Dublin. Graduates of Waverley will long remember the rich and thrilling voice in which he read Latin poetry aloud, seeming to — as one graduate put it — 'call Horace smiling from his tomb and Vergil from the realm of the shades.' This same noble organ was for years to be heard in performances given by the Salterton Little Theatre, of which Professor Vambrace was at one time Vice-President. His most notable performance by far was as Prospero in *The Tempest*, of which *The Bellman* critic of that time, Mr Swithin Shillito, wrote: 'It was said of Kean's Shylock, "This was the Jew, That Shakespeare drew"; still borne aloft upon the wave of poetry evoked by Walter Vambrace (away with all Misters and Professors in the presence of Genius) your annalist can but murmur, "This IS the Mage, From Shakespeare's page." '

After fifteen minutes' careful work Ridley had revised this paragraph to read thus:

> Professor Vambrace, an austere scholar, was associated with many causes. To his students he brought a store of scholarship from famed Trinity College, Dublin. Graduates of Waverley will long remember the voice in which he read Latin poetry aloud, seeming, as one graduate has put it, to call Horace from his tomb and Vergil from Hades. The late Professor Vambrace had a strong histrionic bent and was for some years an amateur performer with the Salterton Little Theatre.

It was not much, and it might be years before it bore fruit, but it made him feel a little better.